STEPHEN HALES: SCIENTIST AND PHILANTHROPIST

Stephen Hales:
Scientist and philanthropist

D.G.C. ALLAN AND R.E. SCHOFIELD

SCOLAR PRESS
LONDON

First published 1980 by Scolar Press
90/91 Great Russell Street, London WC1B 3PY
Scolar Press is an imprint of Bemrose UK Limited

© D. G. C. Allan and Robert E. Schofield 1980

Set in Monotype Baskerville by
Gloucester Typesetting Co. Ltd
Gloucester

Printed in Great Britain by
Western Printing Services Ltd
Bristol

BRITISH LIBRARY CATALOGUING IN PUBLICATION DATA
Allan, D G C
Stephen Hales, scientist and philanthropist.
1. Hales, Stephen
2. Scientists – England – Biography
I. Title   II. Schofield, Robert Edwin
509'.2'4   Q143.Hr
ISBN 0 85967 482 7

Contents

Preface

Stephen Hales was one of the most celebrated Englishmen of the eighteenth century. His scientific researches in animal and plant physiology provided a theoretical and experimental model which inspired other scientists for nearly a century; his work on the nature and the activity of air was fundamental in the development of pneumatic chemistry. His ingenuity in invention and the application of science to the social and economic needs of his day brought him international renown. Yet he was, by profession and conviction, a clergyman who served as a minister in two parishes for the greater part of his life and his major public efforts were devoted to his church and to philanthropic endeavours. He was associated in the activities of the Society for Promoting Christian Knowledge (s.p.c.k.), was one of the Georgia Trustees (for the colonization of Georgia), and was a founding member of the Society for the Encouragement of Arts, Manufactures, and Commerce (now the Royal Society of Arts). He was admired by contemporaries as various as Alexander Pope and John Wesley and, for the modern reader, might well serve as an example of the most admirable qualities of his age and country.

Yet the only full-length biography of Hales is that of Dr A. E. Clark-Kennedy, whose charming *Stephen Hales D.D., F.R.S.: an Eighteenth Century Biography* (Cambridge University Press, 1929) was an extension of a memorial address at Corpus Christi College, Cambridge, celebrating the two hundred and fiftieth anniversary of Hales's birth. In a conversation we had at the Royal Society of Arts some years ago, each of us revealed that we had been led, by Dr Clark-Kennedy, into 'farther researches' about Dr Hales and we both expressed a wish to add to Dr Clark-Kennedy's work the results of those researches and those new insights which nearly fifty years of changes in social and economic history and the history of science might have brought to the subject. The book which follows is the result of that conversation.

We shared an overall interest in the man and his work, but for each of us there were aspects which were particularly attractive. For R.E.S.,

Hales's scientific writings held a special significance as the culmination of a British Newtonian tradition and a major influence on the work of later scientists as diverse as Benjamin Franklin, Joseph Priestley, and Antoine Lavoisier. For D.G.C.A., it was Hales's part in the foundation of the Society of Arts and his earlier paternalistic philanthropic enterprises which seemed especially important. So we agreed to divide the labour: R.E.S. worked on the scientific and technological aspects of Hales's life and D.G.C.A. on the personal and philanthropic. After a brief preliminary chapter on Hales's family and his early education (by D.G.C.A.) there is an analysis of the influences moulding his early scientific thinking (by R.E.S.) and an account of his work as a parish priest (by D.G.C.A.). Then follow two chapters on his principal scientific books (by R.E.S.), the *Vegetable Staticks* of 1727 and the *Haemastaticks* of 1733, and another (by D.G.C.A.) on his work during the years 1722–52 for the s.p.c.k., the Associates of Dr Bray and the Georgia Trust. His interest in practical invention and the application of science *c.* 1739–61 (by R.E.S.) and in the foundation and early years of the Society of Arts, *c.* 1753–61 (by D.G.C.A.) are then described. The book ends with an account of his work as a Royal Chaplain, from 1750 until his death (by D.G.C.A.) and an analysis of his scientific reputation and influence (by R.E.S.).

We have received assistance and encouragement from numerous institutions, custodians of records and other scholars. This we acknowledge wherever possible in our notes.

We are grateful to the governing bodies of the following institutions for permission to quote from their Hales mss.: the Linnean Society, the Royal College of Physicians, the Royal College of Surgeons, the Royal Society of Arts, the Society for Promoting Christian Knowledge, the United Society for the Propagation of the Gospel, the Wellcome Institute of the History of Medicine.

R.E.S.   D.G.C.A.
CLEVELAND, LONDON, CLEVELAND   LONDON, CLEVELAND, LONDON

Chronology

1677	Stephen Hales is born on 17th September at Beakesbourne in Kent.
1687	Mary Hales, mother of S.H., dies.
c. 1689–93	S.H. taught by Mr St Clare and Revd Richard Johnson.
1692	Thomas Hales, father of S.H., dies.
1693	Sir Robert Hales, grandfather of S.H., dies.
c. 1694–96	S.H. taught by Revd Mark Hildeseley.
1696	He enters Corpus Christi College, Cambridge.
1700	He receives his B.A. degree.
1702	He is pre-elected to a fellowship of Corpus.
1703	He takes up his fellowship and is subsequently made M.A. and ordained deacon.
1705–09	He investigates arteries of animals and constructs an orrery.
1709	He is nominated curate of Teddington and ordained priest.
1714	He conducts experiments on force of blood in animals; his brother Robert goes to Hanover on behalf of the S.P.C.K.
1716	Robert Hales is appointed Clerk to the Privy Council.
1717	S.H. attends his first meeting at the Royal Society; the first enlargement of Teddington Church during his incumbency takes place.
1718	He is elected F.R.S. His nomination as rector of Porlock causes him to resign his fellowship of Corpus.
1720	He marries Mary Newce in March.
1721	She dies in October.
1722	He is elected a Corresponding Member of the S.P.C.K.
1723	He exchanges the living of Porlock for Farringdon in Hampshire, which then becomes his summer home.
1724	Dr Thomas Bray appoints him a trustee of the D'Allone bequest.
1727	He publishes the *Vegetable Staticks*.

1728	William and Robert Hales get into difficulties.
1729	William Hales dies.
1730–51	S.H. attends meetings of Dr Bray's Associates.
1731	He publishes a second edition of *Vegetable Staticks*.
1732–52	He attends meetings of the Georgia Trust and Common Council.
1733	He publishes the *Haemastaticks* and is created D.D. by Oxford University.
1734	He anonymously publishes a *Friendly Admonition*.
1735	Robert Hales dies.
1739	S.H. publishes *Philosophical Experiments* and is awarded the Copley Medal by the Royal Society.
1740	He serves as a Trustee to examine Mrs Stephens's remedy.
1741	He reads his account of ventilators to the Royal Society.
1743	He publishes *A Description of Ventilators*.
1748	The second enlargement of Teddington Church takes place.
1750	S.H. is appointed chaplain to the Princess Dowager of Wales.
1753–54	He is active in the foundation of the Society of Arts. The third and fourth enlargements of Teddington Church take place.
1755–61	S.H. serves as Vice-President of Society of Arts.
1758	He publishes *A Treatise on Ventilators*.
1761	S.H. dies at Teddington on 4 January.

The farther researches we make into this admirable scene of things,
the more beauty and harmony we see in them.
STEPHEN HALES, *Vegetable Staticks* (1727)

His [Hales's] experiments and enquiries,
relative to the theory of vegetation,
are the basis of all our subsequent information.
SIR J. E. SMITH, *Correspondence of Linnaeus* (1821)

VENTILATOR: an instrument contrived by Dr Hales
to supply close places with fresh air.
SAMUEL JOHNSON,
Dictionary of the English Language (1755)

Though a Man of a Baronet's family,
and of one of the best houses in Kent,
yet was his [Hales's] Humility so prevalent,
that he did not disdain the lowest offices, provided they tended
to the good of his fellow creatures.
GILBERT WHITE to Robert Marsham (1791)

CHAPTER I

Family background and
early education

In that edition of *The Baronetage* of England which gave so much pleasure to Sir Walter Elliot of Kellynch-Hall there may be found three
'handsome duodecimo pages' devoted to the family of 'HALES, of
BEAK(E)SBOURNE, KENT', and headed with a date of creation, 12 July 1660, as ancient and honourable as the Elliots' own.[1]
Another and slightly earlier *Baronetage* gave five *quarto* pages to Hales of
Beakesbourne,[2] but two of these pages were largely made up of long
footnote references to a younger brother far removed from succession
to the title. The scientific achievements and philanthropic works of
Stephen Hales, B.D., F.R.S.,[3] there listed, added lustre to the family
name, and are of course the principal subjects of the present study.
Equally the fact that this celebrated and benevolent philosopher was 'a
man of a Baronet's family, and of one of the best houses in Kent', struck
the minds of his contemporaries, even when it was to contrast his rank
in society with his humility of demeanour.[4] His willingness to carry on
bizarre experiments irrespective of public criticism, and his assumption
of an almost patriarchal authority over his parishioners, may both have
been in part derived from a sense of assurance given to him by his birth:
while some of his success in the prosecution of public causes undoubtedly depended on the influence of his family.[5] Some account of
his forbears and relatives may therefore provide, in the conventional
manner, an opening for this biography of Stephen Hales.

The family originated at Hales in Suffolk, hence the name, and then
migrated to Kent in the late Middle Ages. From Sir John Hales, Baron
of the Exchequer in the reign of Henry VIII, sprang three branches of
the family which held estates and influence in Kent by the seventeenth
century: the senior but apparently the least wealthy, 'Hales of Dungeon,
Canterbury', the junior and richest 'Hales of Woodchurch', and the
intermediate 'Hales of Beakesbourne' from whom Stephen Hales was
descended.[6] Like other leading families of that fertile county, the
Haleses combined the skills of estate management with traditions of
social leadership and responsibility. Dr Allan Everitt, the historian of

the Kentish community for the period, has written of a 'corporate sense shared by many counties. But [which] contemporaries agreed . . . was particularly marked in Kent, and modern research confirms their impression. The origins of the gentry help to explain it . . . between 80 and 90 per cent of the gentry as a whole, including virtually all the "county" families were reckoned gentle before the Tudor period . . . It is not surprising,' continues Dr Everitt, 'that such a community . . . should develop an ethos of its own.' This he believes was made up of a sense of duty to dependents, and the social structure that underlay such patriarchalism.[7]

The household into which Stephen was born had at its head his grandfather, Sir Robert Hales of Beakesbourne, and included his father and mother, besides his numerous brothers and sisters, with other relations as well as the servants who would be counted in those days as members of the family. Sir Robert might have echoed the words of his fellow Kentishman Sir George Sondes, who thought the role of the master of a household was to see its members 'perform the outward duties of God's service, as prayer and going to church, and to show them the way by his own godly example', and claimed he had fulfilled his obligations to be charitable and to be hospitable to rich and poor alike. In his will Sir Robert Hales acquitted 'the Executors of my late son Thomas Hales [Stephen's father] of all that he owes me or may seem to owe me by reason of cohabitation and housekeeping for many years'.[8]

Though Robert Hales welcomed the King's return in 1660 and received his Baronetcy within two months of the Restoration, he had not in previous years shown the same enthusiasm for the Royal cause as earned his Woodchurch cousins the especial favour of the Court. He did not sit in Parliament after 1660 and appears to have been content to remain aloof from national affairs for the remainder of his long life. The subsequent support given by his grandsons to the Revolution settlement suggests that he bequeathed them 'Whiggish' principles and the religious strictness of two of them – Robert and Stephen – may have been partly derived from the Puritan background of this sometime 'lay leader of the Kentish Independents'. Thomas, the elder grandson, later carried on his family branch's political traditions as a Member of Parliament but he was said to be 'a man of pleasure' and, by an ironic paradox, to be unlikely to undertake the important work of converting his Jacobite cousins from 'Popery'.[9]

Sir Robert's son and heir and Stephen's father was Thomas Hales, the elder, of whom little is recorded save his numerous progeny. He was born 'about 1640' and seems to have studied, in reverse of the usual order (perhaps because of the unsettled circumstances of the period) first at the Inner Temple and then at Magdalen College, Oxford. In 1662 he married Mary Wood, a fourteen-year-old Hertfordshire heiress, and two years later the first of their twelve children was born, nine of whom were to survive. He died in 1692, his wife having pre-deceased him by five years. Stephen, then fourteen, was the youngest boy, and the next but youngest of all the children.[10]

Stephen tells us nothing of his parents and their influence on his up-bringing. His eldest brother, Thomas, now heir to the Baronetcy, was twenty-six years of age in 1692 and had, like his father, been admitted to the Inner Temple. In 1688 he had made a much-prized match with the sister and heiress of Sir Charles Pym of Brymore in Somerset thus joining, in the words of a modern authority, 'two great estates by this important marriage'. After his grandfather's death in 1693 he succeeded to the title, and although old Sir Robert's remaining lands passed to the next brother Robert, he supervised the management of all the estates and continued to reside in the family home at 'Howletts' in Beakes-bourne, which Stephen revisited in later years.[11]

Sir Thomas served as Member of Parliament for three periods be-tween 1701 and 1747. He was called 'a man of pleasure' and evidently made the most of his visits to London. His son and heir, Sir Thomas Hales (II) also had a parliamentary career, so that Stephen would have at least one relative and for many years two in the House of Commons who could assist him in the myriad negotiations with public authorities he undertook on behalf of charitable causes. Sir Thomas (I) was ac-quainted with Sir Hans Sloane and Robert, first Baron Romney, Stephen's Royal Society associates, though there is no evidence to suggest that he took an interest in his brother's complicated experiments. His connection with Sir Hans may have been as a patient of the great physician, and Lord Romney was a fellow Kentish man who became his son-in-law. The marriage of Thomas Hales (III) to Mary Marsham, Lord Romney's sister, in 1723 cemented Stephen's association with the Marsham family which gained him the friendship of two members of the Upper House and enabled him to assist in the foundation of the Society of Arts in the early 1750s.[12]

In order of seniority amongst Stephen's brothers after Thomas came Charles, Robert and William. Charles lived until 1747, when the

Beakesbourne Register notes his death in the Low Countries;[13] throughout these years there is no sign of an association with Stephen. Nearer in age to Stephen were Robert and William – nineteen and eighteen respectively in 1692. Robert was made heir to the bulk of the family fortune by their grandfather and in a few years departed on a protracted grand tour, when he acquired a remarkable skill in foreign languages and a detailed knowledge of the Protestant interest on the Continent.

From 1716 to 1728 he was to hold the important position of Clerk to the Privy Council in Ordinary and be specially concerned with diplomatic affairs.[14] William was apprenticed in 1693 to a wealthy London goldsmith, whose partner he became in an important firm of bankers. He was made a freeman of the Goldsmiths' Company in 1703 and a liveryman in 1705.[15] We do not know if he had much to do with Stephen until misfortune struck both him and Robert in later years. Robert, on the other hand, came into close contact with Stephen through the Society for Promoting Christian Knowledge which their mutual friend Thomas Bray founded in 1698. The Society's Secretary from 1708–1743 was Henry Newman who became the confidant of both Robert and Stephen and who shared some of Stephen's scientific interests. Though Stephen did not join the s.p.c.k. until 1722, we have abstracts of letters exchanged by the brothers in Henry Newman's hand, probably written when Robert was working hard as a roving ambassador on behalf of the Society in Europe (1700–14). Robert spent his estate freely on behalf of the Society and other good causes and by 1721 was beginning to be pressed by creditors. That was the year of the South Sea debacle and William's banking firm failed. The climax came eight years later when William was charged with forging a promissory note valued at £6,400 and Robert was apprehended as 'confederating' in the offence. Then Stephen came forward and stood bail for Robert, and appears to have assisted him financially until his death in 1735. William died of gaol fever in Newgate soon after his trial and we may assume this strengthened Stephen's concern for prison reform. Robert's widow and elder daughter came to live with Stephen, and he was to make the latter his heiress.[16]

Stephen was also to retain some association with his sisters: the youngest, Elizabeth (two years his junior), married the Revd John Metcalfe, when Stephen himself performed the ceremony; Ann, the next youngest (six years older than Stephen), whose husband's name,

4

Samuel Milles, Esq., of Herne, figured with Stephen's in a family settlement; Catherine (eight years older than Stephen) did not marry and continued to live with Thomas at Howletts, where presumably Stephen would have met her over the years. The oldest of his sisters was Mary (eleven years his senior), who married the Revd and Hon. Robert Booth, Dean of Bristol and Archdeacon of Durham, and it was to one of her ten children that Stephen wrote the only purely personal letter whose contents are known to us today. He wrote it to Mary's fourth son Nathaniel Booth in 1741, and it was published many years afterwards in the *Gentleman's Magazine* as an 'original letter from Dr. Hales'. It consoles Nathaniel on the death of his sister, and though it was probably written in some haste and distress, it marshals the comforts of religion in the same simple and direct style he used in his scientific writings.[17]

It has already been suggested that old Sir Robert Hales passed on to some of his grandchildren an attitude of gravity and religious zeal. Himself a former student of Corpus Christi College, Cambridge, he was said 'with his family' to have been a 'constant hearer' of the 'very pious' Thomas Ventris, a graduate of Corpus and an ejected Puritan minister. Dr Clark-Kennedy suggested that Ventris's influence on Sir Robert led to Stephen's own admission to Corpus Christi in 1696,[18] yet there appears to be no evidence of non-conformist influences affecting the education of Stephen Hales. Whatever memories his father and grandfather may have cherished of their Puritan past, they were content that their progeny should be reared in the Church of England. For Stephen Hales the true faith would always be 'the Protestant Religion by law established' and if he inherited from his forbears the habits of personal piety they had cultivated during the Commonwealth, he also learnt the respectful acceptance of the restored fabric of Church government which his family showed as near neighbours to the Primatial See of Canterbury.[19]

In a brief autobiographical note composed at the age of sixty-five, Stephen stated that he was sent to Cambridge after having been 'educated in grammar learning under Mr. St. Clare at Kensington, and under the Rev. Mr Richard Johnson at Orpington in Kent', while Bishop Hildesley claimed, shortly after Stephen's death, that his father, the Revd Mark Hildesley, 'had the honour of his earliest erudition as a private preceptor, at his rectory house in Kent'.[20] From this meagre evidence we can only speculate that Stephen's schooling took the following form.

When he was about eleven years old he was sent to a Kensington boarding school kept by a Mr St Clare. That such an individual existed and kept house on a substantial scale in Kensington – a place with some reputation as a centre for private education – from 1688 to 1692 can be deduced from entries in the parish rate book. Otherwise nothing seems to be known of Mr St Clare and his school, though it cannot be a coincidence that the Revd Richard Johnson also conducted a school there from a date in the 1690s until 1707, when a notice appeared referring to 'Mr. Johnson's late Boarding-School . . . where is taught by experience'd Masters whatever is usual in other Boarding Schools, to fit youth either for the University or for Common Business'.[21] It may well be that Johnson took over St Clare's school, though this would have been after Stephen had left, for Stephen recalled that he was educated 'under Mr. St. Clare at Kensington, and under the Rev. Richard Johnson at *Orpington in Kent*'. [Author's italics]

Although Johnson is a far more fully documented figure than St Clare, we must again rely on inference in regard to the part he played in Stephen's education. Until 1689 he was a near neighbour of Stephen's family, being Head Master of the King's School, Canterbury, and rector of Nackington, a village next door to Beakesbourne. After he refused to take the oath of allegiance to William III, and quarrelled with the governors of the King's School, he lost both his living and his teaching position. Evidently he taught private pupils for a while at Orpington after 1689 before setting up or, perhaps, taking over, the boarding school in Kensington. We can at least assume that Stephen benefited from Johnson's celebrated 'extensive and accurate acquaintance with the grammatical properties of the Latin tongue', and his determination to reform the 'common methods of teaching them'.[22]

The next change in Stephen's schooling perhaps occurred when his grandfather died at the close of 1693. For the boy would have become the responsibility of his elder brother, now Sir Thomas Hales of Beakesbourne, Bart. We can conjecture that Stephen would have been brought home from Orpington at this crisis in his family's affairs and that at some time after April 1694, when he was nearly seventeen, he was sent to Murston, a village north of Beakesbourne (though nearer home than Orpington), where Mark Hildesley was the newly-inducted vicar. We may assume that the initiative came from Thomas, because it was he who had presented Mark Hildesley to the Murston living.

In view of Stephen's subsequent friendship with Bishop Hildesley

6

(born 1698) it is a little surprising that he should have omitted the Bishop's father from his list of teachers. Probably he regarded the private tuition he had received from Mark Hildesley as too informal for inclusion in the *Athenae Oxiensis*, and was content to mention only the 'grammar learning' he had received from the professional school-masters, St Clare and Johnson. So there is no reason to doubt what the Bishop would have been told by his father and which he recounted some sixty-seven years later. The gloss deriving from Stephen's fame as a scientist ought possibly to be discounted. The Bishop's full statement ran:

My father had the honour of his earliest erudition, as a private preceptor, at his rectory house in Kent; but soon discovering his too improveable genius, especially in the philosophical way to be confined to a country parson's institutions, he was sent to Cambridge, which I believe was not originally intended.[23]

We shall see that once his brothers had sanctioned this important step in his education, Stephen Hales entered a new environment which he would not leave until he was in his early thirties and where he would mature intellectual interests far beyond the influence which had sought to mould him in his early years.

CHAPTER II

Scientific education and background

Despite Bishop Hildesley's memories, nothing is known of Stephen Hales's early interests or abilities in the sciences.[1] Indeed, the first clear indication of any association with scientific matters appears during Hales's years at Cambridge University, specifically during his tenure there as a college fellow. Of the twelve years of Stephen Hales's residence at Corpus Christi College detailed information is available only for the last five. What he read and learned during the years at Cambridge when he qualified for the bachelor and master of arts degrees can be determined only by an inference which assumes that the educational practices found in one college or tutor can be generalized for all the others. To a large measure this cannot really be asserted. The pattern of compromise and neglect by which the University had adjusted to the Statutes of Queen Elizabeth (and the few modifying letters-patent of succeeding monarchs), as these became impractical or inconvenient, had produced a confusion of conflicting rules and precedents which allowed the colleges and their students considerable latitude in teaching and learning. During the course of the eighteenth century this permitted the notorious degeneration of Cambridge (and her sister university, Oxford), and while the situation had not, during Hales's years at the University, deteriorated that far, it was still largely a matter of pupil and tutorial initiative if a student was to acquire the education available to him.[2] It is clear, from Hales's later career, that he used that initiative, but how he used it during his early years at Cambridge remains unknown.

Hales enrolled in Corpus Christi College in the Easter term of 1696, at the age of eighteen. As was then customary he commenced residence the following Michaelmas term (autumn of 1696). The college he entered was one of no particular distinction, save a traditional association with the county of Norfolk and the See of Canterbury, a minor affinity for antiquarian pursuits, and a notable attachment to the Protestant Succession.[3] His class was a typical one of ten students, six of whom were from Norfolk.

Hales would not formally have been bound to any particular curriculum, though it may reasonably be assumed that he entered college with the intention of becoming a clergyman. In any event his course of study is unlikely to have varied from that generally followed in Cambridge colleges, where undergraduates were expected to study Latin grammar, some Greek, rhetoric, moral philosophy and ethics, logic and metaphysics, arithmetic, algebra, geometry (including chronology and geography) and trigonometry, as well as some astronomy and natural philosophy. As Hales continued to the M.A. he would add theology, some Hebrew, and more astronomy and natural philosophy to his programme of studies.[4]

In this programme the university professors can have been of little assistance, for none of them lectured regularly during Hales's years of formal study. Under the circumstances, the choice of a tutor was of primary importance to the student's education. From the first term in residence to the completion of the Master's degree, each student was expected to have a tutor, who was to be his guide and friend, responsible for his discipline and finances, and uniquely in charge of his education. Hales was assigned to the Revd Robert Moss, who, with Charles Kidman, appears to have divided tutorial responsibilities at Corpus, at least during Hales's first six terms.[5]

Assignment of a tutor was normally the responsibility of the college master, unless the student's family made a specific request. In this instance, there appears no reason why Hales's family would have done so. Certainly Moss would have been a more than adequate guide to most of Hales's studies as an undergraduate. In those areas where he lacked particular qualification, he might have employed an assistant, but seems not to have done so, perhaps from a reluctance to split tutorial fees. At least there is no record that Hales obtained additional tutorial supervision, neither for the undergraduate exercises of his final year of the B.A., nor for the three years of preparation for the M.A., when he must have directed his own studies as Moss had departed Cambridge for London. The record of his academic achievement would indicate that this was quite sufficient. He kept his 'acts and opponencies' and took the senate house examinations at the usual time, during his eleventh term in residence, and was placed twenty-second in the *Ordo Senoritatis* of the University in a competing class of 127 for the Lent term of 1699/1700.[6] He received his B.A. that term, was pre-elected a fellow of Corpus in April of 1702, became a fellow the following February, and qualified for the Master of Arts degree in Easter term of 1703.

9

The ability of Cambridge's colleges, even as unreformed, to prepare students for careers in the church has seldom been questioned and, from Hales's successful career as a clergyman, it is clear that he was so prepared. It is as a scientist, however, that Hales made his reputation. What did he learn of natural philosophy during this period, and from whom? This question remains unanswered and perhaps unanswerable. Neither Moss nor Kidman distinguished themselves in scientific studies and nothing, prior to 1704, is known of Hales being taught by any of the tutors or lecturers in Cambridge. From the general undergraduate curriculum at Cambridge, he must be assumed to have studied considerable (if elementary) mathematics and some natural philosophy. It is reasonable to suppose, however, that very little of his actual instruction can have been in the Newtonian natural philosophy of which he later became so distinguished an exponent. So little is it true that Cambridge was the home of Newtonianism when Hales studied for his B.A. and M.A. degrees, that it might be more accurate to state that Newtonian philosophy was all but unknown in the University.

Newton had, of course, lectured in mathematics, optics and mechanics from the Lucasian chair in mathematics, but few persons attended these lectures. In any event by the time that Hales arrived in Cambridge, Newton had already departed to fill the position of Warden of the Mint. He retained his Lucasian professorship, without lecturing, until 1699, when he appointed William Whiston his deputy. Whiston, however, did not commence lecturing until January 1700/01 and no university lectures in mathematics or natural philosophy were given in the interim. Not that this was significant to Hales's education, as students were discouraged from attending university lectures, but it does demonstrate that in natural philosophy as in all other subjects the primary responsibility for learning lay with the students and their college tutors. Most of the latter, and that surely includes those of Corpus Christi, were then teaching Cartesian philosophy and many were to continue doing so as late as 1730. Nor is this particularly surprising. Even had the tutors been aware of Newton's work, they had sparse instructional materials from which to teach. The *Principia* was unsuited for elementary instruction and, only when Richard Bentley's *Eight Sermons Preach'd at the Honourable Robert Boyle's Lecture* were published in 1692 was Newtonian philosophy at once placed in the mainstream of British theological apologetics. Bentley's book was rapidly adopted for tutorial use in college classes of moral philosophy.[7] It failed, however, to provide sufficient detail for significant use in natural philosophy.

In 1694 Samuel Clarke, of Gonville and Caius College, defended a Newtonian proposition for one of his 'acts', in the schools, and in 1697, he published the first edition of his Latin translation of Jacques Rohault's *Traité de Physique*. The translation was made at the suggestion of Clarke's Cartesian tutor and though it begins the practice of adding Newtonian notes in opposition to the Cartesian text, the annotations are chiefly derived from Newton's optical papers of the 1670s. Not until the edition of 1702 (just one year before Hales obtained the M.A.) did Clarke's *Rohault* attain a significant confrontation of Cartesian text and Newtonian annotation.[8] That same year David Gregory's *Astronomiae Physicae et Geometricae Elementa*, and John Keill's *Introductio ad veram physicam* appeared, both Newtonian works based on their authors' lectures at Oxford. Gregory's *Astronomiae*, a five hundred page folio, was not for beginners, but Keill's work marked the beginning of purely Newtonian texts. Together with Clarke's *Rohault*, it permitted a start in teaching elementary Newtonian natural philosophy. It is indicative of the slight impact of Newton on Cambridge during these early years that many colleges continued to teach Cartesianism, and though several made use of Clarke's increasingly polemical editions of *Rohault* (the edition of 1710 consistently argues against the Cartesian text), others used Descartes' own writings. As late as 1708, the Cambridge University Press published an edition of still another Cartesian text, Jean Le Clerc's *Physica, sive de Rebus Corporeis*. About 1707, only one year before Hales departed from Cambridge, Richard Laughton, a tutor of Clare College, began to build a reputation as a teacher by suggesting some Newtonian propositions to be defended in the schools; at the same time, however, a fellow tutor at Clare, Robert Greene, presented his pupils with an anti-Newtonian 'Greenian' philosophy, later described in his *Principles of Natural Philosophy* (1712) and *Principles of the Philosophy of Expansive and Contractive Forces* (1727).

Thus, it can hardly be assumed that Hales was formally instructed in Newtonian philosophy, because of some supposed pervasive Newtonianism at Cambridge between 1696 and 1703. There is, nonetheless, ample evidence that before he left Cambridge in January 1708/09, Hales had already become acquainted with the Newtonian mechanical philosophy and with most of the authorities from whom he derived the Newtonian physiology and chemistry which lay at the roots of his major scientific work of subsequent years. A combination of circumstances, in Hales's life and at Cambridge, makes it probable that these were acquired during the five years between his obtaining the M.A. degree and his departure to become perpetual curate of Teddington, Middlesex. When Hales became a Fellow of Corpus in 1703, he entered a position for which there were neither duties nor responsibilities. Unless a fellow became a tutor or university professor (and Hales did not), life in a college residence could be exceedingly dull and empty. As Hales probably was remaining in residence at Corpus only until the Teddington living, an indirect gift of his family, became vacant, it is unlikely that he planned to keep the rigorous Divinity acts and exercises required of a resident fellow. He had, therefore, complete leisure to engage himself in any line of study he might choose.

This leisure was available to him shortly after Whiston began a regular course of lectures in Newtonian natural philosophy from the Lucasian chair. Moreover, Newton's *Opticks*, which presented that philosophy on a basis at once less technically demanding and more broadly relevant to the whole range of scientific problems, was first published in 1704. Within two years another edition, in Latin but broadening the scope still further through an additional set of seven queries, was published. In 1703 Joan Francis Vigani, who had lectured privately for years at Cambridge, was named Professor of Chemistry, and provided a chemical laboratory at Trinity as part of Bentley's efforts to concentrate science teaching in that college. Vigani continued lecturing periodically until 1712.[9] Bentley also attempted to establish an astronomical observatory at Trinity and, for that purpose, employed a young protege of Newton and Whiston, Roger Cotes, who was, in addition, named first incumbent of the Plumian Professorship of Astronomy and Experimental Philosophy, established in 1704. Cotes lectured in astronomy and, with Whiston, in pneumatics and hydrostatics at least from 1707.[10] During the same period lectures in anatomy and physiology were apparently delivered privately by James Keill and, from about 1706 and a time thereafter, by George Rolfe, who was named Professor of Anatomy in 1707.[11]

That Corpus Christi, and with it Stephen Hales, was caught up in this flood of scientific activity is made clear in the *Memoirs* of William Stukeley, who was admitted to Corpus, as a medical student, in November 1703. Stukeley's tutor, in subjects of natural philosophy and mathematics, was Robert Danny, who read to his pupils in arithmetic, algebra, geometry, trigonometry, astronomy and philosophy; among the books they used were Samuel Clarke's edition of *Rohault* (probably the edition of 1702) and his Boyle Lectures. Stukeley also saw 'many Philosophical Experiments in Pneumatic Hydrostatic Engines & Instruments performed . . . by Mr. Waller', Fellow of Corpus from 1695 and Humanity lecturer there, who was to succeed Vigani as Professor of Chemistry in 1713.[12] Stukeley also records attendance at the chemical lectures of Vigani, botany expeditions into the surrounding country, visits to the rooms of John Gray, a medical student junior to Stukeley at Corpus, whose uncle, Stephen Gray, then assisting Cotes with the Trinity observatory, showed them some electrical experiments. He witnessed Rolfe's dissections (and probably had previously heard James Keill's lectures, for he visited Keill in 1708 at Northampton) and, in a room provided by his tutor, Stukeley claims to have performed chemical experiments and animal dissections.

Through all these activities Stephen Hales accompanied Stukeley: botanizing trips, chemical experiments and dissections, electrical demonstrations, even studies of the 'doctrine of Optics & Telescopes & Microscopes' and of astronomy. Hales was unlikely to have been strongly educated in medical subjects prior to 1703 and, given his practical bent, he may well have reasoned (correctly) that medical learning would be useful to a parish clergyman. He could, that is, have joined Stukeley as a fellow tyro in medical learning and this is how Stukeley describes their relationship. But Stukeley wrote after Hales had achieved fame as a scientist and, never backward in pushing his claims, was clearly anxious to associate himself, as an equal, in Hales's scientific education. Now Stukeley's teachers, Danny and Waller, would be newly educating themselves, as they taught others, in Newtonian philosophy. As Hales was over twenty-five to Stukeley's seventeen, it seems more likely that he joined the teachers in activities in which Stukeley participated as a junior pupil. Some of Stukeley's remarks support this interpretation of their relative positions. It was Hales who designed a machine to represent the motions of planets according to Newton's system (an orrery); Stukeley, an accomplished draughtsman, drew a picture of that machine. When the botanizing party went 'simpling together', Stukeley was set the task of drawing a map of the region and sketching the additional specimens to be put into a revision of John Ray's *Catalogus* of Cambridgeshire flora. And surely that room in the college, given to Stukeley by his tutors for chemical

13

experiments and dissections, is the same as the 'private Elaboratory in Bennet College', where, later Cambridge tradition held, Hales planned 'those Statical Enquiries which have opened a new road into Nature'.[13] Certainly Hales was later to declare that his experiments on animals had begun some twenty years before publication of those on vegetables (i.e., about 1707) and one of the anatomical preparations (a lead cast of the lungs) which Stukeley claims to have made at Corpus is identified, in the biographical sketch of Hales written by his friend, Peter Collinson, to be the invention of Stephen Hales.[14]

Whatever may have been the circumstances of Hales's scientific studies at Corpus it is clear that he had been introduced, either directly or through the works of Samuel Clarke, John Keill and William Whiston, to Newton's *Principia* and his *Opticks*, that he knew of James Keill's work in anatomy and physiology (there is reference to a personal communication from Keill in the *Haemastaticks* as well as to works by Keill in both volumes of the *Statical Essays*); that he was acquainted with the pneumatic and hydrostatic studies of Whiston and Cotes and had received an introduction to chemistry in the lectures of Vigani. When the second volume of John Harris's *Lexicon Technicum*, containing an exposition of the ideas of Newton, John and James Keill, and of their friend, John Freind, was published in 1710, Stephen Hales's name was on the list of subscribers. The *Vegetable Staticks*, published in 1727, lists among the most prominent authorities cited, the names of Newton, James Keill and John Freind. Any examination of the major influences on Hales's work must, therefore, begin, at least, with a study of the general attitudes expressed by these men, and it is of small concern that most of the available information appears in books published after Hales had left Corpus.[15] Except for the *Hydrostatical and Pneumatic Lectures* of Roger Cotes, the relevant books were all published before Hales had written the first of his most important works, the *Vegetable Staticks*, and most of them are explicitly named in that book.

Although the general attitudes of Newton and the early Newtonians provided an epistemological (and theological) frame for Hales's natural philosophy, the details of Newton's astronomy or mechanics do not enter his considerations. Most of Hales's original work was done in areas now defined as animal and plant physiology and pneumatic chemistry. For these the significant Newtonianism was the theory of matter and its action described in the *Principia* and the *Opticks*, as interpreted by the Newtonians Hales had read, and as applied by them to the subjects of his research.[16] As broadly discussed by Samuel Clarke and John Keill, for example, this meant that all matter ultimately consisted of small, hard, physically indivisible particles (or 'Corpuscles') possessed of *vis inertia* and endued with powers of attraction and repulsion acting at a distance across void space. The particles variously combine and move under the influence of these forces, and all phenomena were ultimately to be explained by the various magnitudes, figures, textures, positions, motions and forces between complex particles formed of these primitive ones.[17] This 'dynamic corpuscular' view is expressed most clearly by Newton in the Queries added to the 1706 Latin *Opticks* (particularly Query 22), though it is at least adumbrated in the 1687 *Principia* and 1704 *Opticks*. Neither the query form in which it appears in the *Opticks* nor the repeated positivistic assertions in the *Principia*, by which the view is qualified or even denied, were taken seriously by Newton's followers, though many were prepared to agree that the forces were not inherent properties of matter, but instead revealed the mediate presence and action of God in the Universe. This interpretation would not presumably have been unacceptable to Hales, but he does not examine the metaphysical details of his Newtonianism. Accepting both particles and forces without question, Hales was concerned with their application to the understanding of experimental practice.

He would not have learned the application of this Newtonian dynamic corpuscularity to chemistry through the lectures of Vigani, whose *Medulla Chymiae* (first published in 1682 but enlarged and republished four times) and the extant record of his lectures (approximately 1699–1700), do not reveal much more than a pharmaceutical chemist interested in the empirical compounding of medicines. There are occasional disparaging remarks about van Helmont and Tachenius and a few favourable comments about Nicolas Lemery, whose Cartesianism sometimes appears in Vigani's occasional mechanistic explanations of chemical phenomena.[18] Nor would Hales have learned Newtonian chemistry from his post-Cambridge reading of the works of Lemery (even in the translation of James Keill), Boyle, John Mayow, Etiènne Geoffroy or George Wilson, to all of whom he refers in the *Vegetable Staticks* (1727) or *Haemastaticks* (1733).[19] Hales also cites the chemical writings of Herman Boerhaave, but it appears that he rather influenced than was influenced by them. For the origin of Hales's mechanistic chemistry one must go to John Freind and to Freind's friend and mentor John Keill.

In 1708 John Keill published, in his *Philosophical Transactions* paper,

'In qua Leges Attractionis aliaque Physices Principia traduntur', an extension of Newton's dynamic corpuscular Queries of the 1706 *Opticks*. Thirty theorems detail the construction of heterogeneous substances from homogeneous primitive particles as a consequence of a non-gravitational attractive force between them. Keill assumes that force decreases inversely as some greater power than the square of distance and attempts to reduce explanation of such phenomena as cohesion, fluidity, elasticity, crystallization, precipitation, congelation, etc., to mechanical laws involving compound particle size, shape and attractive force.[20] His discussion is necessarily qualitative (for he could determine values for neither force nor particle size), but his ingenuity inspired the more detailed application of the same principles to chemistry by John Freind. Freind's *Praelectiones Chemicae* of 1709 supposedly prints lectures delivered at Oxford in 1704, but is so clearly dependent upon the ideas expressed in the Queries to Newton's *Opticks* of 1706 and in Keill's paper of 1708 that it is hard to imagine that it had not been substantially modified before publication.[21] Freind declares that short-range forces of attraction are clearly evidenced in the very nature of things. To Keill's use of particle size, shape and attractive force, he adds a greater dependence upon momentum in explaining chemical phenomena. He is not interested in discussing the causes of the forces, nor the unique and invariant properties of substances, but only in the chemical operations, such as dissolution, calcination, precipitation, etc. Like Keill's, his work is essentially qualitative; like Keill, Freind concerns himself only with attractive forces and, like Keill, he does not consider gases at all in his explanations of phenomena. For the origin of Hales's singular use of repulsive forces in a chemical context applied to gases, we must turn to the pneumatic studies of Whiston and of Cotes.

Exactly what Whiston and Cotes may have said during Hales's years at Cambridge cannot now be determined, but some information on their teaching may be extracted from their subsequent publications. In 1714 William Whiston and Francis Hauksbee published a syllabus of the course of lectures in natural philosophy they were delivering in London. According to Whiston, that course was based on the lectures he and Cotes had first delivered in Cambridge in 1707.[22] References in the syllabus to: lifting weights 'by a Chain of inflated Bladders, with its application to Muscular Motion': to examination of 'the more hidden Properties of the Air', and its influence on the causes of magnetism, elasticity of springs, cohesion of matter and sphericity of fluid drops, capillarity, sounds, fire and flame, and the life of animals: and to the uses of a manometer in the measurement of air pressure in bladders, etc., do give some indication of the nature of the pneumatic demonstrations which Hales witnessed while at Corpus Christi. Roger Cotes's hydrostatic and pneumatic lectures were published posthumously by his cousin, Robert Smith, in 1738. Smith suggests that the lectures were left unchanged from the form and substance delivered by Cotes from 1707, and their tone is certainly that of an early stage in the evolution of eighteenth-century Newtonianism. Cotes is most outspokenly anti-Cartesian in his denunciation of *materia subtiles* as a 'way of juggling' now to be laid aside (this despite his editing of the 1713 *Principia* which re-introduces the subtle fluid of the aether). He concerns himself primarily with simple hydrostatics and pneumatics, at the level of Archimedes, Pascal and Boyle, but there is no doubt of his acceptance of particulate matter acting through powers of attraction and repulsion. This becomes important in his explanation of capillarity and of the elasticity of the air, which is a consequence of repulsive forces between air particles, reciprocally proportional to their distances, as was demonstrated in the second book of the *Principia* and further confirmed by late additions to the *Opticks*. As Hales could later have remembered the suggestion, in John Keill's paper of 1708, that the ascent of sap in plants and trees might be explained by attractive forces, so he might have recalled that Cotes had made a similar suggestion, as well as a still more pertinent and explicit reference to the increase or decrease of the elastic force of air by the subtraction or addition of attractive substances.[23]

The references by Keill and Cotes to the motion of sap in plants were probably the only botanical carry-over from Hales's education to his work on plant physiology, for though he worked with plants, he never was a botanist. In later life he claimed once to have known 'most English plants'.[24] This may be a distant recollection of those 'simpling expeditions' mentioned by Stukeley, but the very term 'simpling' reveals the purpose of the expeditions as the collecting of medicinal plants, probably in connection with Vigani's emphasis on materia medica. John Ray's Cambridge catalogue, which only briefly outlines his system of classification, was clearly used for its locations not for intrinsic botanical instruction, and Hales makes no reference to Ray's *Philosophical Transactions* papers on plant anatomy or physiology. By the time Hales came to write the *Vegetable Staticks* he had informed himself on the plant anatomy studies of Marcello Malpighi and makes some use of Nehemiah

17

Grew's *Anatomy of Plants*, but the plant book he is most familiar with is the eminently practical *Gardener's Dictionary* (1711) of Philip Miller. He might have read Grew's work as early as his Cambridge days, but there is no obvious reason why he should have done so, and the nature of his work with plants is such that the dynamic corpuscular mechanisms of John Keill and Roger Cotes, and particularly the applications of these to animal physiology by James Keill, would be of considerably more significance than the work of Ray, Malpighi or Grew.[25]

Inspection of the *Vegetable Staticks* and of the *Haemastaticks* will reveal that, next to Newton, the person whose work most influenced Hales was James Keill. It was Keill's *Medicina Statica Britannica* which, indeed, provides the pattern and motivation of Hales's studies on vegetables and it was Keill's mechanistic physiology, as revealed in his *The Anatomy of the Humane body abridged* and his *Account of Animal Secretion*, which suggested the problems for investigation, inspired the design of the experiments, and provided the mode of their interpretation for the *Haemastaticks*.[26] James Keill represents the culmination of that speculative mode of physiological explanation usually called the 'iatro-physical' (meaning literally 'medical-physical') but, particularly as it developed in Britain, a better name might be iatro-hydrodynamicist, for its primary interest was in the motion of body fluids studied from the physician's point of view. Having decided that the greater part of the animal body was fluid, this school of physician-physiologists reasoned that both normal and abnormal functions of the body were to be explained by changes in the quantity, texture or velocity of motion of the various kinds of fluids. The major influence of Newton on the British members of this group is in their disdainful rejection of Cartesian 'aetherial, subtile matter' and their persistent attempts to quantify their interpretations (regardless of the inadequacy of their data). James Keill raises the speculative impulses of the group to a height of sophistication, adding experimental determination of some of the parameters and, under the influence of Newton's *Opticks* and his brother's paper of 1708, the concept of dynamic corpuscularity. When he declares that the body consists of tubes or vessels full of blood, or of the fluids separable from blood, he presents mathematical-experimental arguments producing a quantitative estimate of the fluid-solid ratio. He describes computations by which to evaluate Pitcairne's estimate of the force by which the lungs act or that exerted by the stomach on food. He enters into a long and elaborate computation (based on measurements of tubular cross-sections, velocity of blood from cut arteries, volumes of parts of the vascular system as cast in wax, etc.) of the force of the heart. Arguing that the blood consists of variously sized particles formed of primary particles under attractive forces, Keill produces explanations of muscular motion and of the range of glandular humours. From his own experiments, and those reported by Robert Boyle, Keill is convinced that air penetrates the substance of the lungs and mixes with the blood. There the air is strongly compressed by surrounding, mutually attractive particles of blood; but action of the will releases into muscular fibres, still smaller (and therefore more attractive) particles of animal spirits which attract blood particles more strongly than they attract one another; air particles are thus released from their inelastic state and expand, shortening the muscle and producing motion. Finally, supposing the blood to consist of no more than five compound particles, these five can join in as many as twenty-six different simple combinations, and many more elaborate ones. As the five particles have different quantities of motion, the effects of attraction between them will vary, in different places in the body, as a function of blood velocity in those places. The glands secern sieve humoreal combinations as a function of their size, and are positioned in the body at just those places where the blood moves with a velocity appropriate to produce the right combinations.[27] Here we can see exhibited nearly every one of the parameters Hales was later to be concerned to measure: heart pressure; blood velocity in various parts of the body, and its variation with circumstances; strength of body fibres; dimension of lung surface, etc. Here also is the concern first shown with the physiological effect of changes in air elasticity, blood viscosity and attractive force between particles. In Keill's physiological work, Hales found the last necessary addition to his scientific education in preparation for his own research. He was now prepared for the extended investigations which were to bring him fame as a scientist in his own right and which he would need to undertake side by side with his vocation as a parish priest.

CHAPTER III
Parish priest

When he left Cambridge early in 1709 to take up his post at Teddington, the science which had dominated Hales's last years at Corpus Christi must have ranked low in his immediate considerations. Those responsibilities of parish priest for which he had primarily prepared himself were now to be his, and there is every indication that he was always to regard his clerical role as his most important activity. Although Hales was ultimately to achieve his greatest successes in science and technology, the simplicity of character and serene self confidence which marked his entire life were rooted in his family origins and in his position as priest.

Hales began his long ministry in the Church of England at the time of the Sacheverell 'phrensy' and of the re-awakening of hope amongst nonjurors and Jacobites. Throughout his life he was to be an associate of High Churchmen and a venerator of Princes. Yet at no time did he preach or write in bitterness against Dissent or deviate in his support of the Protestant Succession. Family influences could well have made him adopt these attitudes, and he would have certainly have been encouraged to maintain and develop them during the formative years of his intellectual development at Corpus Christi College, Cambridge. Unlike many other Oxford and Cambridge Colleges in the reign of Queen Anne, Corpus Christi was said to be firmly attached to the Revolution and the succession in the House of Hanover. Hales's own tutor, Robert Moss, became successively Chaplain in Ordinary to William III, Queen Anne and George I, and obtained lucrative preferments which included the rich Deanery of Ely. In spite of his apparent ambition for worldly advancement, which distinguishes him from his pupil, Moss was earnest and active in his priestly vocation. His popular *Sermons and Discourses on practical subjects*, his support of hospitals and charity schools, and his private benevolence set a pattern for Hales to copy and were at one with the redeeming side of Latitudinarianism.[1]

In February 1708/9,[2] when he was thirty-one years old, Stephen Hales was presented to the 'perpetual curacy' of the Thameside parish of

Teddington in Middlesex and he served there until his death in 1761. The living was nominally in the gift of the Lord of the Manor, but when in 1671 the Bridgeman family increased the incumbent's stipend from £6 6s to £87 4s (twice the value of Hales's Cambridge fellowship), it received the right of alternate presentation.[3] Hales was connected with the family and this probably explains why he was chosen to receive the curacy by Sir John Bridgeman.[4]

Though not immune from the influences of the metropolis from which it was but fourteen miles distant, Teddington was very different from the bustling parishes of London. It was a village community of some 400 persons congregating around the little church of St Mary's and the modest manor house, which stood together near the river landing place, and in scattered dwellings interspersed with two or more inns, ranged along a high street. Away from this nucleus stood the house of the Bridgeman family, and one or two other 'gentlemen's residences', for the parish shared some of the fashionable reputation attached to neighbouring Twickenham and Richmond. Large low level open fields and a 450 acre common made up the landscape of the parish and provided food and labour for the majority of the inhabitants. The river-bank was its border for nearly two miles and inland it reached to the great parks of Bushey and Hampton Court. For Hales it proved a congenial environment for half a century of work in many spheres, and though successive generations of his parishioners could not quite maintain the standards he required of them he was long remembered in the parish with affection and admiration.[5]

Seven years after his induction at Teddington, Hales was presented to the living of Porlock in Somerset by the Lord Chancellor, the Rt Hon. William Cowper who may have heard of his work at the Royal Society. Dr Clark-Kennedy has pointed out the remoteness of Porlock, which was 150 miles from London, on the borders of Exmoor, but he incorrectly concluded that Hales 'probably never even went to see his new parish'. The s.p.c.k. still preserves a record of a letter it received from Hales in September 1722, 'Desiring a Packet of the Society's Books . . . may be directed to him at Porlock, near Minehead in Somerset, by the Taunton Wagon'.[6] This would have been his last visit as Rector; earlier in the year he had arranged to exchange the living, and, on 9 February 1722/3, he was installed as Rector of the beautiful village of Farringdon in Hampshire, which became his summer home for many years. At Farringdon, Hales found accounts of ancient customs and festivities in the

Parish records which attracted his interest, and he noted that the Rectory garden was adjoined by a field of two acres, which presumably made it convenient for agricultural experiments.[7] By holding an ecclesiastical living or benefice first at Porlock and then at Farringdon, Hales was made ineligible to continue in his Cambridge Fellowship which he had been allowed to keep so long as he was simply the Perpetual Curate of Teddington. Since his sadly brief married life to the daughter of a Hertfordshire clergyman had terminated with the burial at Teddington in October 1721 of 'Mary Hales, my dear Wife', we may assume that Teddington became his main home, certainly from 1718 and probably before. There was no parsonage in the parish, so round about this date Hales purchased a 'copyhold dwelling House', with an acre and a half of gardens and 'Barns, Outhouses and Stables', where presumably he fitted up his famous laboratory.[8]

Professor Sykes has shown that the eighteenth century clergy of the London Diocese, to which Hales belonged, were 'the exception against the general sentence of slackness and inefficiency which is passed on their order as a whole'. Hales had received ordination at the hands of Dr Compton, and he undoubtedly strove to fulfil the trust committed to him by the aged Bishop.[9]

In his sermons Hales repeatedly stressed the Christian duties of charity and love.[10] It was a commandment, he taught, 'to be tender-hearted, gentle, meek, long-suffering, full of compassion, to abound in every good Work': He believed that, 'Among all the Christian Virtues', there was none 'more acceptable to God, or beneficial to Man, consider'd in his civil Capacity, than Benevolence'. Although he taught that human goodness was insufficient in itself and that 'the Love of God, and Obedience to his Word, and Humility and Faith in his Name and Promises, *the noble Principles of Christian Charity*, must always be acknowledged infinitely more excellent than the most perfect natural Tenderness of Man', he urged that this 'necessary and important Caution' should not 'be thought a Discouragement to good Works . . .'[11] Man should glorify God by 'living in the Practice of all virtuous Actions' as well as by 'Acts of Piety and Religion'. He used the promise of salvation and the threat of damnation to instil obedience to these precepts: '. . . If we neglect these his gracious Offers . . . then we may be assured, that God will exert his vengeful Wrath and Power, in our everlasting Perdition and Destruction.'[12]

At ordinary Sunday services Hales fulfilled his duties through sermons and readings from the scriptures. For the less frequent service of Holy Communion, he required his parishioners to prepare themselves by self-examination, restitution of wrong done to others, and charity and faith. On 6 December 1722, we find Hales writing to the S.P.C.K. from Teddington and ordering a supply of its books to 'be sent as soon as maybe, because he is desirous to distribute them with some other Books he has by him on the Sacrament . . . to be useful in preparing his Parishioners for the Xmas Sacrament'.[13] Although he bought large stocks of S.P.C.K. literature over the years, he ventured on one occasion to criticize an apparent departure from its generally strict standards. In April 1731, he wrote to the Society, objecting to its use of the text: 'and that even the just man falleth seven times in a day' in one of its manuals, which he believed had 'given a plea to some disorderly loose persons'.[14]

As a corresponding member of the Society, Hales was allowed to buy its books at a reduced price, and he took advantage of this facility from his election in 1722 until shortly before his death in 1761. For his parishioners he bought Bibles, Books of Common Prayer, catechisms and *The Whole Duty of Man* and as we shall see, played some part in the nationwide distribution of its more specialized literature.

Amongst the books in the first three 'packets' he ordered from the Society were 250 copies of the tracts 'Against Swearing' and 200 of the tracts 'Against Drunkness', publications which the Society had been distributing since the first year of its foundation. Hales's experiments on blood circulation had given him a particular abhorrence of drunkenness and in 1734 he published for the Society his anonymous *Friendly Admonition to the Drinkers of Gin, Brandy and other distilled Spirituous Liquors*, which it was still distributing in the nineteenth century. Hales was to campaign against spirit drinking through what he called his 'open public testimony . . . for near thirty years', but he also endeavoured to check the habit and other irregularities of conduct within the parishes under his charge.[15]

At Farringdon, he told the S.P.C.K. in 1726, he found himself 'placed among a sober and Industrious people'. In 1741 he calculated that the expectation of life there was one-third longer than at Teddington and that the life span at Farringdon was 'nearly the regular course of nature in this healthy air. For there are few in this Parish who disorder themselves, or impair their health by intemperance or debauchery. Most of them employ themselves in husbandry, the rest in laborious handicrafts . . .' He maintained his good opinion of his country parish in his old age, calling it, in a letter he wrote to David Hartley in 1757, 'one of the

23

most orderly Parishes in England'. Teddington, however, was too near to the evil influences of London:

I wish I could say the same of Teddington [he continued in his letter to Hartley], which being unhappily within the Gin Bills of Mortality, grows continually from bad to worse.[16]

Hales condemned drunkenness not only because of the harm that it did to men's bodies but because of what he called the '*bewitching of Naughtiness* in these fiery liquors'. He wished to maintain both the sobriety and morality of his parishioners. For what was considered the flagrant offence of fornication Hales imposed the ancient discipline of public penance (growing rarer in its use at this time), on eleven persons between 1723 and 1743. At Teddington he left a memorandum in the Parish Register of 'Persons who have done Public Penance in this Parish'. There was one performance on 16 February 1723, three on 16 April 1732 and one on each of the dates 13 June 1733, 16 October 1737 and 8 February 1740. At Farringdon according to a similar entry in the Register, only four penitents were disciplined. The custom was for the penitents to be clothed in a white sheet, given a white rod to hold, and to be made to stand barefoot outside the church until just before the Litany was recited, at which point they were brought inside to hear the sermon and to be prayed over. Mark Hildesley was 'edified' at the retention of this 'primitive' custom in his diocese of Man and we may assume that Hales thought it no less salutary. Writing to Hildesley in 1758, he remarked, 'that "we have lost all discipline in church and state", as the late excellent Bishop of London observed, in his last charge to us clergy, in St. Martin's church; whence he inferred, that the parochial clergy ought therefore to exert themselves with the more zeal to their parochial duties'.[17]

The sacred buildings to which the people came for sermons, sacraments and penance were also the object of his care. The church of St Mary at Teddington presented a special problem since it was in bad repair when Hales came to the parish and was too small for the continually increasing population of the village. In 1716 the church roof was repaired and a gallery and extension 'on the south west corner of the Church, viz. from the Church door to the Tower' constructed at a cost of £172 6s 10d. To raise this sum Hales organized a complicated rearrangement of pews and pew rights, involving the drafting of proprietorial instruments. Eighteen years later Hales took the initiative in enlarging the churchyard. 'About the year 1734' he afterwards noted in the Parish Register, 'I prevailed with Mr. Perkins then the Lord of the Manor to enlarge our church yard 15 feet on the North Side and 18 feet on the East Side in all 2190 square feet,' and he recorded that a further '65 feet on the East Side' was given by Mr Perkins' son in 1754. The church itself was again altered in 1748, 1753 and 1754:

Mem. – That it being found by long experience that the three Bells, which are inclosed in the Tower of this Church, can be heard at but a very little distance when the wind blows contrary, to the great inconvenience of the Parishioners, especially those who live the more distant: it was in the year 1748 agreed to inlarge three of the Tower Windows: and . . . to place a lantern on the Tower, in the room of the Shingled Spire, in which to hang a loud Bell, to be heard at a much greater distance, not only for the benefit of the serious and well disposed, but also as a constant memento to the Careless, the Negligent and the Profane; who with the wicked in Job are but too apt to say, '*Who is the Almighty that we should serve Him? And what profit should we have if we should pray unto him?*' (Job 21 15). The inscription on the Bell is '*Worship God.* 1748.' The weight of the Bell is 179 Pounds. The whole expense was £51.07.00.

A further enlargement took place in 1753 as the Church was:

too small to contain the number of Parishioners that ought to resort thither to join in the Worship of Almighty God. By consent of the Parishioners met in vestry, it was agreed to have it inlarged by building a new Aisle on the North Side, at the same dimensions as the South Aisle.

Then came the rebuilding of the Church tower:

and in the year 1754 the old Timber Tower which stood on the west end of the church was pulled down; and a new Brick Tower built . . .

Hales does not record his own generous donation of £200 which helped make up nearly half the cost of these enlargements.[18]

Through Hales's influence regular collections were made for the relief of paupers at the Sunday offertory and the Teddington Vestry saw to the efficient enforcement of the Poor Laws. The *Victoria County History of Middlesex* describes the methods of the Teddington Vestry in the mid-eighteenth century as 'concentrated largely on obtaining settlement certificates as a method of controlling applications for relief. They also paid some of the poor to open the gates which barred the main roads at the entrance to the village . . . almshouses [built *c.* 1740–45] . . .

25

were used as cheap or free dwellings for poor families, not as conventional workhouses'. The same authority speaks of Hales's frequent attendance and his 'very important part in the village life'.[19]

One purely secular contribution he made to the amenities of the community consisted in supervising the provision of a new water supply, 1754–55, a task which called for mathematical calculations of weights and measures, and must have been a source of some satisfaction to him as an application of the 'statical' method to an obviously valuable social purpose. He entered an account of the undertaking into the Parish Register:

1754. Mem. – That in order to have a constant Stream of fresh water thro' the Town, a Channel or Drain was dug about ten feet deep and 64 yards long . . . intercepting all the main springs . . . [and] a constant Stream of water was obtained which runs at the rate of about 30 tons in 24 hrs; and probably double that quantity of water might be procured if the channel was dug 64 yards further. The whole expense of this was £45.8.3-1/2, 15 guineas of which was paid by the Lord of the Manor, the rest by the contribution of the Gentlemen of three guineas each.

. . . In the year 1755 . . . a new ditch was cut . . . [and this not working] the drain was cut 64 yards more in length across the Springs which produced double the quantity [of water] . . .

The quantity of water which ran from the Springs was estimated by fixing in clay at the mouth of the covered Drain a small Trough, and placing inside it a vessel containing two quarts, which filled in three Swings of a pendulum beating seconds . . . By which means it was found that more than sixty Tons of water ran there in twenty-four hours.[20]

Farringdon, though more pliant in spiritual matters, was less receptive to his experimental ideas. In 1746 he told a correspondent: 'I have met with a great deal of that backwardness you mention in mankind to try new things, though never so reasonable. Though I furnished every Family at Farringdon with a Reed Cane [for preserving corn]; yet I do not find that it was used by any but at My House, and there with the desired good effect.' Undeterred he was seen at the close of his life, 'in the street' at Farringdon 'with his paint-pot before him, and much busied in painting white with his own hands the tops of the footpath posts that his Neighbours, might not be injured by running against them in the dark'. Hales's success as a parish priest in Middlesex and Hampshire was exemplified in the public tribute paid to him by the Dean of St Paul's who described him in 1754 as 'an excellent man, who hath been long an Ornament to his Profession, as a Clergyman, and to his Country as a Philosopher', and by his election as their Proctor by the Clergy of the Diocese of Winchester for the Convocation which met in the same year.[21]

Though Hales worked to the full as a parish priest he spent, in the words of Robert Master, his 'leisure . . . in a most studious and useful manner, through Improvements in Natural and Experimental Philosophy'. His Newtonian background would have allowed him no doubts about the compatibility of his profession and his scientific interests. The wonders of nature were a proof of the existence of God as Richard Bentley, with Newton's blessing, had long since proved in his Boyle lectures confounding atheism. In the preface to the *Haemastaticks*, Hales quoted the text Bentley used for his first sermon on *The Folly of Atheism*, 'The fool hath said in his heart there is no God,' and he also echoed words used in Bentley's third sermon *A Confutation of Atheism from the structure of Human Bodies* in his own on *The Wisdom and Goodness of God in the Formation of Man*. In 1692 Bentley had spoken of:

the many constituent parts of the bodies of men, all admirably compacted into so noble an engine; when we consider how innumerable parts must constitute so small a member as the finger, we cannot but look upon it or the whole body, wherein appears so much fitness, and use, and subserviency to infinite functions, any otherwise than as the effect of contrivance and skill, and consequently the workmanship of a most intelligent and beneficient Being.

Some sixty years later Hales reaffirmed that:

What is commonly ascribed to Nature, is the immediate Action of the Author of Nature. And the governing Power of God, is his creating Power continually repeated; so that his governing and preserving Power are, as it were, a continuance of his creating Power: We are not only at first fearfully and wonderfully formed, but fearfully and wonderfully preserved . . .

. . . What a vast Variety of Parts, differing from each other, are nourished by the same Blood, whereby *we are cloathed with Skin and Flesh, and fenced with Bones and Sinews*, and all these Parts are, not only in themselves of an admirable Texture, but also justly adapted to be useful to each other? With what excellent Art is that curious Hydraulick Engine the Heart formed, forcibly to impell the Blood and Rapidity through the minute Channels, and Meanders of the Body?

Bentley's last three Boyle lectures confounded atheism 'from the Origin and Frame of the World' on the basis of the then recently published gravitational theories of Newton. Hales again invoked Bentley to

27

justify his own notational studies of plants and animals. The introduction of the *Vegetable Staticks*, Hales's first book, ran:

The farther researches we make into this admirable scene of things, the more beauty and harmony we see in them: And the stronger and clearer convictions they give us, of the being, *power and wisdom of the divine Architect, who made all things to concur with a wonderful conformity, in carrying on, by various and innumerable combinations of matter, such a circulation of causes,* and effects, as was necessary to the great ends of nature . . .

Thus, in relation to those Planets which revolve about our Sun, the great Philosopher of our age has, by numbering and measuring, discovered the exact proportions that are observed in their periodical revolutions and distances from their common centers of motion and gravity: And that God has not only comprehended the dust of the earth in a measure, and weighed the mountains in scales, and the hills in a balance, Isai, xl. 12. but that he also holds the vast revolving Globes, of this our solar System, most exactly poised on their common center of gravity.

Twenty-four years later in the 'Crounian' Sermon Hales expounded the same idea and reaffirmed his belief in the creation:

What a multiplicity, variety, beauty, usefulness, and subservience to each other, may we with Pleasure observe, in contemplating the Works of Creation? Not only the Grandeur of this our solar System, and the other heavenly Bodies, declare the Glory of God, but also the exceeding Minuteness of microscopical Animals, and of their component Parts, shew forth the Skill and Power of the Creator.[22]

Since man was so evidently formed in the image of God it was worthwhile taking care to preserve the human frame from disease and abuse. Hales believed that scientific experiment not only disclosed the wonders of God but assisted in their maintenance; and thus 'researches into the Nature of Our Bodies' contributed to the 'Welfare of Mankind'. His investigations into 'animal oeconomy' were, he admitted, 'disagreeable', and their appalling cruelty did not go uncriticized even in his harsh period, yet they too, he believed, would provide the physician with useful knowledge and provide 'new and farther motives to adore and praise our All-Glorious Maker in his Works'.

He had begun to experiment on animals when he was a junior Fellow of Corpus and would, during the same period, have become accustomed to the appearance of blood and entrails through his companionship with Stukeley, who boasted of his indifference to such sights with the typical bravado of the medical student of all times. Hales continued his experiments as a parish priest at Teddington when he earned the well known reproaches of Alexander Pope who settled at nearby Twickenham in 1719. The scope and purpose of these experiments will be described in chapter V. He published them to the world in 1733 and in the same year wrote to another scientist/clergyman, the Revd John Mickleburgh, admitting that he had caused the death of sixty animals and stating that since further experiments 'would probably occasion the death of 2 or 300 Animals, so I do not think it proper for one of our Profession to engage any further in it'. Even for the sake of 'God's image' man, Hales could no longer justify the sacrifice of his other creatures.[23]

CHAPTER IV

The *Vegetable Staticks*

Stephen Hales made his first public appearance as a scientist before the Royal Society on 5 March 1718/19 when he informed 'the President that he had lately made a new Experiment upon the Effect of the Sun's warmth in raising the Sap in trees', and read a paper on that subject to the Society. He was thanked and urged to continue his experiments.[1] This request, in the phrase of Peter Collinson, 'was like the charge given by *Pharoah's* daughter to the mother of Moses to take care of her son'.[2] So eagerly and successfully did he continue those studies that on 14 June 1725 he showed the Society the greater part of a treatise which, as expanded by a chapter on factitious airs, was published in April 1727 as the *Vegetable Staticks*.[3]

With the publication of the *Vegetable Staticks*, Hales at once attained first rank as a scientist. This single work introduced the study of experimental plant physiology, was essential in the founding of pneumatic chemistry, and provided the eighteenth century with a prototype of experimental science. Yet prior to his paper of 1718 no indication exists in Hales's researches of any significant interest in plant physiology nor of any chemical investigations on gases. The extant record, including a statement by Hales himself in the preface to the *Vegetable Staticks*, suggests that from as early as 1707 to as late, at least, as 1713 his experiments related to animals with particular emphasis on the haemodynamic problems he was later to treat in his book, the *Haemastaticks*.[4] Hales does say that even then he had wished to 'discover the force of the sap in Vegetables', but in this he was to remain unsuccessful until 1720 (two years after his first paper on plants), while the majority of dated experiments in the *Vegetable Staticks* come from the period between 1724 and 1727. How did it happen that a promising course of animal experiments was interrupted for a series on plants, what led him to the emphasis on airs, and from where did Hales derive those experimental techniques which were at once so successful in themselves and so canonical in the work of succeeding plant physiologists?

It is true that most of the problems to which Hales addressed himself were of long standing. As early as 1693 an English translation, by John Evelyn, of Jean de La Quintinie's *The Compleat Gardner* declared that there existed:

. . . no part of Natural Philosophy yielding more excellent matter for contemplation, or being more fertile in useful and delightful experiments than that which teaches of Vegetation. For I know there are abundance of fine and curious questions proposed in it: as for instance whether the sap circulates in Plants as the blood does in Animals? Whether the roots do actively attract or only passively, without any action on their side, receive the juice which serves for the nourishment of every Plant . . .?[5]

Moreover, such scientists as Marcello Malpighi, Nehemiah Grew and John Ray had concerned themselves with aspects of these problems, but their work had approached the subject anatomically and by analogy with animals. No doubt it was this same analogy between plants and animals which encouraged Hales to encompass the former in his physiological experiments, but the works of Malpighi, Grew and Ray had all been published for roughly a quarter of a century when Hales commenced his study of plants; it is hard to see any of them as inspiring Hales in the *Vegetable Staticks*.

Though there is no one section in the work of 1727 which reveals what his paper of 1718/19 had contained, the subject of that paper suggests a proximate cause for the study on plants more probable than any influence from Malpighi, Grew or Ray. In volume twenty-nine of the *Philosophical Transactions* for 1714–16, there is a paper by Richard Bradley, 'Observations and Experiments relating to the motion of the Sap in Vegetables'. It is unlikely that Hales heard this paper when it was read before the Royal Society and he does not explicitly refer to it, but it appeared in print in what may well have been one of the earliest volumes of the *Philosophical Transactions* available to Hales as a fellow of the Society. Furthermore, it appeared at just the time he must have commenced his own work, and it raises many of the issues which Hales was to investigate: sap motion and possible circulation, root action, differentiation of function of bark layers, pith and wood, and variation in sap character.[6] In spite of its title, however, Bradley's paper is not an experimental one and though it repeats the animal-plant analogy (and therefore might suggest a transference of Hales's animal-experiment techniques to plants), we have still not explained the origin of that 'statical' mode of examination which was to prove so significant an approach for Hales.

The importance of 'this statical way of inquiry' is emphasized by Hales, who essentially credits it with the 'considerable advances' which he was able to make beyond the studies of such 'ingenious and inquisitive' investigators as Grew and Malpighi [*V.S.* xxv]. Subsequent generations, lacking the necessary referents, have confused Hales's 'statical way' with experiment or at best with experiments leading to those numbers, weights and measures in whose exact proportions, Hales tells us, the 'all-wise Creator' observed the making of all things [*V.S.* xxxi]. No doubt a chief aspect of Hales's technique did involve just this quantitative approach, which from the inspiration of 'the great Philosopher of our age', Sir Isaac Newton, became an essential feature of experimentation for Hales and other natural philosophers of the eighteenth century. But 'statical', used in Hales's sense, implies more than this; it requires a concept of functional equilibrium and throughout his *Statical Essays*, as Hales was later to call the two volumes of *Vegetable Staticks* and *Haemastaticks*, the critical parameters are measured always in both input and output stages:

. . . *viz.* by enquiring what quantity of fluids, and solids dissolved into fluids the animal [or plant] daily takes in for its support and nourishment: And with what force and different rapidities those fluids are carried about in their proper channels, according to the different secretions that are to be made from them: And in what proportion the recrementitious fluid is conveyed away, to make room for fresh supplies; and what portion of this recrement nature allots to be carried off by the several kinds of emunctories and excretory ducts. [*V.S.* xxxii]

This was a technique first made famous by the studies of Santorio Santorio (Sanctorius), published in 1614 under the title, significantly, of *de Statica Medicina*. For thirty years Sanctorius periodically measured his consumption of food and drink, his body weight and its changes, and the amounts of excrement, setting these off against one another in the first widely known attempt at a quantitative physiology. His experiments were well-known in Britain and the 'insensible perspiration' deduced by Sanctorius to 'justify' his accounts had become a cornerstone of iatrophysics.[7] Yet Hales, who was a disciple of the iatro-physicists, who certainly cites Sanctorius in the *Haemastaticks*, and who frequently makes use of the concept of insensible perspiration, need not have known of the century-old *Statica Medicina* at first hand. For James Keill, whom Hales cites most frequently next to Newton in the *Statical Essays*, and who was

32

his mentor in human anatomy and physiology, had published a *Medicina Statica Britannica*, as an appendix to his *Tentamina medico-physica*, in 1718, the year that Hales delivered his first paper. And Keill's version of medical statics has the advantage of association with the Newtonian dynamic corpuscularity which is a second distinguishing characteristic of Hales's work.

The first chapter of the *Vegetable Staticks*, 'Experiments showing the quantities imbibed and perspired by Plants and Trees', establishes the 'statical' pattern for the whole. The early experiments bear some initial resemblance to the willow-tree experiment made famous by van Helmont and mentioned again by Boyle. Like van Helmont, Hales waters plants growing in sealed pots and measures changes in weight of plant and pot. But van Helmont, concerned to demonstrate transmutation of water into 'earth', compares only the initial and final weights. Hales is interested in transport phenomena. Limiting his experiments to short periods (twelve to fifteen days), during which his mature plants scarcely changed their weights, he measures the amounts of water added and changes in weight of plant and pot, each night and morning. Subtracting the amount of water evaporated through the sides of the earthen pots, he concludes that the remaining differences between weights added and weight of increase represent the amounts of water 'perspired' – i.e., transpired. He then measures the surface area of leaf and stalk and computes the rate of transpiration, determines surface area for the root systems and computes rate of fluid absorption, and finds the cross-section of stalk (correcting for proportion of solid to hollow parts) to compute the velocity of flow between root and leaves.[8] He compares these values for different climatic conditions and for different plants, noting, for example, the major difference between evergreens and deciduous types and thus explaining the former's survival in winter. He also compares transpiration rates of plants to perspiration for man, using values given by James Keill in *Medicina Statica Britannica*, and, correcting for vapours lost in expiration, concludes that weight for weight, the amounts of fluid passed through plants is substantially larger than that passed through man.

Hales then devised a crude potometer for a series of variations on these experiments. First the roots, then the severed ends of branches or vines (with and without leaves and/or fruit) and finally the stubs from which the branches had been removed, were cemented within a glass tube filled with water. In each case the change in water level provided a direct measure of fluid intake. Again variations with temperature, humidity, time of day, season and size of exuding surface were noted. Direct measurement of transpired fluids was also suggested by cementing a rooted stump or branch stub within a glass tube, in which exuded moisture might be collected, measured and examined.

This last technique was, however, generally not used to find the quantity of 'perspired' fluid but as part of a study of the mechanism of fluid flow. A stump or branch section, without leaves, exuded sap sufficient only to keep the end moist. With leaves remaining (on other branches of a tree, for example), the 'imbibing force' through a branch stub was sufficient to raise the mercury level in a 'U-tube' manometer attached to the end of the potometer. Inverting a branch or plant with an attached potometer containing as much as seven feet of water failed to increase sap flow if the leaves were removed or the leafed section was itself inserted in a tube of water. Hales concludes, contrary to the opinion of John Keill and Roger Cotes, that: '. . . Tho' the capillary sap vessels imbibe moisture plentifully, yet they have little power to protrude it farther, without the assistance of the perspiring leaves . . .'9

Other sections of this first chapter show Hales concerned with mechanisms and mechanistic explanations of botanical phenomena. He provides an ingenious explanation of tropism: a sunflower turns in the direction of greatest stem shrinkage due to differential perspiration in direct sun-light. Rot and mould diseases of hop vines find an explanation in direct analogy with the iatro-physical theory of fevers. Damp weather retards transpiration, slowing the motion of sap which stagnates in the vines. Stagnant sap becomes corrupt – as can be seen in the degeneration of exuded vapours collected in receivers – and stagnant, corrupt sap causes plant diseases as stagnant blood causes animal disease.

The chapter continues with a return to 'statical' studies in an investigation of the source of moisture in the earth. Dew and rainfall combine for liquid input; from this are subtracted the values found for average evaporation from the earth surface and transpiration from plants and, Hales concludes, that rain and dew together supply stores '. . . so abundantly sufficient to answer the great quantity of water . . . that we need not have recourse, for supplies, to the great Abyss . . .' [*V.S.* xxxii]. Finally, consideration of the influence of temperature on evaporation and transpiration leads Hales to a series of experiments with a set of 'botanical' thermometers, graduated on a 'vegetation' scale. The lowest point was freezing, or the 'utmost boundary of vegetation on the side of cold,' the highest was midway between freezing and the heat of boiling water, fixed 'as the utmost boundary of vegetation, on the warm side, . . . such a degree of heat separating and dispersing, instead of congregating and uniting the nutritive particles [*V.S.* xxxiii].' With these thermometers Hales measures the 'heat' of blood, milk, urine, dung heaps, exteriors of animals' bodies, interiors of stoves and green-houses, average noon-tide in sun and shade, varying with season, and, most important to his purpose, variations with depth, time, and season of the 'heats' of the earth. Again he is concerned ultimately with a vegetation mechanism, and concludes that the warmth of the sun is sufficient, at root depths, to vaporize underground moisture which, being confined under pressure of earth above, is able to penetrate the roots with some force.

Chapter two continues the investigation of vegetative mechanisms. Here the 'statical mode' of inquiry is less in evidence, but the essential Newtonianism of Hales's thinking is brought into prominence. By an ingenious variation of the manometer experiments he must first have learned from Cotes and Whiston, Hales measures 'the force with which trees imbibe moisture.' One end of a glass tube, filled with water, is cemented to the cut end of a root, the stub of a branch or the severed end of the branch itself: the other end of the tube is inserted into a basin of mercury. The height to which mercury rises in the tube to replace water imbibed by the test object is a measure of the 'imbibing force'. Again the experiment is varied for types of plants, differing ages and states of vegetation, varying amounts of leaves, sunshine, warmth, humidity, etc. He notes that 'imbibing' can proceed in any direction – from the root upward, from a branch stub laterally, or, in a severed branch downward. The force is less a function of direction than of transpiration. He concludes that the mechanism of sap motion is the (statical) equilibrium of capillary action and transpiration.

. . . plants imbibe moisture . . . up their fine capillary vessels; which moisture, as it is carried off in perspiration . . ., thereby gives the sap vessels liberty to be almost continually attracting of fresh supplies, which they could not do, if they were full saturate with moisture. [*V.S.* 56]

Recognition of the role of capillary attraction in this phenomena turns Hales's attention to that attraction by itself:

We see . . . many instances of the great efficacy of attraction; that universal principle which is so operative in all the very different works of nature; and is most eminently so in vegetables, all whose minutest parts are curiously ranged in such order, as is best adapted by their united force, to attract proper nourishment. And we shall find . . . that the dissevered particles of vegetables, and of other bodies, have a strong attractive power when they lay confused. [*V.S.* 54]

Dried peas, placed in water in an iron pot, imbibed water and expanded with sufficient force to raise a 184 pound weight placed on the cover. '. . . 'tis doubtless a considerable part of the same force which is exerted, not only in pushing the Plume upwards into the air, but also in enabling the first shooting radicle of the Pea and all its subsequent tender Fibres, to penetrate and shoot into the earth' [*V.S.* 54]. Wood ashes imbibed water with a 'force' sufficient to raise the level in the aqueomercurial guage as much as seven inches. These and similar experiments, indicating that the imbibing action is not a function of vegetable organization, send Hales to Query 31 of Newton's *Opticks*, where it is observed that the same attractive principle responsible for the rise of mercury in capillary tubes may also explain the action of sponges and that of 'the glands of the bodies of animals, according to their several natures and dispositions, [which] suck in various juices from the blood' [*V.S.* 56]. This notion would also have been familiar to Hales from his reading of James Keill's *Tentamina medico* . . . (called, in its first edition, *Essays on Animal Secretions*), which considers in some detail the attraction by the glands of various particles from the blood.

The third chapter relates the only entirely accidental discovery described in the *Vegetable Staticks*, and even that one would not have been made had Hales not been looking for related phenomena or been without the experience, gained in animal experiments, of measuring fluid pressures. Fixing the freshly-cut stump of a vine into a vertical glass tube 25 feet long, Hales observed that the sap rose steadily, night and day, until it reached a height of 21 feet. This pressure did not appear except during the 'bleeding season' in early spring. Hales cannot explain the anomalous occurrence of root-pressure during this part of the growing season (nor has anyone since reached an entirely satisfactory explanation), but he can extend his investigation to a comparison of sap pressures in vines to blood pressures in animals. By employing his 'mercury gage' – the U-tube manometer – he finds the pressure of extruded sap is sufficient to raise a mercury column 38 inches, the equivalent of 43 feet

$3\frac{1}{2}$ inches of water, at the stump, and lesser amounts at different branch stubs along the vine. The pressure at the stump was nearly five times greater, Hales says, than the force of blood in the crural artery of a horse, seven times that in a dog, and eight times that in a fallow deer.

This is the first published reference to Hales's experiments on animals, but except for a brief description of his method, he does not develop the subject.The existence of root-pressure suggests that the mechanism of sap flow – capillary action continued by transpiration – might be invalid for vines and, pursuing this line of enquiry, he directs his attention to that consideration. By a series of experiments on vines continued into the growing season, he finds that the extrusion force is reversed by the familiar 'imbibing force' of transpiring leaves and stalk, and again notes the influence of sun, humidity and temperature. With a slight modification, he can again conclude that '. . . the capillary sap vessels, out of the bleeding season, have little power to protrude sap in any plenty beyond their orifices . . .' [*V.S.* 59]

Throughout this early part of his work Hales has assumed that sap does not circulate in plants. This 'assumption' is so necessary to his statical computations, that he may have demonstrated, experimentally, the lack of circulation at an early stage of his investigations; such experiments, whenever they were performed, are, at any rate, described in chapter four of the *Vegetable Staticks*. In a series of experiments so beautifully conceived that they have since become staple demonstrations in botany courses, Hales sets about to demonstrate the direction of sap flow in plants. Deeply notching a branch alternately around its circumference and along its length, he set the severed end in a container of water. As the branch inspired water (though in less quantity than an unnotched branch) and its leaves remained green (though for less than normal time) sap must have passed laterally between sap vessels, for no single line of passage remained unbroken between end and leaves. Similarly notched branches on trees remained alive with green leaves: in no instance, though direct passage of sap was intercepted, was there transpiration or evaporation of fluid at the notches. The power of transpiration to effect sap flow in any direction (up or down) is demonstrated: first with a large severed branch which inspired water through a cut tip, when the butt end was sealed, and second, and more dramatically, when a tree remained alive and green, though its roots were above ground, when its upper branches were incorporated with those of two other trees.

Nonetheless, though there may be a periodic counter flow of sap, in an ebbing with condensation in the cool of evening or in the distribution of moisture imbibed as dew or rain by the leaves, it can be demonstrated that there is no regular descent of sap in circulation. In spring vegetation, the lower bark is damp first, then progressively higher until the top branches are found moistened. The lower part of a notch, cut through the bark of an imbibing branch, bleeds freely, showing ascent of sap between bark and wood. The upper part of that notch remains dry, as does that of a notch cut through bark and new wood. Sap does not descend at or through the outer, new wood, though, in this case it must ascend through inner wood. A statical argument to the same end appears in an ingenious inversion of Harvey's familiar 'proof' for the circulation of blood.

We see in many . . . Experiments, what quantities of moisture trees do daily imbibe and perspire: Now the celerity of the sap must be very great, if that quantity of moisture must, most of it, ascend to the top of the tree, then descend, and ascend again, before it is carried off by perspiration. [*V.S.* 77]

Nor can one argue that nutrition requires circulation. As James Keill, and other iatro-physicists, have stated, nutrition is a Newtonian, mechanical, attractive process:

. . . the great work of nutrition, in vegetables as well as animals – is chiefly carried out in the fine capillary vessels, where nature selects and combines, as shall best suit her different purposes, the several mutually attracting particles which were hitherto kept disjoined by the motion of their fluid vehicle. . . . [*V.S.* 83]

In animals this vehicle, the blood, runs a long circulatory course, during which selection and combination occur, before it is discharged. The velocity necessary for circulatory sap flow would be too great for the particles it contains to be withdrawn in this manner. Lack of circulation is compensated for by the greater amount of particle-carrying fluid which passes through the plants, as, for example, that in the sunflower, bulk-for-bulk, seventeen times larger than for man.

During some of his experiments, particularly those with vines, Hales had noticed bubbles of air rising through the sap. In the fifth chapter he turns to an examination of this phenomenon, in the first instance to demonstrate that air '. . . is taken in by vegetables, and is perspired off with the sap thro' the leaves', but also, one suspects, to set the stage for

38

the magisterial chapter on 'analysis' of air which was to follow. He shows that an imbibing branch will take in air as it draws water up a tube from a cistern. By using an air pump he demonstrates that air will enter roots or branches through the bark, pass through 'the whole and inmost substance of the wood' (*via* those passages identified by Grew and Malpighi as air vessels), and emerge at a severed end. Soaking the bark in water closed the pores, observed by Grew in trunks and leaves, and stopped the admission of air. Now it was 'well known that air is a fine elastic fluid, with particles of very different natures floating in it, whereby it is admirably fitted – to be the breath of life, of vegetables, as well as of animals . . .' [*V.S.* 85]. Hales's experiments show 'that the air freely enters plants, not only with the principal fund of nourishment by the roots, but also thro' the surface of their trunks and leaves, especially at night, when they are changed from a perspiring to a strongly imbibing state' [*V.S.* 87]. That part of the air entering by the roots is supposed to come from the earth, in which it is mixed in both elastic and unelastic states and from which it can be released, by soaking in water or, in an explicit reference to the next chapter, by a distillation in which fire rouses the fixed air to elasticity.

All the work reported in the sixth chapter was done between 1724 and early 1727. During this time Hales turned his attention from plants to examine '. . . in how great a proportion Air is wrought into the composition of animal, vegetable, and mineral Substances, and withal how readily it resumes its former elastick state, when in the dissolution of those Substances it is disengaged from them' [title to chapter six, *V.S.*]. No external events seem to have occurred sufficient to have directed Hales's attention from physiology to what, in retrospect, appears as pneumatic chemistry. The publication of Hermann Boerhaave's chemical lectures in their first, spurious edition, the *Institutiones et experimenta chemiae* in 1724, might be thought significant except that Hales's references to this work are to its English translation by Peter Shaw and Ephraim Chambers, as the *New Method of Chemistry* of 1727, too late to have been a major influence on the *Vegetable Staticks*. Moreover, Hales's views of the nature and function of the air are very different from those of the 'spurious' Boerhaave text while the official version of that text, which appeared dated 1732, contains (somewhat contradictory) revisions based on a reading of Hales.[10] The major influences on Hales, with regard to chemistry, were Newton and John Freind, about both of whom he writes:

. . . it appears by many chemio-statical Experiments that there is diffused thro' all natural, mutually attracting bodies, a large proportion of particles, which, as the first great author of this important discovery, Sir *Isaac Newton*, observes, are capable of being thrown off from dense bodies by heat or fermentation into a vigorously elastick and permanently repelling state: And also of returning by fermentation, and sometimes without it, into dense bodies: . . . It is by these properties of the particles of matter that he solves the principal Phoenomena of Nature. And Dr. Freind has from the same principles given a very ingenious *Rationale* of the chief operations in Chymistry. [*V.S.* xxvii]

But the Queries in which Newton suggests these ideas had appeared in the 1706 Latin and the 1717 English editions of the *Opticks*, while Freind's *Chemical Lectures* had been available in Latin from 1708 and in English translation from 1717. Insofar as a reason can be assigned for Hales's turning in 1724 to the study of pneumatic phenomena, it must be found in a conjunction of his earlier studies and the internal logic of his physiological experiments – especially from that appearance of air bubbles rising in the sap of plants described in his fifth chapter. It is one of the many indications of Hales's abilities as an experimenter that he should have made so much of what must, to many previous observers, have seemed so insignificant a phenomenon.

Over forty per cent (ninety-two pages) of the *Vegetable Staticks* is devoted to a study of air which was to be the starting point for eighteenth century pneumatic chemistry. Yet it is by no means clear that Hales intended the interpretation of his work which was to inspire his successors. Before Hales, air was regarded as an element instrumental in chemical change but not a constituent in chemical composition; after Hales, air (or the airs) was generally accepted as playing both a constituent and an instrument role in chemistry. The change was, at least in part, demonstrably a consequence of Hales's work, but Hales himself is ambiguous on this point. Even in the title to the chapter, the use of the term 'wrought into the composition' does not necessarily mean that air forms a part of that composition, while the text of the chapter employs such terms, to describe the role of air, as 'lodged in', 'arises from', 'is raised from a fix'd to an elastick state', or 'changed from a repelling elastick to a fixed state'.[11] Once the nature of chemical compounding was made clearer (and Hales's work contributes to the defining of that process), the ambiguity of Hales's expressions went unnoticed. Nonetheless, the emphasis of Hales's study is not upon the nature of composition, nor its changes through addition or subtraction of air.

The property of air which fascinated Hales – fascinating him to the point of near-obsession in his later years – was not its substantiality, but its activity. Accepting the corpuscular philosophy, as modified by Newton, Hales believed matter to consist of particles possessed of a power, or powers of attraction. Hales's mentors in natural philosophy, John and James Keill, John Freind and Samuel Clarke, had demonstrated the application of this principle to the explication of a wide variety of phenomena. They, however, had employed those powers of repulsion, which Newton had also ascribed to the fundamental particles, reluctantly or not at all. Hales was the first person, after Newton, to see the necessity of both attraction and repulsion in an active, organized universe.

. . . if all the parts of matter were only endued with a strongly attracting power, whole nature would then immediately become one unactive cohering lump; wherefore it was absolutely necessary, in order to the actuating and enlivening this vast mass of attracting matter, that there should be everywhere intermixed with it a due proportion of strongly repelling elastick particles, which might enliven the whole mass, by the incessant action between them and the attracting particles. [*V.S.* 178]

Now Newton had referred to repulsion between particles in connection with electrical, magnetic, optical and chemical phenomena, but only in the treatment of elasticity of air had he developed a quantitative law of repulsion approaching that developed for attraction.[12] It was in this connection that John Keill and Samuel Clarke referred to repulsion. More significantly, it was in this connection too, that Hales, when attending the pneumatic and hydrostatic lectures of William Whiston and Roger Cotes, would have seen the notion of repulsion used and demonstrated with apparatus such as the mercury manometer he was later to employ in his own experiments. And it was probably from Cotes (for it is definitely in the published form of Cotes's lectures) that Hales first learned of the type of experiments he was to perform for his sixth chapter, in which air was 'generated' or 'consumed' in chemical operations on various substances.[13]

Neither Whiston nor Cotes have, however, what Hales was to develop – a notion of air as that singular substance of 'strongly repelling elastick particles' which enlivened other matter by its interaction with it. For Hales air becomes a 'protean principle'. Under normal conditions its particles repel one another but are attracted by particles of other matter. In a free, atmospheric, state it might have floating in it unelastic (attracting) particles of acids, sulphurs, salts, etc., which can reduce its elasticity and therefore its activity. In some circumstances its particles can become bound, fixed and unelastic, where they contribute to the union of concreted matter in other bodies. By chemical processes of fermentation (mixing with acids, alkalies, water, etc.) or distillation (heating), the fixed air can be roused to activity, recover its elasticity in breaking free of bodies, and thus enliven the mass.[14] The experiments of chapter six are designed primarily to determine what processes, acting on what substances, change the elastic properties of air, and to what degrees.

The methods Hales adopted were very simple, for his achievement lay more in conception than in execution, but the conceptualization which aided experimental design also limited it. A measured quantity (volume and/or weight) of the substance to be 'distilled' or 'fermented' is placed in a retort which, by itself, neither produces nor absorbs air. The stem of the retort is cemented to one end of a glass tube in which a substantial quantity of the air has been displaced by water rising from the container in which the other end of the tube rests. As air is released – that is restored to elasticity – or absorbed – made unelastic or fixed – in distillation or fermentation of the test substance, the water level in the glass tube falls or rises. After allowing sufficient time for the system to return to normal temperature (correcting for heat expansion but also permitting absorption of excluded gases in water), Hales measures the volumes of the airs produced or absorbed by determining the volume of water necessary to restore the water level to its initial position in the tube. Although he occasionally computes the weight of this air, from the specific gravity measurements of Francis Hauksbee, Hales is interested in changing elastic properties of the air, not in its substance. He never observes the lack of equality between weights before and after his experiments and, although he confirms that air released in the process is 'true air' (it does not condense with change of temperature and conforms to Boyle's law) he never really notes any difference in quality of the airs he studies.

In the course of his experiments, Hales 'distils' or 'ferments' a variety of animal and vegetable substances: blood, tallow, horn, wood, wheat, peas, etc., and mineral substances: nitre, pyrites, tartars, shells, bladder and gall stones. In retrospect it can be assumed that he must have obtained a number of different gases, including carbon monoxide and dioxide, nitrous and nitric oxide, ammonia, sulphur dioxide, hydrogen and oxygen, for example. Yet in the few instances in which he describes any variation in behaviour of the gases he produces (as, for example, the inflammability of that dislodged in the fermentation of iron by acid), he ascribes the anomaly to the presence in the air of adventitious unelastic particles. Clearly, Hales was unable to see, in his experiments, what subsequent observers have found it easy to discover in them. Nonetheless, in connection with those concepts of elasticity which provided his frame of reference, he could be both perceptive and ingenious, drawing, for example, from a combination of experiment, theory and computational deduction, a demonstration of his contention that air could change from an elastic to an unelastic state:

... there arose from a piece of heart of *Oak*, 216 times its bulk of air. Now 216 cubick inches of air, compressed into the space of one cubick inch, would, if it continued there in an elastick state, press against one side . . . with an expansive force equal to 3310 pounds weight . . . and . . . against the six sides of the cube with a force equal to 19860 pounds, a force sufficient to rend the *Oak* with a vast explosion: tis very reasonable therefore to conclude, that most of these now active particles of the new generated air, were in a fix'd state . . . before they were roused and put into an active repelling state by . . . fire. [*V.S.*120]

The role of fire (or heat) in transforming fixed into elastic air led Hales to investigate other instances of fire-air interaction: from his experiments on distillation and fermentation he turned to a study of combustion and respiration. In the course of his investigations he repeated many of the experiments previously described by John Mayow. Mayow, however, was an iatro-chemist and drew his conclusions in terms of the acid-alkali spirit interactions popular to that school of thought; Hales's mechanism led him to very different interpretations. Where Mayow saw a spirituous portion of the air removed by combustion or respiration, which ceased when that part was exhausted, Hales saw the elasticity of the air destroyed by the addition of unelastic vapours, until the air was so saturated with absorbing particles that its activity had to stop. Applying this theory to an experimental investigation of respiration in animals, by determination of the specific gravity of lung substance, microscopic examination of the diameter of lung vesicles, and measurement of inflated lung capacity, Hales computed the surface of the lungs in contact with the air. As the blood was also 'spread into a vast expanse, commensurate to a very thin surface of air', in the 'innumerable meanders' in the lungs, and separated from the air by very thin partitions, it seems that the lungs were formed to provide an opportunity for the blood to attract particles of air through those partitions.

Now his previous distillation and fermentation experiments had shown that blood does contain particles ready to resume the elasticity of air, but it is surely not purely coincidental that James Keill had postulated elastic particles in the blood to explain muscular motion.[15] Nor is the mechanism postulated for the addition of that air through the lungs (for it might be added by way of food, 'which contains great stores of it'),unrelated to Hales's iatro-physical concept of lung action. By experiments on dogs, he shows that respiration involves the action of the thorax to dilate the vesicles, allowing blood to pass through them, where it is divided into smaller particles. But if the air is surcharged with acid fumes and vapours, its particles will contract the vesicles; they may also clog the free ingress of air by their grossness, and reduce the elasticity of the air so that it fails to distend the vesicles sufficiently to permit passage of blood. The fatal effect of noxious vapours is not, therefore, the lack of vivifying spirit in the air, but its loss of elasticity; '. . . suffocation . . . consists chiefly in the falling flat of the lungs, occasioned by the grossness of the particles of a thick, noxious air, they being in that floating state most easily attracted by each other . . .' [V.S. 153].

If combustion and respiration processes were, like those of distillation, explicable in terms of changing elasticity of air, then heat need not be regarded as substantial. Hales completes his analysis of combustion with a critique of the view of 'Mr. Homberg, Mr. Lemery, and some others' that fire is 'a particular distinct kind of body'. The 'heat of fire consists principally in the brisk vibrating action and reaction, between the elastick repelling air and the strongly attracting acid sulphur . . .' found in the fuel [V.S. 161–2]. Continuing his objections to a material theory of heat, held also by 'the pious and learned Dr. Nieuwentyt' and the 'learned Boerhaave', Hales explicitly adopts the contrary opinion of Newton. He even (for the first and only time in the *Vegetable Staticks*) invokes the idea of a highly elastic aetherial medium, whose elastic force, increased by the brisk action and re-action of particles of fuel and ambient air, is sufficient to explain intense degrees of heat. Hales, however, was no more kindly disposed to the aether of Newton than were his mentors and the majority of his immediate contemporaries. For the most part he found the vibratory motion of air particles and those of the heated substance sufficient to produce the heat and the heating effects he wished to explain. By this means, for example, he understood the consequences of 'distillation' of minerals, etc., while fire itself was to be understood as those particles of air, acid and sulphur which were most vigorously moved in heating. It is this view of fire, rather ambiguously expressed, which Hales adopts in his conclusion '... that the sulphureous and aereal particles of the fire are lodged in many of those bodies which it acts upon, and thereby considerably augments their weight ...' [*V.S.* 163]. As he does not believe that fire is a substance *sui generis*, this must be taken to mean that calces are increased in weight by the air (including its adventitious particles) within which the bodies are heated. Still more perceptive – and prophetic of future events – is Hales's statement:

From this manifest attraction, action and re-action, that there is between the acid, sulphureous and elastic aereal particles, we may not unreasonably conclude, that what we call the fire particles in Lime and several other bodies, which have undergone the fire, are the sulphureous and elastic particles of the fire [i.e., that combination of heated air and sulphur called fire] fix't in the Lime; which particles, while the Lime was hot, were in a very active, attracting and repelling state; and being, as the Lime cooled, detained in the solid body of the Lime, at the several attracting and repelling distances they then happened to be at, they must necessarily continue in that fix't state ... But when the solid substance of the Lime is dissolved ... being thereby emancipated, they are again at liberty to be influenced and agitated by each other's attraction and repulsion, upon which a violent ebullition ensues, which ... ceases not, till one part of the elastick particles are subdued and fix't by the strong attraction of the sulphur and the other part is got beyond the sphere of its attraction, and thereby thrown off into true permanent air. [*V.S.* 162–3]

Hales continues his application of the Newtonian concept of attracting and repelling particles in the next, and last chapter of the *Vegetable Staticks*, where he combines all of his previous discoveries on the action of leaves, movement of sap and nature of air into a mechanistic explanation of plant growth and nutrition. The leaves assist in drawing up the sap, admit dew, rain and particles of light, and serve the plant as lungs to admit air, with alterations of temperature supplying the office, in vegetables, of the expansive thorax in animals. Light, as Newton has observed, can be converted into gross bodies and thus enters the composition of plants. More significantly, a combination in the plants of air particles with the mutually attracting particles of sap produces a nutritive state in which the attracting power is greater, in sum, than the repelling power. The combination, therefore, increases in consistency from a fluid to a viscid, ductile state and thence is compacted into hard substance, according to the different degrees of cohesion of the principles involved.

Growth occurs in the sections of a plant before final compacting, either as the active aereal particles distend the ductile parts or as the fluid (sap and/or water) within the spongy fibres is expanded by heat of the sun before transpiration occurs. In both cases primary growth takes place in the tender, younger shoots, or sections, of a plant; between knots or partitions which are provided by design as walls, against which the expansive pressure acts.

The essentials of Hales's explanation of plant nutrition and growth are derived from James Keill, Nehemiah Grew and G. A. Borelli. Keill describes the selection and combination of particles of very different degrees of mutual attraction into different animal substances, out of the blood whose motion is appropriately retarded at the proper places for the better coalescences of secretions; Grew earlier observed contrivances in plants whereby motion of the sap is retarded and viscid nutriment might result, while Borelli supposed that growth was an extension of soft animal or vegetable matter distended like soft wax. But Hales's ideas combine the notions of his predecessors into a much more comprehensive and coherent system, while he alone went on to design experiments whereby some of these speculations might be tested. The method he adopted bears that deceptive simplicity which became the hallmark of a Hales experiment. He pierced young shoots of vine, honeysuckle, sunflower, etc., the leg bone of a half-grown chick, the young leaves of trees and flowers with evenly spaced holes marked with a composition of red-lead and oil. Several months later, when the test object had grown, he measured the distances between the marks and observed that the growth was not evenly distributed but varied as the different parts were variously capable of extension.

The chapter culminates in an exuberant speculation that even the generation of plants might find explanation by the same concepts. The *farina foecundans* abounds in sulphur, sulphur strongly attracts air. Hence the farina is placed on the apices at the tips of the stamen, whereby it

46

is dispersed by the least breath of wind to surround the plant with an atmosphere which is inspired by the plant in its strongly imbibing state, especially towards evening.

And if to these united sulphureous and aereal particles we suppose some particles of light be joyned . . . then the result of these three by far the most active principles in nature, will be a *Punctum Saliens* to invigorate the seminal plant: And thus we are at last conducted, by the regular Analysis of vegetable nature to the first enlivening principle of their minutest origin. [*V.S.* 203]

With this optimism, and a conclusion which recites the general schema of the experiments performed, and recommends their conclusions to the practical considerations of gardeners and farmers, the *Vegetable Staticks* ends. Never before had experimental ingenuity, theoretical understanding and conceptual imagination been so closely connected in a study of plants; not for nearly a century, till the work of the German plant physiologist Julius von Sachs, were they again to be so connected and applied.

CHAPTER V

The *Haemastaticks*

Not until 1733, six years after the publication of the *Vegetable Staticks*, did Stephen Hales again publish on a scientific subject. When he did so, it was not in continuation of those researches on plant physiology and pneumatic chemistry which had won him reputation. In spite of his declaration that, 'What I had at first intended only as additional Observations and Experiments to the first Volume is now grown into the size of another Volume', his new work neither grew out of the *Vegetable Staticks*, nor did it merely describe investigations performed since the publication of that work. The title to the new volume reveals its nature: *Statical Essays: Containing Haemastaticks; or, An Account of some Hydraulick and Hydrostatical Experiments made on the Blood and Blood-Vessels of Animals. Also An Account of some Experiments on Stones in the Kidney and Bladder; with an Enquiry into the Nature of those anomalous Concretions. To which is added An Appendix, containing Observations and Experiments relating to several Subjects in the first Volume . . .* Vol. II.[1] Although two long sections (slightly more than half the whole) do indeed continue the work described in the first volume, they are comparatively unimportant; the more significant part of the *Haemastaticks* relates to those experiments on animals that Hales began when a Fellow at Corpus Christi, Cambridge, interrupted for the work on plants and on air, and resumed with greater confidence after the favourable reception of the *Vegetable Staticks*. The *Haemastaticks* has neither the sophistication nor the speculative originality of the *Vegetable Staticks*, possibly, in part, because so much of the work described in it was conceived early in Hales's scientific career, but also because that work is a running experimental commentary on the physiological speculations of others. His experiments still show that marvellous simplicity of genius and their long-range importance is indicated by the remark, 150 years after their publication, that '. . . the two books (the *De Motu Cordis* [of William Harvey] and the *Haemastaticks*) might fitly be regarded as a kind of *principia* for the physiological student'.[2] Nonetheless, Hales had come to the subject of vegetable physiology and pneumatic chemistry as an innovator; both the concepts, and the experiments designed to elucidate and test them, were of his creation. His work in animal physiology is instead part of a long train of physiological explanation stretching back to Descartes, Galileo, Harvey, Borelli, Bellini and Sanctorius; Hales's contribution was only (admittedly a very big only) the design of experiments which were ultimately to moderate severely the enthusiasms of iatro-physics.

Hales's immediate inspiration was drawn from a school of British anatomists and physiologists: Archibald Pitcairne, Richard Mead, George Cheyne, John Freind and James Keill, who added, not always effectively, the quantitative concerns of Newtonians to the kinematic mechanisms (i.e., explanations solely in terms of particle size, shape and motion) of the iatro-physicists. The major emphasis of this British school, based perhaps on a patriotic pride in William Harvey, was on body fluids. Indeed, to them, the body primarily consisted of fluids, related to or derived from the blood, and of the conduits of these fluids. 'All Diseases consist either in a Change of the Quantity of Fluids, or a Change of the Velocity, or a Change in their Quantity and Texture,' wrote Pitcairne.[3] Body heat was caused by attrition of the blood in circulation. Fever resulted from a change in texture of the blood, or variation in its particle size, when it suffered some obstruction in its motion and became viscid. The function of respiration was mechanically to reduce the particles of blood to a size proper for their passage through the pulmonary vessels of the heart. Digestion was a mechanical division of the food into particles capable of passing through the lacteals. Glandular secretions were formed by the permutations and combinations of of the primary particles of the blood and were separated from the blood by the various glands, appropriately situated in the body at those particular velocities of circulation, where the quantity of motion of compatible secondary particles made for their easy withdrawal.[4]

All of these Newtonian iatro-physicists indulged in elaborate, quantitative, hydrodynamic arguments, based on estimates of blood-pressure, size, shape and convolutions of blood-vessels, strength and elasticity of vessel walls, and resistance to fluid flow. Two of them, John Freind and James Keill, performed experiments – Freind with substances added to the blood to change its viscidity and the elastic properties of the vessels, and Keill to measure cross-sections of the vessels, volumes of heart-chambers and the velocities of blood-flow from cut arteries and veins.[5] For not one of them, however, was there sufficient data even to justify his calculations, to say nothing of the 'precision' with which the results

49

were reported. Examples of the values given for some of the essential parameters, prior to Hales's critical measurements of them, include: Pitcairne's declaration that the lungs exert a force of 100 pounds on blood globules, and the stomach a force of 12,951 pounds on food; Borelli's supposition that the force of the heart was 180,000 pounds (an estimate substantially reduced by Keill to not more than 16 and not less than 5½ ounces), and Keill's statement that the blood flowed in capillaries as much as 5,223 times more slowly than through the aorta. Clearly there was a need for some accurate measurements for these parameters, so important to iatro-physical theories of physiology and disease. It was to this task that Hales had devoted himself for many years and on which he finally issued his report, in the *Haemastaticks* of 1733.

The *Haemastaticks*, unlike the *Vegetable Staticks*, is not formally organized into chapters, but progresses continuously from one set of experiments to another. This gives the appearance of an experimental empiricism in which, as one description puts it, 'Hales simply rambles on and on, each experiment suggesting another, so that he was led almost imperceptibly to study a great many physiological phenomena'.[6] This appearance is, to say the least, deceptive, for it ignores the range of theoretical literature on which Hales's work is, by implication, an experimental commentary. The *Haemastaticks* does read like a scarcely ordered experimental notebook, but the justification for the experiments is to be found in those speculations on animal physiology relating to haemodynamic profiles, circulation (in the capillaries), lung action and the force and strength of animal parts which were common currency to readers versed in the iatro-physics of the time.

Hales's first, and major, experimental innovation was the direct measurement of blood pressure, in the crural artery, carotid artery, and jugular vein, of a variety of animals – horses, oxen, sheep, a fallow deer and dogs. Initially he employed an end-manometer, or long glass tube, cemented into the severed end of an artery or vein. Pressure is measured by the height to which blood is forced up the vertical tube. Later conceiving that this method stopped '. . . the course of a considerable stream of Blood . . . and that consequently the Force of the Blood must be proportionably increased in all the Veins or Arteries' [33], Hales substitutes a lateral-manometer, in which the artery or vein is cemented within a tube-section from which the long manometer-tube projects vertically at a right-angle. Blood pressure is, again, determined by the height to which blood is forced from the pierced vessel up the long tube.

Not content with the first direct measurement of any blood pressure, Hales elaborates the experiment by noting changes in pressure as a function of the state of excitement of the animal, its deep breathing, muscle straining, etc., and repeats his measurements at various stages of blood depletion. Having measured the force of blood in the carotid artery, the next stage in determination of a haemodynamic profile was the measurement of ventricle volume and area. This Hales achieves, adapting a technique of James Keill, by making a wax cast of the heart. Rather than injecting molten beeswax with a syringe, Hales pours it down a vertical tube, more closely to approximate the dilation force of of the injected cavity. Cutting open the left ventricle (and, in process, measuring the thickness of the muscular coat), he removes the wax-cast whose volume, he assumes, is 'nearly commensurate to the Quantity of Blood received into this Ventricle at each *Diastole* and . . . thence propelled into the *Aorta* at the subsequent *Systoles*' [19]. That volume is measured by displacement of water, while the surface of the ventricle is equal to the total area of pieces of paper cut just to cover the surface of the cast.

The total force sustained in the heart is now to be obtained as the product of arterial blood pressure, as measured at the carotid, by the surface area and the force sustained by the muscular fibres in any transverse section as the product of blood pressure by the area of that section. Of still more interest is the possibility now opened for computation of the velocity at which the blood is propelled from the ventricle on contraction. This Hales determines as the product of ventricle capacity by the measured area of a transverse section of the aorta. And from this value, and the various pulse rates, he computes the cardiac output, giving the value, for each experimental animal (except the fallow deer, whose timidity precluded obtaining a 'normal' pulse rate) in the time required for its equivalent weight, in blood, to pass through the heart.

It is presumably on the bases of comparative values for variously sized animals that Hales supposes 'what is probable, that the Blood would rise 7+1/2 Feet high in a Tube fixed to the carotide Artery of a Man' [40]; and with the area of the left ventricle of the human heart set equal to 15 square inches, computes the force of the heart to be 51·5 pounds – a value substantially closer to the presently accepted range than either Borelli or Keill were able to achieve. And with Keill's measurement of the area of the orifice of the aorta, the average human pulse rate, and various estimates (by Keill, Harvey and Richard Lower) of human cardiac output, it is possible to determine a haemodynamic profile for man to range in a table along with those for horses, oxen, sheep and dogs.

One consequence of these experiments is Hales's observation, implicitly critical of iatro-physical theories of disease:

. . . even in the same Animal the Force of the Blood in its Vessels, is continually varying, according to the different Kinds and Quantities of Food, the various Distances of time after taking Food, the more or less plethoric State of the Blood Vessels, also from Exercise, Rest, different States of Vigor or Vivacity of the Animal, and many other circumstances. . . . For the healthy State of Animals is not confined to the scanty Limits of one determinate Degree of vital vigor in the Blood. But the Allwise Framer of these admirable Machines has so ordered it, as that their healthy state shall not be disturbed by every little Variation of this Force, but has made it consistent with a very considerable Latitude in the Variation of it. [31–32]

There is a similar criticism of iatro-physical theory in Hales's comment that excessive sweating (the cold, clammy sweats of faint persons or the 'colliquative Sweats' of those in pain, fear, etc.) is not due to a greater protrusive force of the blood, but to some general relaxation of the pores. The practical considerations which led Hales to engage in the 'disagreeableness of anatomical Dissections' [xlvi], are explicitly revealed, for the first of many examples, in his recommendation that the

practice of bleeding be carried over 'several distant times, where it is requisite to take away a great Quantity of Blood', as the body can, in time, adjust itself to restore, in some measure, the vigour of the blood rebated with extreme 'evacuations'.

His measured criticisms of iatro-physical parameters did not disenchant Hales with iatro-physical theory; though over-all force and velocity of the blood might vary significantly in the healthy state, it was in the lesser vessels where obstructions, producing illnesses, were to be expected. Hales turns from a determination of haemodynamic profiles to a study of peripheral circulation, the mechanism of its continuation, the resistance offered there to blood flow, and the change of circulation rates. As part of his first set of experiments, he had already noted that systolic impulsion of blood into the major arteries produces a dilatation there which is followed by contraction as the systole ceases.

By which curious Artifice . . . the Blood is carried on in the finer Capillaries, with an almost even Tenor of Velocity, in the same manner as spouting

Water in some fire-Engine is contrived to flow with a more even Velocity . . .
by means of a large inverted Globe. . . . [23]

Given that the velocity of capillary flow ought, therefore, normally to be
steady, what is its value? In that first set of experiments the observation
is made that the total cross-section of arterial branches is always greater
than the trunk from which they arise, so that the 'Velocity of the Blood
will be proportionably abated in them' [24]. The task now is to determine the degree of that 'abatement' as the blood passes from arterial
branches into their capillaries.

Direct measurement of capillary blood velocity is difficult to achieve,
but Hales succeeds, for certain of the larger capillaries, in obtaining at
least a comparative measure. Pouring warm water down a tube and
into the descending aorta of a dog, he notes that the water takes three
times as long to complete its passage through the 'innumerable small
capillaries' and out the orifices, cut by slitting open the gut, than it takes
to pass through the orifice of the mesentary artery, when the gut is
removed. This technique is, however, inapplicable for the finer and
finer capillaries, and for an estimate of blood velocity in these, Hales is
forced to adopt the methods of his predecessors and follow the paths of
lesser arteries and capillaries as they branch from one another, estimat-
ing their numbers, sizes, the resistance to flow offered at sharply-angled
branches, etc. The orifices of those capillaries at the slit gut were, on the
average, found equal in diameter to a hair, while capillaries branching
from them (traced by injection with vermilion) decreased in size to such
a fineness that only one corpuscle at a time might pass through them.
Water, at a force equal to that of the heart, merely oozed through the
hair-sized capillaries; how much larger must the resistance be to the
more viscid blood in lesser capillaries, notwithstanding that the sum of
the cross-sections of these capillaries is considerably larger than that of
the aorta?

Now the force of the blood in the arteries depends upon the proportion which the quantity of blood ejected by the heart bears to that which
can pass through the capillaries into the veins. It is the resistance in the
capillaries which explains the difference in force (ten or twelve to one)
of the blood in the arteries and the veins. But what is the force in those
capillaries? To determine this, Hales adopts his favourite statical computational technique. Suppose the capillary to be twice the diameter of
a blood corpuscle (as measured by 'Leewoenhoek'). The product of this
area by the pressure measured in the arteries gives a force, from which

E   53

one subtracts that part of the pressure caused by resistance in the veins. One might add to the resultant force for blood impelled into the capillaries the momentum of that impulsion, but this would be small, as the resistance to blood flow is so large.

From these studies of peripheral circulation, two major conclusions, again critical of iatro-physics, result. The resistance to blood flow in the capillaries may vary so widely, with varying fluidity of blood and constriction of the vessels, '. . . so as probably never to be exactly the same, any two Minutes, during the whole Life of an Animal . . .,' and the state of the blood or its vessels is so dependent upon conditions of motion, temperature, food, etc., that '. . . Nature has wisely provided that a considerable Variation in these [states], shall not greatly disturb the Healthy State of the Animal' [56]. Even more disconcerting than the failure to relate peripheral blood flow and disease was the smallness of blood pressure in the capillaries. Hales says that it was a conjecture that the hydraulic force of blood might explain muscular motion which, as early as 1706, had led him into physiological investigations. But 'from the very small Force of the arterial Blood among the muscular Fibres, we may with good reason conclude how short this force is of producing so great an Effort as that of muscular Motion . . .' [58].

To what cause then is this 'Mystery of Nature' to be ascribed? Hales supposes, from the vigour and activity of muscular energy and its regulation by the nerves, that it must be explained by some elastic 'animal spirit' conducted by or along the nerves, and capable of being destroyed or paralysed by sulphureous fumes. Considering the particulate mechanism, involving elastic air, proposed by James Keill for explaining muscular motion and Hales's previous work on pneumatic elasticity and its 'fixing' by sulphureous particles, it is somewhat surprising that he does not elaborate some pneumatic process of muscular activity. Instead he hints at an electrical explanation, citing some papers published by Stephen Gray (but surely, in his mind, harking back to electrical experiments witnessed as a fellow at Corpus) on the transference of a 'vibrating electrical Virtue' in or along animal fibres. He also notes some microscopic observations on the change of form of muscular fibres in a frog's belly, suggesting this as a mode of investigation of muscular action, but the problem is too difficult to solve and Hales moves instead to a consideration of the mutual action of blood flow, muscular action and pneumatics in the more accessible region of the lungs.

In spite of their readier accessibility, the lungs did not provide an

54

easy field of investigation. Hales emphasizes their importance in the haemodynamic system by measurements which contrasted their weight and fluid capacity with those of the fleshy part of the body which they serve, but the complications of lung structure make it difficult to determine those parameters of blood velocity and pressure required for a mechanical analysis of their function. As the same amount of blood must pass through the lungs each minute as passes through the heart, an elaborate computation, involving lung surface and the area of the vesicles, permits an estimate that nearly twenty-eight times the lungs' capacity must pass through them each minute. Microscopic examination of blood flow in the capillary arteries of a frog shows a velocity in the lungs forty-three times that through its muscles. Together, statical comparisons and direct observation reveal, at least, that blood velocity in the lungs is very large, but neither method gives any information on blood pressure. The cross-sections of the pulmonary artery and aorta being roughly equal, the velocity of blood expulsion from left and right ventricle may be assumed to be the same, but it does not follow that the forces of expulsion are equal. Given the larger capacity of the body and greater resistance of its arteries and capillaries, a larger impelling force is required to send blood through the body than through the lungs; hence the muscle walls of the right ventricle are less thick than the left. Yet the force of the right ventricle cannot be measured by Hales's direct method, for the animal 'must needs dye' while the manometer tube is fixed to the pulmonary artery. Hales therefore attempts a determination by measurement of the force necessary to impel water through the lungs. But warm water forced via the pulmonary vein filled the lungs and stopped; forced via the pulmonary artery, the water poured freely into the bronchi and down the windpipe, without reaching the pulmonary vein. Yet the vesicles were not burst, for a mixture of blood, water and nitre forced at greater pressure along the same path filled the lungs without reaching the vein or escaping into the bronchi. The method proved inadequate for determining cardiac output, but suggested that something more than the force of the right ventricle was needed to promote passage of blood through the lungs.

After a series of vivisection experiments, in which air pressure inside and outside the lungs is equalized by opening the thorax, Hales concludes that 'a farther Dilatation of the Coats of the Vesicles with inspired air; thereby probably to unfold the corrugated Extremities of the Arteries and Veins' [78], must be added to the force of blood in the pulmonary artery if blood is to pass through the lungs. But surely something must happen to the blood in the lungs to require their elaborate structure and operation. Hales concedes, without much examination, that the mechanical action of the lungs in 'Attenuation and separating the Blood Globules' [105], for their passages through the heart is doubtless one considerable use of them, but he is concerned to demonstrate another. He does not doubt that animal heat is a consequence of the agitation and friction of particles of blood against each other and against the resisting walls of the circulatory system and, by virtue of the blood's great velocity in the lungs, it seems clear that it acquires a principal part of its heat there. But heat not much beyond the natural amount coagulates the blood, and Boerhaave, describing the ill effects of breathing hot air and observing the invigorating effects of the cool air which a heated man pants after, infers that the blood must also be refrigerated in the lungs. Hales concludes that this refrigeration occurs by the contact of the blood, through the thin walls of the vesicles, with constant supplies of cool air and, by the amount of heat acquired by expired air, determines the degree of cooling. Breathing warm air on the bulb of a thermometer held in his mouth, he finds the temperature raised 36 degrees in 3 seconds. Communicating this information to J. T. Desaguliers and Charles Labelye, along with data on the quantity of blood passing through the lungs per minute and of the air inspired during the same time, Hales obtained from them the 'Degree of Refrigeration which the blood received from the inspired air'. They assumed that 'actual heat was to sensible heat as momentum is to velocity', i.e., that quantity of heat is related to temperature by the mass of the substance heated. They found that the air in the lungs cools the blood there by '2·98 degrees of heat' each minute, and Hales computes, from this information, that were a man to hold his breath for a minute, his body temperature would rise by 0·08487 degree!

For reasons he does not entirely make clear – though surely his experiments in diluting the blood in living animals which prove 'the meer keeping the Arteries full with any Fluid will not support Life . . .' [115], provide part of the explanation – Hales is convinced that the blood is no 'meer languid inert Fluid' [108]. He had already demonstrated, in his studies of the heating of the blood, that its active principles did not involve electricity. As the most compact and firm, though elastic, parts of the blood are the globules whose red colour suggests the presence of sulphur, making them the more susceptible and retentive of

56

heat, it would appear that the blood's heat is produced by the agitation of these particles rubbing against each other. But though particles of some fluids acquire electricity as well as heat by agitation (as Hales demonstrates with mercury), experiment shows that blood does not. This does not disprove the friction-heat relationship, however, as other fluids in agitation or effervescences, such as mercury and aqua fortis, water and oil of vitriol, and iron fillings and aqua fortis, grow hot without becoming electrical [90–6]. What then is the source and nature of the blood's activity? ''Tis probable . . . that the Blood may in the Lungs receive some . . . important Influences from the Air' [105–6], other than cooling. This influence cannot be a consequence of any inspired force, for air passes to and fro too easily and with too small a velocity; nor can it be from additional gravitation force acquired in the lungs, for James Keill's estimate that the weight of the air in the lungs equals 50,443 pounds contains a 'manifest Mistake' [106]. We cannot suppose there is a 'strongly repelling Degree of Ferment or Effervescence in the Blood, in its healthy State' but the parts of that fluid, 'actuated with so considerable Degree of Friction and Heat' must be in a vibrating state. These vibrations are restrained, within due bounds, by the attractive power of sulphur, whose reaction with air is responsible for all vegetable ferments and probably also produces the ferments in the blood.

This dynamic corpuscular suggestion, so reminiscent of Hales's speculations in the *Vegetable Staticks* is, however, elaborated into a discussion which appears almost iatro-chemical. The healthy state of the blood requires a due equilibrium between these active principles, lest a fixed and depressed state tend to an acid acrimony or a raised and exalted one tends to alkaline acrimony. 'When we consider . . . by what innumerable Combinations of Causes this *Equilibrium* is liable to be disturbed, we cannot wonder that our Health is so often interrupted, and the Period of Life most uncertain as to its Duration' [109].

Those experiments, intended indirectly to determine the force of blood flow and begun with forcing warm water into the lungs, are now diversified with similar studies for the stomach and glands – particularly the kidney, liver and bladder. Hales begins by flooding the circulatory system of a dog with warm water at arterial pressure and observing the 'universal dropsy', produced as the water passes through pores and ducts impassable to the more viscid part of the blood, distending the fatty vesicles, swelling the muscles, salivary and other glands, and filling body cavities. Water soaked through the arteries into the muscle fibres

57

of the stomach, the abdomen and the gut. It oozed from the mesenteric artery into the gut, but none passed from the gut into the veins though the pressure was raised to 9½ feet. Applying water, under pressure, directly to the kidneys, he found them distended to hardness, but no water passed into the ureter or bladder and none would pass through the blood vessels of the bladder into its cavity. The liver also would become swollen, whitened and hard, yet pass no water through to the vena cava; but the gall bladder, pancreas and spleen, while somewhat distended, would permit the passage of water under pressure. Hales concludes that the 'Secretions, which are different according to the different Texture of the secretory Vessels and which are made from the arterial Blood' are not produced as a consequence of the force of the blood, but more gradually and sparingly through an 'alternate pulsive force of the arterial Fluid, and attractive Power of the fine secerning Vessels; assisted also by constant Vibrations', mutually and incessantly active in animal fluids and solids [125].

His observations on the passage of light fluids through vessel walls and fibres give Hales yet another opportunity for those practical, quasi-medical, recommendations which justify, to him, the making of these 'disagreeable anatomical dissections'. The experiments on the lungs led to suggestions for surgical operations in the thorax; explanations of pleurisy 'when the Blood by its Siziness does with difficulty pass, tho' impelled with such Force as to distend the Vessels, and thereby cause pungent Stitches' [82]; and a description of asthmas as the filtering, through the pores of the pulmonary artery and lungs into the bronchi, of the thin, watery fluid which surcharges and dilutes the blood in colds. The necessity of maintaining an equilibrium between active principles in the blood led to speculations on the deposition of 'gross tartarine gouty Particles' from the cooling blood in the extremities furthest from the heart, where the progressive force of the blood is least. Now Hales can continue with a caution on the disturbances caused to regular secretions by undue variation in the quality of the blood, particularly, with reference to a cause of continuing concern to him, in the case of habitual hard drinking, when surcharging the blood with these liquors produces that 'cold watry stomach', of which drinkers so frequently complain, as the fluid passes easily through the vessels into the stomach.

The 'hydraulic and hydrostatical Method of examining the animal Canals' by forcing water through them also presented the possibility

'. . . to see, what Effects different Liquors have on those solids, either in relaxing . . . or in contracting and strengthening them . . .'[127]. Such properties were known for many substances through the long experience of physicians, still '. . . a fuller Demonstration . . . may be of Service in confirming the known Explications of the Operations of Medicines, and in farther clearing up the Reasons of such as are more doubtful'.[7]

The technique adopted was that earlier used, in which liquids were poured, under pressure, down the descending aorta of a dog and their passage, through the severed capillaries of the slit gut, was timed and compared. Warm water relaxed the vessels, the first pot taking 52 seconds to pass, the seventh only 40. Brandy contracted them, the first pot increasing passage time to 68 seconds, the fifth taking 72. On relaxing the vessels again with warm water and then pouring cold on the guts and through the arteries, the arteries were so contracted that the fourth pot took 80 seconds longer than a pot of warm water had taken. A strong decoction of Peruvian Bark (cinchona) contracted the vessels as did those of oak bark, chamomile flowers, and cinnamon, while Piermont (carbonated) water also appeared to have a styptic quality. Some of these experiments were complicated by dropsical expansion of body fibres which began to compress the vessels and slow the passage even of warm water.

The explicitly pragmatic justification for this set of experiments comes in general observations on the therapeutic value of the perfusates as medicines for fevers, dropsies, profuse sweating, etc., but the most explicit remarks are again directed toward the effects of drinking 'strong spirituous Liquors'. Hales's conclusions are somewhat contradictory. It is probable that liquids which constringe the vessels also increase the force of arterial blood and therefore invigorate, though they attenuate, the blood. Increased resistance to blood flow causes accumulations, in parts, which must then be impelled with greater force, acquiring more heat and being the more attenuated and digested. This, presumably, is good. Brandy, on the other hand, not only constricts the vessels, but, as is 'well known', thickens the blood and humours, further increasing the friction in the contracted vessels. Furthermore, as Boerhaave observes in his *Elementa Chemiae*, when brandy is mixed with water, the mixture acquires a glowing heat. This result is bad, for the glowing heat is soon lost, whereby habitual drinkers suffer a cold, relaxed state, following their warm and exalted one, and are driven to drink again for relief. Moreover, the dilatation of warmed blood-vessels in the brain permits

59

'too plentiful secretions being made' into its substance, causing intoxication and sleep. Perhaps the explanation of the seeming contradiction is to be found in Hales's conclusion to the set of experiments, inconclusive for all the apparent successes of his trials:

Thus what we take in, either as Food or Physick will have different Effects on our Solids as well as Fluids, according to their different Natures; and . . . it greatly imports, that they be rightly adapted to the different Constitutions, so as either to invigorate, contract or relax the Fibres of the Solids, or to change the Qualities or Quantities of the Fluids as occasion shall require. [139]

There follows an abortive set of experiments ultimately intended to reveal the course of the arteries as they divide into capillaries and thence pass into the veins. Hales observes that the circulatory system must first be flushed clean of blood and outlines his methods of using warm water and air at a pressure equivalent to that of arterial blood, lest the vessels be burst. He notes that parts of the body resist flushing, but the major failure is in his injection technique by which he had hoped to fill the emptied passages with a hot, coloured (with vermilion or indigo) mixture of rosin, tallow and turpentine varnish. Though he did not succeed as well as he had expected, and only relates his attempts so '. . . that more skilful Anatomists may judge whether they shall think it advisable to pursue the Matter further . . .' [146], he had a minor success in microscopic tracing of the anastomosis of arteries and veins in the gall-bladder.[8] In that organ sufficient vermilion had been left to trace 'here and there an extream Artery injected to the very Coat of the Vein, which it enters at right Angles'; and from this observation Hales generalizes on the natures of the arterial and venal systems, each dividing from larger trunks into branches, 'like the spread Fingers on the Hand', these into finer branches at right angles, and these into others, which finally dip into one another, 'without the interposition of any glandular Cavities' [150].

The one problem remaining, of those suggested by iatro-physical theory, was the strength of various animal parts, and to this Hales turns in the final physiological section of the *Haemastaticks*. Fixing a U-tube mercury manometer to one end of the carotid artery of a dog, he forced air into the artery (placed in water to observe leaking) and found a pressure of 5·42 atmospheres was required to burst it; this was 26·7 times that of normal arterial pressure. Similar experiments on the carotid artery, and jugular vein of a mare, and the jugular vein of a dog gave equivalent results: '. . . the great strength of the Coats of these Vessels . . . are Proof against its most lively and vigorous Sallies, when agitated by the different Passions, or by strong or brisk Actions of the Body' [160]. And as the force against the sides of a cylinder is proportional to the surfaces, though the walls of the finer arteries and veins are thinner, it is probable that their strengths are as much superior to the force of the blood in them as are these of the larger vessels. The coats of the finer secretary vessels and lymphatics are, however, not near as strong, for they do not sustain the impetus of arterial blood but only the slower and more diluted parts 'secerned' for nutrition, perspiration, etc.

These experiments are followed with a report of some, made some ten years earlier (c. 1723), on the strengths of the periosteum and ligaments. It took 119 pounds to draw off the head of the instep bone of a nine-week old calf, the breakage occurring at the symphysis. Leaving the periosteum on the bone, it took 550 pounds to sever the head of the bone, leaving 431 pounds as the strength of the periosteum. Pulling asunder the hock joint required 830 pounds. To these figures, Hales adds those determined by Musschenbroek for bursting silk thread, human and horse hair, spider thread, flax, the gut string of a musical instrument, leather thongs of calf and of oxen hide, and twisted rope.

Hales now extends his 'hydraulic' experiments to determine bursting strength of the intestines and stomach. Observing the height of the column of water sufficient to burst the stomach of a dog, and from measurements of the surface of a distended stomach, it appears that a pressure of 39 pounds is sufficient to force the fibres of the stomach. 'Which shows how greatly *Borelli* and *Pitcairne* were mistaken' in their estimate that the stomach exerted a force of 12,951 pounds on food, for 'the Force of those Fibres cannot in a live Animal be greater than the Force which will tear them asunder as soon as dead' [178]. It is more likely that the pressure of the full stomach on contained aliment is nearer 20 pounds, and so small a pressure cannot effect digestion. This is more properly to be attributed to mastication and comminution by the teeth; mixture with saliva (containing elastic air) and stomach fluids; the ferment of the 'active and expansive Principles' of the mass encouraged by the warmth and the peristaltic muscular action of the stomach; and by the 'incessant reciprocal Action and Reaction of the *Diaphragm* and Muscles of the Abdomen . . .' [180].

Here we see, as earlier in the instances of muscular motion and effect of blood, that simple mechanical explanations have had to be complicated by the addition of active principles. Hales's intent, in the *Haemastatics*, was not to disprove iatro-physical theory and, so far as he was able, he retained mechanical interpretations for physiological phenomena. But repeatedly, in areas for which simple mechanisms were almost canonical as explanations, Hales's experiments had led him into implicit criticism. He does not, however, conclude his work with a summary of iatro-physical criticism or with suggestions for its elaboration or sophistication. Though one may sense an uneasiness in his mind, it is possible that he never formulated a comprehensive objection to this physiological theory of his youth. Certainly the animal physiology part of the *Haemastaticks* ends as abruptly as it had begun – the budget of information of nearly thirty years' experimentation on animals was emptied.

The volume of the *Haemastaticks* was not at an end, however, for there remains the several additions, 'relating to several Subjects in the first Volume', appended to the text. The first of these repeats and extends experiments and observations on vesicle calculi briefly mentioned in the *Vegetable Staticks*; it can more effectively be dealt with in chapter VII which deals with Hales's explicitly practical investigations. So also can the brief section describing a sea-gauge he invented with the assistance of Desaguliers. The remaining near-eighty pages contain a miscellaneous collection of experiments and observations, most of them related only by their association with the *Vegetable Staticks*. Count Marsilli is quoted to confirm Hales's opinion that rivers and springs are supplied by rain and dew, Desaguliers and Beighton cited to support an observation on the rarity of water vapour. The motion of sap in trees is confirmed in references to workmen's experience and to observations on sea plants by Marsilli. Of the random additions, perhaps the most interesting relates to the role of air in the substantial growth of trees. Hales suggests that air, in its elastic state, need not touch and have its course determined by air vessels in the trees, any more than rays of light, in reflection, actually touch the reflecting body at the point of reflection [267].

The longest, and most coherent, section of this appendix relates, as one might expect, to those experiments on air which were of such conspicuous importance in the *Vegetable Staticks*. Hales's first concern is to extend his experiments on releasing air from liquids. After reporting some work with mineral waters – in which he was aided by a private communication from his old mentor, James Keill (which dates part of these investigations prior to 1719, when Keill died), Hales examines the amounts of air rising from ale and other fermenting liquors. Here he observes that some air is always returning to its fixed state in the liquid as other air is released and, in this double action and its variation with temperature, finds the source of some of the confusion reported in his earlier volume. It seems clear that not all of the air released from fluids is held fixed in them, but it cannot be inferred that the interstitial air is inelastic though it fills less volume in the liquid than when released. Ice contains bubbles of air, but the cold which froze the water would decrease the expansiveness of the air rather than release it.

Hales is, however, still most concerned with the release of air from a fixed, inelastic state in solids to an elastic state. He observes that there are other instances in nature, 'where the same Particles are sometimes in an elastic, and at other times in a fixed State' [279], and he instances electricity and water in the frozen and vaporous states, '. . . as all the Parts of this System are in a constant oscillatory Motion, so all Matter seems to be agitated by a repulsive and attractive Force' [280].

It will puzzle the *Epicureans* to give a rational Account how from a Chaos, a meer Necessity of Nature, and the casual Concourse of Atoms, so considerable a Quantity of Matter . . . should be endued with this double Capacity, of changing *pro re nata* from a strongly attracting fixed State, to a permanently and vastly elastic State, and vice versa; this wonderful Property . . . which is so necessary for carrying on the constant regular Processes of Nature, must needs be owing to the Direction of an allwise Being. [281]

Those observations on the air released from nitric acid and Walton pyrites, which were so to intrigue Joseph Priestley when he identified it as a new kind of air (nitric oxide) and used it in early eudiometry, are extended here with farther experiments, leading to speculations on the nature of lightning. Hales supposes that clouds serve as a partition between pure air above and 'sulphureous Vapours' below, which suddenly mix and effervesce with so rapid a velocity as to kindle the vapours and produce light.

The importance of the air, as an operative fluid in nature, is such that Hales adds twenty-one pages of experiments on effervescent mixtures, extracted from Musschenbroek's Additions to the *Tentamina Experimentorum* of the Academia del Cimento. Musschenbroek's concern, in these experiments, is, however, the changes of temperature produced by chemical mixtures and he concludes, from them, that there is a real inherent elemental fire, which produces cold by leaving the substances. Hales disagrees.:

. . . when we consider, how vastly great the attractive and repulsive Force of many of the Particles of Matter are, near the Point of Contact, it seems not improbable that the acquired Heat of effervescent Mixtures may be owing to the intestine Motions arising from those contranitent and much agitating Powers. [318]

He even goes on to suggest that the effects of these powers will be varied with infinitely different combinations, some producing heat, as they increase the effervescent vibrations of particles, and others cold, by retarding them. But he has to conclude this section and, in effect, the appendices to the book on a note of frustration similar to that which, by inference at least, permeated the animal physiology of the *Haemastaticks*. The parameters essential to a Newtonian mechanistic explanation of heating remained unmeasured and unmeasurable:

. . . as we cannot pry into the various Position of these Particles, in their several Combinations, on which their different Effects depend, so it will be difficult to account from any Principle, even though a true one, for the very different Effects of effervescent Mixtures. [319]

Musschenbroek and Desaguliers, each independently and at about the same time, also confessed their inability to determine the essential operative parameters of a Newtonian mechanism while, some thirty years later, Henry Cavendish, still attempting a mechanical explanation of heat, ran foul of the same problems of temperature change in chemical mixtures.[9]

By the application of the same Newtonian concepts and principles of scientific inquiry which had produced the serene confidence of the *Vegetable Staticks*, Hales had been brought to the doubts and uncertainties of the *Haemastaticks*. The conceptual value of Hales's work soon disappeared, but the permanent value of his experiments remained to challenge and inspire his successors, who replaced Newtonian mechanisms by the materialism of imponderable fluids and vitalistic physiology.

CHAPTER VI

Work for the S.P.C.K., the Bray Associates and the Georgia Trust, 1722-1752

Throughout the years of experimentation and writing for the *Vegetable Staticks* and the *Haemastaticks* – activities which, when added to his assiduous attention to parish duties, might be thought sufficient for any one man – Stephen Hales was expanding his clerical interests and extending his limited parochial experience into philanthropic activities operating on a national, even an international, scale. The first of these was associated with the Society for Promoting Christian Knowledge which provided him with his first opportunity to share in the work of a philanthropic organization operating on a national scale, and therefore marks the effective beginning of his long period of public works. At Cambridge during his years as a Fellow in residence at Corpus he had, according to Stukeley, 'gathered subscriptions to make the cold bath about a mile and a half out of town',[1] and, as early as 1716, he had raised money to begin his first enlargement of Teddington Church; but it was not until the next decade that circumstances arose to give free rein to his abilities as a volunteer administrator.

The Minutes of the s.p.c.k. for 8 May 1722 record the agreement of the Society, 'that the Rev. Mr. Stephen Hales Minister of Teddington in Middlesex be recommended to the Society for a Corresponding Member'[2] and though they do not mention Robert Hales by name, we may assume it was on his recommendation that Stephen was admitted to the Society. Dr Lowther Clarke has described the conditions laid down by the Society for Membership at this time: 'Loyalty to the Monarch and his Government was insisted on. Corresponding Members were chosen only after careful enquiry into their personal life and religion, the Bishop concerned being consulted if necessary.'[3] There can be little doubt that Stephen Hales would have passed such tests with ease.

As a corresponding member of the s.p.c.k., Hales purchased its publications not only for distribution amongst his parishioners but for the benefit of other like-minded individuals. He bought packets of the Society's books in 1723 for Lady Torrington and Mr Metcalfe of Sunbury,[4] in 1728 for Mr Young of Barbados, in 1729 for the Revd Mr

Gardner of Walton-on-Thames, in 1730 for Mr Butler of Warlinghurst Park in Sussex and for the Dean of Middleham,[5] and in 1736 and 1741 for Lady Blount.[6] On at least two occasions he received gifts of money to buy the Society's books for the use of the poor, and was also twice given money by anonymous benefactors for the general purposes of the Society.[7] His letter to the Society of December 1722, requesting for 'A Lady of his acquaintance . . . 50 New Testaments for a Charity School', was presumably intended for the charity school at Teddington which was one of many established by the Society for 'promoting Christian Knowledge, especially amongst the poorer sort of people'.[8] The Society published the annual sermons which eminent divines preached in support of the Charity School Movement and Hales occasionally bought copies for distribution to benefactors and friends of the Society.[9] Christian education in Wales was a special concern of the Society, and Hales collected money for the distribution of books and the support of Charity Schools in the Principality despite criticism that he should not have encouraged the use of the vernacular.[10]

The Society championed the Protestant Religion by aiding French and Spanish converts from Roman Catholicism and German Protestants who wished to escape from Roman Catholic rule. Hales gave some assistance to both these causes. In 1733 he took lodgings for a certain Don Louis de Las Torres only '2 miles distant' from Teddington and thus near enough for him to supervise the arrangements. In the same year, he arranged for Monsieur Jean Vat, a Swiss Magistrate, to conduct some Lutheran refugees from the rule of the Prince Archbishop of Salzburg to Rotterdam, where they could embark for England on their way to the newly founded colony of Georgia.[11]

As a 'Corresponding' member, Hales was not expected to attend meetings in London, yet his interest in all aspects of the promotion of Christian knowledge and, in particular, his friendship for the Society's founder, Dr Thomas Bray, led him into work which, by the 1730s and 40s, would require frequent journeys from Teddington to the metropolis.

The S.P.C.K. had begun with a meeting of four friends of Thomas Bray – the enthusiastic advocate of catechistical learning and parochial libraries – on 8 March 1698/99. In its early years it was concerned with missionary work abroad as well as the establishment of charity schools and the circulation of religious literature, but after 1701 it largely resigned overseas activity to another of Bray's foundations, The Society

66

for the Propagation of the Gospel in Foreign Parts (S.P.G.).[12] Though Hales never became a member of the S.P.G., he thought highly of its work, passing on contributions he received from his parishioners and bequeathing it 'the sum of one hundred Pounds to be by them layed out, as occasion shall offer, in purchasing books on the pastoral duty, to be from time to time given to the several successions of Ministers and Missionaries in our plantations in America'.[13]

After the S.P.G. had become successfully established Bray found other outlets for his immense energies. In 1705 he established a trust 'for erecting Parochial Libraries' which founded sixty-four libraries between then and the year of his death, 1730,[14] when its work would be carried on by yet another of his enterprises, The Associates of Dr Bray, amongst whom Hales had been numbered since their genesis in 1723.

In October 1723 Dr Bray received a legacy of £900 from the estate of Abel Tassin, Sieur D'Allone, to be used for the conversion and education of negro slaves in the West Indies. Soon after, Bray fell dangerously ill and was advised to form a body of trustees to administer the bequest. On 15 January 1723/24, Bray executed a feoffment appointing Lord Perceval, Robert and Stephen Hales and William Belitha (Stephen's neighbour at Teddington) to be his associates in carrying out the trust.[15] Bray recovered from his illness and seems to have put the D'Allone Bequest to one side until two more great reforming projects came to the fore. In 1727 the 'miserable state' of the inmates of White-chapel Prison, which was near to Bray's Parish Church of St Botolph's, Aldgate, came to his notice and revived his long-standing interest in prison reform. Through the prompting of Bray and others, a Committee of the House of Commons, investigating flagrant abuses in London's prisons, sat in 1729. This was the year that William Hales died of Gaol Fever in Newgate, when Stephen would have had good cause to share its feelings.

The Committee secured an act releasing large numbers of debtors from prison and Bray worried over the future of the freed prisoners. Accordingly he determined, in spite of recurrent illness, that:

he would before he died find out a way to have a Settlement made for the Relief of such honest poor Distressed Families . . . as by Losses, want of Employment or otherwise are reduced to poverty and such who were persecuted for their professing the Protestant Religion abroad, to be happy by their Labour and Industry in some part of His Majesty's Dominions in America. So he sent for Mr. James Vernon,[16] the Rev. Dr. [sic.] Hales, Ld.

Perceval and Mr. Oglethorpe and 2 or 3 more and proposed their entering into an association . . . for the Carrying on his Design of a Colony, and two Designs of his own viz't for Instructing the Negroes in the British Plantations in the Christian Religion; (for which there is £960 now at Interest under good security) [;] for setting Parochial Libraries in Great Britain, and for other Good Purposes.[17]

On 15 January 1729/30 Bray executed a second feoffment adding twenty-four new persons – including Vernon, Oglethorpe and Captain Coram – to the D'Allone trust. The document mentions as reasons for the enlargement of the trust, Robert Hales's desire to be discharged 'on account of diverse affairs which may probably require his passing into parts beyond the seas', which was a euphemistic way of referring to his legal and financial problems, the difficulties of 'the other Associates [who] are by their family occasions often called from London' and the fact that Dr Bray himself was 'in a declining state of health'. Bray signed it on his sick bed and after his name comes Robert and Stephen Hales's and William Belitha's, with seals impressed with the Hales arms following each signature. Then there is a space with a similar seal, reserved for Lord Perceval, who was not present at the signing.[18] One month later, on 15 February, Dr Bray died,[19] and on 5 March the initial meeting took place of the 'Trustees for Mr. D'Allone's Charity for the Instruction of the Negroes in the Christian Religion and Establishing a charitable Colony . . . and other good purposes' which was to be the first of sixty-one such occasions which would bring Stephen Hales up to London during the next twenty-one years.[20]

The establishment of a 'Charitable Colony' in America, was potentially the most costly and complicated of the Trustees' projects, requiring an extension of both their financial resources and legal competence. Before their first meeting Oglethorpe was already assured of £5,000 from another charitable bequest, and the Trustees agreed with him that this sum should be devoted to the colonial scheme. They also accepted a proposal in July 1730 that they should petition the King in Council for a grant of land south of the Savannah River in South Carolina with the necessary authority to carry out the scheme, thus beginning a complicated legal process which would not be completed until the Georgia Charter passed the Great Seal some two years later.[21] In the meantime the 'Associates of Dr. Bray' as the Trustees now called themselves, contributed small sums of their own 'for the Designs in general'; and organized themselves for their other tasks. On 30 July 1730, the Minutes record that each Associate agreed to lodge 'Sufficient Instructions, where any letter may be directed to' and there is an appropriate entry for: 'The Reverend Mr. Stephen Hales at his House in Teddington near Hampton Court'. Another tells that 'Mr. Hales paid £5:5s from Mr. Belitha, to the Designs in General . . . Mr. Hales paid £3:3s of his own for the Designs in General and thanks were returned to him for the same.'

At the next meeting of the Associates, held in October 1730, Hales though not himself present was appointed to a committee 'to consider all letters and all matters relating to Parochial Libraries'. Surviving minutes show that the committee met on at least two occasions later in the year, both of which were attended by Hales. Its principal business was to arrange for the 'sending' of parochial libraries to places in Wiltshire, Bedfordshire and Norfolk.[22]

At the fifth recorded meeting of the Associates (Thursday 12 November 1730 at 9 o'clock in the morning, with Hales present) consideration was given to the disposition of 1,200 copies of Dr Bray's edition of *Erasmus his Ecclesiastes*, which the Doctor had bequeathed to the Associates. The Minutes noted:

. . . that the Design of Dr. Bray was that one of those Books should be given to every Library in Oxford and Cambridge, and another should be sent to each Tutor, and as many more as should be thought proper for the Tutors to lend to their Pupils . . .

Hales evidently undertook to find out the extent of the demand for these books at his own university. He wrote about the matter on 15 December to the Master of Magdalene and received a detailed reply.[23] Two years later he wrote to the S.P.C.K. promising to provide ten copies of the book for John Mickleburgh at Trinity College.[24]

In 1731, Hales played some part in the establishment of a parochial library at Chertsey. The Minutes for 12 August record the receipt of 'a letter from the Rev. Mr. Hales signifying Sir William Perkins desire for a Parochial Library for Chertsey' and the same source for 11 November notes that Hales, who presided at the Meeting, 'reported that Sir William Perkins had received the Books which were sent from the Associates towards founding a library at Chertsey [and] that he will have proper presses made to preserve them . . .'. By the end of 1737 the Associates could claim that 'since the late Dr. Bray's death' they had 'endowed between twenty and thirty libraries', some of which were in

New England and, of course, Georgia. Among the books sent to New England in 1735 were 50 of the 250 copies of Hales's own work 'against Drinking Brandy' which he had himself presented to the Associates.[25] On 6 October 1736 Hales presided at a meeting of the Associates which received 'a Catalogue of the books in the Georgia Office'. This reference to 'the Georgia Office' is indicative of the formal separation of the Bray trusts and the colonial enterprise which had taken place in 1733.[26]

Yet though the accounts of the Bray Associates and the Georgia Trustees had been separated, the two charities continued to meet together each year to hear an anniversary sermon. So it was that on 21 March 1733/34, Stephen Hales preached (as the title page of the printed sermon had it) 'before the Trustees for Establishing the Colony of Georgia in America, and before the Associates of the late Rev. Dr Thomas Bray, for converting the *Negroes* in the *British* Plantations, and for other good purposes, at their Anniversary Meeting in the Parish Church of St. Brides, Fleet St'.[27]

Taking as his text 'Bear ye one another's Burdens, and so fulfil the Laws of Christ', he devoted the first half of his sermon to the arguments in favour of charities and good works which were quoted in chapter III. His hearers may well have wondered at what stage he was going to touch on the work of the Trustees and the Associates. But after a long digression exposing the absurdities of atheists and free-thinkers, he resumed his main theme:

We of this Age and Nation have much Reason to bless God, that he has put it into the Hearts of many, most zealously to join in promoting many great and excellent Designs, insomuch that it may well be accounted as the distinguishing Character of this Age, that it has been so happy in beginning, and so successful in carrying on many noble Designs for the Welfare of Mankind, and the real Interests of Religion, not only in this Island, but also to the most distant Parts of the World

Such are the generous and disinterested Aims of this Society, who are unanimously united for the establishing a Charitable Colony, not only for the Relief and Benefit of many of the Unfortunate and Distressed in our own Country, but also for an Asylum to such as are persecuted and forced for Conscience Sake to quit their native Country, and wander about destitute and afflicted . . .

He then proceeded to deal with a 'particular Branch of this kind of Charity for the advancing of which we are *Associated*, Viz. to promote as far as in us lies, *the Conversion of the poor Negro Slaves in the British Planta-*

tions'. Planters, he declared, who prevented their slaves from becoming Christians could never be Christians themselves: 'This is, in Effect, to renounce Christianity, thus wilfully and designedly to keep poor *Slaves* in Ignorance.'[28]

Hales's arguments were not, of course, original, yet his cause, though pleaded many times before, was of the utmost urgency. Francis Darwin, writing in 1890, found the sermon 'dull', but Lord Perceval (then Earl of Egmont), who was present at its delivery and had a contemporary's understanding of its subject matter, thought it 'excellent'.[29]

The Minutes of the Associates give some details of Hales's contributions to the Associates' 'Good work of converting the Negroes'. At a meeting held on 3 February 1735, he was appointed to a committee to wait on the Bishop of London 'to engage the Society for Propagating the Gospel in Foreign Parts to assist . . . [the Associates] in procuring his Majesty's letters to his Governors in the Plantations to encourage the establishing Catechists in those Colonies for converting Negroes'.[30] Although he was out of town when the committee met the Bishop on 5 March, he was present at a conference held with a committee at the s.p.g. on 21 April to consider the more limited action which the Bishop had proposed. Little progress was made at the conference for the Bishop said, according to Lord Egmont, 'Their Committee were not empowered to agree to anything, but only to report what passed in our conference, and promised that when the Society were come to a resolution we should be acquainted therewith.'

The Society's 'resolution' was far from satisfactory. Lord Egmont noted on 25 June: 'Stopped at the Georgia Office, where the associates of Dr. Bray met; we were, myself in the chair, Mr. Smith, Mr. Anderson, Captain Coram, Mr. Bedford, and Dr. Hales. A very cold and evasive writing was read, being a minute of a Board of the Society for propagating the Christian faith in foreign parts.'[30]

This rebuff from the senior missionary society did not prevent the Bray Associates from continuing to collect money for missionary activity or from contributing on a small scale to the maintenance of missionaries. In the latter case, indeed, the Associates found the s.p.g. willing to cooperate, and it is not surprising to find that Hales, who remained sympathetic to the Society throughout his life, should have participated in the selection of missionaries as well as in the raising of money.

At a meeting of the Associates held on 3 March 1734/35 Dr Hales was said to have received £50 from 'an unknown Benefactress' to be used for the conversion of negroes. In later years sums paid to him for missionary work in Georgia did not, as has been thought, pass through the hands of the Associates.[31] In 1738, Hales presided at the meeting which authorized the first annual payment of maintenance to one of two Moravian 'catechists' to the Negroes of South Carolina. The Revd Alexander Garden, who was the Bishop of London's Commissary in South Carolina, was especially active in attempts to educate the slaves in the colony. Hales was present at a meeting held on 19 March 1746/47 when Garden was invited to become a corresponding Member and to transmit to them his opinion of what they could do towards promoting the Negroes' instruction.[32] In 1751 an Italian convert from Judaism called Joseph Ottolenghi, who settled in Georgia as a silk grower, was voted £25 a year by the Associates for his services as a missionary to the Negroes, and the s.p.g. added £15 to that amount.[33] This was the year of Hales's last attendance as a Bray Associate. He had worked for the Trust for twenty-one years, during nineteen of which he had been concerned as well with the work of its institutional offspring: that ambitious combination of philanthropy and imperialism, the colony of Georgia.

The Royal Charter for Georgia passed the Great Seal on 5 June 1732. In the stereotyped but none the less magnificent language of royal paternalism, the Charter set out the need to relieve the poor of England, to mitigate the sufferings of foreign Protestants, and to provide for the defence of the southern borders of Carolina. It named twenty-one persons – including Hales and the other Bray Associates who had petitioned for the colony – to be Trustees of the new corporation and to hold office until its powers lapsed in 1752. Additional Trustees would be elected at special annual meetings held in March. The Charter also appointed Hales to the governing Common Council, a body consisting of fifteen members of the Trust.[34]

Hales was unable to obey the summons issued to all Trustees to attend the first formal meeting 'to consult about and transact the business of the said corporation' on 20 July 1732. He was not free to come up to Palace Court, Westminster, and take his oath as a Common Council Man until the fourth meeting on 10 August, when he swore that he would 'well and truly exercise the Office of Common Council Man of the Trustees for establishing the Colony of Georgia in America'. At the next meeting (17 August) he received the commission issued to 'each of the Trustees for collecting Money for the Purposes of the Charter', and he was again present on 23 August when he also attended the second Common Council Meeting. He attended the next three Trustee Meetings – 31 August, 7 and 14 September. On 26 October, the chief business of the Trustees' Meeting was to examine 'several persons who Offered themselves to Go to Georgia'. At the third of these meetings he had fulfilled his obligation as a Common Council man to take the Presidential Chair, while at the beginning of October Hales was chosen with seven others to treat with proper persons for carrying on the first embarkation of settlers.[35]

No Minutes survive to show whether he served with this (or any other of the 52 other *ad hoc* committees to which he was nominated over the next twenty years), but it seems likely that he did so, since he attended the Trustee Meeting on 16 November at Gravesend where the ship *Anne* lay and saw the 'new design'd Inhabitants' mustered on board. Lord Egmont noted that at a similar embarkation in 1735 he and Hales spent five hours on shipboard, and it is likely that Hales showed the same interest on the first occasion, when he was required to assist in supervising the accommodation of 52 men, 20 women, 25 boys and 17 girls. He had already collected for their use several hundred assorted Bibles, prayer books, books of religious instruction, horn books and primers.[36]

Hales attended the next Trustee Meeting held after the embarkation and reported benefactions he had received: 'Viz.Seventeen Pounds from a Lady Unknown for Religious Uses; twenty pounds from a Gentlewoman Unknown for the same purposes'. This was on 23 November and he was also present at the last meeting of the month. In December he attended two out of four Trustee Meetings and one out of two Common Councils, and in January 1732/33 his score was also one out of two for Common Council attendances and two out of four for attendances at Trustee Meetings. At the Trustee Meeting held on 10 January he was deputed 'to return the thanks of the Trustees' to a donor who had presented some useful weapons ('ten Hangers, and belts, and ten Cartouche Boxes and Belts') for the self-protection of the colonists, while at a meeting held in February, which was the fourth held and the third attended by him during the month, his name was associated with more characteristic donations of books and money 'for the Religious Uses of the Colony'. Between 31 January and 15 March 1732/33, the Common Council held four Meetings and Hales was present at them all. The two March Common Council days were used as well for Trustee Meetings at

73

which Hales was also present, and the last had a special significance, being the first of the Anniversary Meetings. Lord Perceval noted in his diary: 'This Day being the anniversary day of our Georgia Society . . . We . . . dined at the King's Arms in Paul's Churchyard, and were with friends about thirty in number.'[37]

Hales had established a pattern of regular support and attendance which he maintained until the expiration of the Trust in 1752. Dr McCain calculated that Hales ranked seventh of the seventy-one Trustees in the number of his attendances and he included his name among ten 'Leading Workers among the Trustees in every department of service'.[38] Hales's total of Attendances was spread over the whole period of the Trust's duration, and he persevered even when the novelty of the enterprise had worn off and the complexities of settling and governing a distant land had become apparent. In March 1737/38 Lord Egmont noted the presence of Hales among six Common Council Men who:

thinking it high time to put the affairs of our Colony on a better foot than it has been of late, to remedy abuses, to prevent unnecessary and unknown expenses to us in Georgia, by certified accounts returned to us, and to reduce the establishment of that province within the £8,000 given us this session, Met by private agreement this day as a Committee of Correspondence.

At the same time he noted his misgivings about the resignations of some Common Council Men and the lack of interest shown by others; 'on the other hand,' he added, 'Mr. Vernon, T. Towers, Myself, Mr. Lapostre, Dr. Hales, Mr. Thomas Archer and Mr. Smith continue their zeal.' On 17 July 1738, he observed, 'to make this Board to-day Dr. Hales came out of the country fourteen miles'; by December he notes that himself, Hales and five others 'were not a sufficient number of Common Council Men to make a board'.[39] Among the Trustees were an influential group of persons who were opposed to spending more than a minimum amount on the religious needs of the colony because of their hostility towards the Church of England. This group inevitably came into conflict with the churchmen of the Trust and Hales found himself involved in the controversy. Lord Egmont 'laboured to stifle' the division, but it came to a head over the question of applying 'the money given . . . by private persons for the religious use of the Colony only to religious uses', as he put it. On 5 February 1735/36, it had been agreed that the residue of the income from land being cultivated with money

74

given for religious uses, after church repairs and a clergyman's and schoolmaster's salaries had been paid should be used for 'other *religious* uses'. John White, leader of the anti-church group, seized his opportunity as chairman to cut out the word 'religious' from the resolution as recorded in the Minutes. This provoked a heated debate ending in an unsatisfactory compromise; nothing was to be said about Church maintenance or the payment of clergy or schoolmasters, but the phrase 'religious uses' was restored to the Minutes.

Egmont himself was a moderate churchman who distrusted what he called 'the Bishop of London's desire for power', and he endeavoured to justify the failure of the Georgia Board to endow the established church there with three hundred acres of glebe land, by pointing out to Dr Bearcroft of the s.p.g., 'that our Colony is made up of Protestants of all denominations'. Bearcroft 'said the Society have a very bad opinion of the members of our Board, and that as to himself, he knew only Mr. Vernon and me that were not enemies to an Established Church. I replied that they injured our gentlemen extremely, and named Mr. Digby, Lord Tyrconnell, and Mr. Oglethorpe and Dr. Hales who were as zealous as any for the Established Church'.

Early in 1737, Lord Egmont found that White and his anti-church party were still active:

I can perceive a manifest coolness in all these gentlemen towards our proceedings, and where they are active it is to guard against any resolutions we may take in favour of the Established Church and particularly the persons of our missioners. Moreover, they use little artful managements to carry their points (of which I and Mr. Vernon and Dr. Hales take no public notice) to carry matters their own way, caballing together and not communicating their thoughts to us.[40]

If Hales felt irritation at these quarrels he left no record of it and he showed no signs of quitting either his place in the Common Council or the general Trust. Most likely he displayed his particular ability to 'look even upon wicked men and those who did him unkind offices without any emotion of particular indignation'.[41]

Hales's interest in the settlement of foreign Protestants in Georgia, and his concern with the religious affairs of the colony was a natural extension of his work as a Bray Associate. His enthusiasm for the aims of the project was shown in his anniversary sermon and he no doubt approved of the Trustees' laws against slavery and rum drinking, though

75

he cannot be shown to have played any direct part in their making. Similarly it may be assumed that he took an interest in the encouragement of silk cultivation since in later years he wrote about the matter to John Ellis and the Society of Arts, yet there is no evidence to show that he was personally involved in the scheme as a Georgia Trustee. His main practical contribution to the Georgia enterprise was securing gifts for its religious and educational work.

The considerable stock of books which Hales had received for the Colony from an unknown benefactor in the first year of the Trust was matched by similar donations which came through his hands in subsequent years. In 1739 Hales himself gave 'a large Common Prayer Book' for the use of the Minister at the newly settled town of Frederica, and in 1749 he was instrumental in securing Dr William Crowe's library for the Colony. When making his own will in 1759 Hales again remembered the need for books in that distant province:

All my bound books at Teddington [he wrote] which my Executor, hereafter named, shall think proper to be sent to Georgia, I give and bequeathe for a public parochial Library to such Town or Parish in Georgia in America, the Governor shall think fit to appoint.[42]

Hales collected £567 15s 6d in monetary donations for the Trust, of which all but £126 15s came from anonymous sources and all of which was intended for religious purposes. As well as books and money he provided certain other objects for the Colony. A map of the area was presented by him at the very beginning of the Trust and was no doubt of considerable value since none of the Trustees had ever visited the land they proposed to colonize and govern. Then there were the 'two brass Cocks for salting Animals whole', given by him in 1738.[43] These were inventions of his own which he had already demonstrated at the Admiralty Victualling Office and which were to be successfully employed on one of Admiral Boscawen's expeditions.[44] Their gift to the Georgia Trust is a reminder of the increasing interest which he was showing at this time in the practical scientific problems connected with life on long sea voyages, and shows how his thoughts as an experimental philosopher fitted into his activities as a philanthropist and Christian propagandist.

CHAPTER VII

Practical invention and the applications of science

In May 1733 Hales had a copy of the *Haemastaticks* sent to his friend, the Revd John Mickleburgh, with a covering letter which declared: 'I do not intend to engage any more in a large Series of Experiments . . .'[1] Now Hales continued to experiment for the remainder of his life, but this letter was, nonetheless, predictive of the future course of his technical activities. The *Haemastaticks* was to be his last major contribution to science. There were some few small scientific papers still to be published, in the *Philosophical Transactions* or the *Gentleman's Magazine* – on electricity, for example, or the cause of earthquakes – but, for practical purpose, his attention would henceforth be directed along other paths.

Given the practical philanthropic nature of his public career, described in the previous chapter, it is not surprising that Hales should attempt to make socially useful the results of his scientific researches. Nor is there anything particularly surprising in his failure to continue original scientific investigation after 1733. Although his pessimistic conclusions to the *Haemastaticks* may have prompted his deliberate decision, it is one that time would probably have required in any event. It seems clear that in the *Vegetable Staticks* and the *Haemastaticks* Hales was actually exploiting the creative insights of his youth – the role of repulsive force in the phenomena of nature, the extension of statical equilibrium concepts to dynamical physiology, and the use of the manometer – into the fulfilment of maturity. This is a common pattern for scientific workers and, particularly when that exploitation has been as complete as in Hales's work, the original vein might well be supposed exhausted in middle-age. Hales was, after all, forty-nine when the *Vegetable Staticks* was published and fifty-five when the *Haemastaticks* appeared. In any event, from 1733 to the end of his life, Hales was primarily to turn from a further extension of his mechanistic ideas in physiology to the application of his considerable ingenuity for the practical uses of mankind.

This was not, of course, a totally new venture. The preface to each of the volumes of the *Statical Essays* proclaims his hope that greater knowledge of animal or vegetable 'oeconomy' might accrue to the welfare of man and the texts realize that hope. The *Vegetable Staticks*, for example, contains advice for the growing of hops and transplanting of trees; the *Haemastaticks*, as has been seen, makes recommendations for corrections in the practice of therapeutic bleeding, surgery, and prescription of medicines. Moreover, as a gifted experimenter with a concern for utility, Hales noted, in the course of his experiments, processes and devices which were later to become the subject of one or more separate practical articles.

A characteristic instance relates to a technique Hales describes in the *Vegetable Staticks* for determining the maximum pressure produced during the course of a pneumatic experiment. His suggestion that a depth-gauge might be designed on the same principle was adopted by J. T. Desaguliers, who describes it in his 'Account of a Machine for measuring any Depth in the Sea, with great Expedition and Certainty . . .', and Hales expands Desaguliers's description into an Appendix to the *Haemastaticks*: 'A Description of a Sea-gage, wherewith to measure unfathomable Depths of the Sea.'[2] The gauge operated rather like a barometer, with air instead of vacuum in the chamber over the mercury. As the gauge sank in water, external pressure forced the mercury to rise, increasingly compressing the resisting air into smaller compass. At the bottom, ballast was automatically released, the gauge rose to the surface and the mercury fell – but its maximum height had been marked by a layer of coloured honey or treacle which floated on top of the mercury column. Maximum pressure (and therefore depth) was to be computed from the change in volume of the air chamber.

The device was tested successfully in the relatively calm and confined waters of the Thames, but Colin Campbell inevitably lost the model he tested in the open sea off Bermuda. Nonetheless, Hales republished the account from the *Haemastaticks*, in its essential features, in the *Gentleman's Magazine* for 1754, adding a reference to the bucket-gauge he had designed for Captain Henry Ellis and first described in the *Philosophical Transactions* for 1750–51.[3]

Another example relates to Hales's paper, 'A Method of conveying Liquors into the Abdomen during the Operation of Tapping', published in the *Philosophical Transactions* in 1744. The immediate origin of this paper was the reading, at an earlier meeting of the Royal Society, of a paper by Christopher Warwick, 'An Improvement on the Practice of Tapping', also published in the *Philosophical Transactions*. Warwick proposed that in the operation of paracentesis, when the abdomen was perforated to remove excess fluid, an equivalent amount of claret, or some other restringent fluid, be injected to 'close the mouths' of 'ruptured Lymphatics' and effect a permanent cure of the condition. As the ailment was probably the result of some cardiac impairment, Warwick's 'cure' could hardly have been lasting – and he subsequently noted that later applications had not succeeded – but the report on the first attempt seemed promising, except that the patient had suffered a temporary syncope during the operation. It was this which Hales proposed to correct by injecting the restringent fluid at the same time as the lymph was removed and at a pressure roughly equal that by which the abdomen was distended. There is no indication that Warwick was at all dependent upon Hales's physiological studies, but Hales's paper clearly derives from them. Not only is the technique for determining pressure of injected and ejected fluids (the height of the liquid in a vertical glass tube) his customary one, but the notion of avoiding syncope by maintaining abdominal pressure had been explained in the *Haemastaticks*:

As the Vigour of the Blood in the Arteries and Veins is . . . increased by the increased Pressure in the Blood-vessels in the *Abdomen*; so is its Vigour much rebated when . . . the Blood-vessels . . . are too little compressed; thus when in a Dropsy a great deal of Water is at once drawn off by Tapping, the Patient is then in danger of dying . . . for which reason . . . it is drawn off not at once but at several times, that in the Intervals the dilated Parts of the Abdomen may have time to contract and thereby duly compress the Blood-vessels . . .[4]

These two examples are trivial ones, especially as neither led to a successful conclusion, but they illustrate an essential feature of Hales's work after 1733. Both are applications of science, and that not simply because they derive from Hales's studies of the *Statical Essays*, but particularly because each involves the use of scientific theory – the depthgauge of the laws of gas pressure and the tapping technique of the theories of iatro-physics. Nowadays Hales's work of this last period of his life is customarily called 'applied science', but such descriptions have, however, failed to note what science it was that he applied and how. The impression is left that the term 'applied science' has been used as a euphemism for technology and technology is not always, or perhaps even usually, at this stage of its development, the application of science. In fact, not all of Hales's inventions, of devices or techniques, can reasonably be called applied science; some are simply the consequences

79

of the manipulative ingenuity of a clever man, interested in practical matters and willing to spend the time necessary for the trial-and-error development of an empirical technique. It is well to emphasize, therefore, that those subjects of Hales's primary technological concern over the last third of his life – the campaign against the drinking of distilled liquors, development and use of mechanical ventilation, and discovery of remedies for the stone – are continuations of his earlier work and explicitly involve scientific theory, either in mode of application or, more usually, as providing the essential rationale for the endeavour.

In 1734, as we have seen, Hales published anonymously *A Friendly Admonition to the Drinkers of Brandy, and other Distilled Spirituous Liquors*. This signalled the beginning of his twenty-seven years of public and private agitation against distilled alcoholic beverages. From 1689, when an Act of Parliament prohibited importation of spirits but opened the trade of distillery to all licensed nationals, the manufacture of distilled spirits had steadily increased in England. By 1724, the manufacture and consumption of cheap raw spirits had reached near epidemic proportions. Attempts to control the situation with a Gin-Act of 1729 failed with its repeal in 1733 on the plea that legislation had not reduced drunkenness but had decreased the sale of home-grown barley. The results of repeal were disastrous and the long orgy which followed is one of the best documented popular social phenomena of early eighteenth century England.[5] Gin shops in London invited passers-by to get drunk for a penny, dead-drunk for tuppence – and provided clean straw *gratis*, on which customers might sleep off the consequences of their debauch. Two of Hogarth's most powerful social cartoons contrast the clean, healthy and prosperous life in Beer Alley to the degeneracy, filth, poverty and crime of Gin Lane.

Not until 1751 was effective legislation initiated to control the situation, but the years between 1733 and 1751 were marked by repeated efforts to gain such control and Hales was to take a prominent role in these. *A Friendly Admonition* appeared in three editions by 1735; by 1754 a fifth edition was published. He himself distributed it as a tract to gaols, churches and hospitals and by the end of the century it had formally become one of the tracts of the s.p.c.k., which republished it at least twice early in the nineteenth century.[6] Hales also consulted with Thomas Wilson in the writing of the latter's anonymous *Distilled Spirituous Liquors the Bane of the Nation*, of 1736, which paraphrases from the *Friendly Admonition* and also states, in the preface:

In the Physical Account, I have been very much indebted to an Ingenious and Learned Gentleman, well known and admired by the whole Faculty (tho' not of that Honourable Body) and whose nice and curious Experiments have struck out many new and surprizing Discoveries in that Science. – the Publick may be assur'd that what is said from him is a Matter of Fact, Consequences drawn from repeated Experiments: I have also submitted this Part to the Judgment of some eminent Physicians, who have given their Approbation of it.[7]

The first part of Hales's treatise on ventilators, of 1743, contains cautions on the 'pernicious use' of spirituous liquors which are extracted in the *Gentleman's Magazine* for the same year; his paper on the causes of earthquakes, published in the *Philosophical Transactions* for 1750 includes an almost gratuitous denunciation of the use of 'fermented, distilled spirituous liquors of all denominations'; and the second part of the treatise on ventilators (1758) repeats his warning to drunkards, a warning republished by William Henry in his *A New Year's Gift to Dram-Drinkers, being an earnest Address to them: from the late S.H.*, of 1762. The *New Year's Gift* also includes a letter to Henry written by Hales a few days before his death still exhorting against the sale of drams, at home, abroad or on the planets.[8] And if all this is not an adequate demonstration of Hales's major and continuing concern over the dangers of distilled beverages, there is his personal statement, in a letter to Bishop Hildesley of 1758, claiming that his public testimony for '30 years, in eleven different books or newspapers', against dram-drinking afforded him the greatest satisfaction of his life.[9]

Yet it is clear, from a reading of his publications, that Hales's concern was more than simple religious or social morality. His *Friendly Admonition* is no typical blue-nosed temperance tract with assurances that eternal hell-fire awaited the sinner who partook too freely of a temporal release from worldly ills. Hales was a cultured gentleman who, no doubt, enjoyed his wines in moderation, and would not have withheld beer or cider from his social inferiors. True, as a clergyman, he did not fail to note scriptural passages against drunkenness and he was clear in his conviction that excess drinking led to sin, if it was not in itself sinful. But Hales was also a scientist. From his reading, his own experiments and contemporary physiological theory he found ample and terrifying explanations for the medical consequences of heavy indulgence in distilled spirits.[10]

When, for example, Hales declares that these liquors 'coagulate and thicken the Blood', goes on to insist that they 'contract and narrow the Blood-Vessels', and states that these are facts 'found to be true, by Experiments purposely made, with Brandy, on the Blood and Blood-Vessels of Animals' [3–4], he is referring, in the first instance, to the section: 'Chemical History of the Serum of the Blood', in Boerhaave's *Elementa Chemiae*, then to his own confirming experiments, and finally to the experiments with perfusates, reported in the *Haemastaticks*, where brandy took, on an average, twenty seconds longer to pass the capillaries of the gut than did warm water.[11] These experiments had been performed on dissected organs, but the assumption that the same phenomena would occur *in vivo*, and with the amounts of alcohol added to the blood in drinking, conformed with iatro-physical theory in explaining the occurrence of jaundice, dropsy, consumption, etc. Thickened blood and narrowed blood-vessels combine to slow circulation and 'cause Obstructions and *Stoppages* in the Liver; whence the *Jaundice* . . .' Slow circulation also induces stagnant blood and, in the heart, 'breed Polypuses, or fleshy substances . . . hindering and retarding the motion of the Blood through the Heart . . .' And stagnant blood permits the mutual attraction of the red parts of the blood and separation of the serum. The red parts are 'consumed and burnt' by the desiccating properties of repeatedly distilled spirituous liquors 'whereby the Blood is impoverished' while the thin, sharp, serum oozes easily through the corroded weakened blood-vessels and produce dropsies.[12] Hales's explanations are not always consistent within their own frame of physiological theory and that theory too clearly had its limitations, but it can hardly be denied that many of his arguments against dram-drinking were, in the fullest sense, the application of his science.

Hales's first explicit publication on the subject of ventilators and associated devices was a paper, read to the Royal Society in May 1741 and printed in extended form in 1743, as *A Description of Ventilators: whereby Great Quantities of Fresh Air may with Ease be conveyed into Mines, Gaols, Hospitals, Work-Houses and Ships, in Exchange for their Noxious Air*.[13] From that time until his death, Hales was to be occupied with activities respecting the ventilator or some variation of the basic principle he felt was realized in it. Between 1743 and 1757 the *Gentleman's Magazine* contains some twenty different references (as notes, extracts, letters or commentaries) relating to Hales and ventilation; three papers by Hales in the *Philosophical Transactions* on the same subject are supplemented by half a dozen papers by others. Another pamphlet, *An Account of a Useful*

Discovery to distill double the usual quantity of sea-water . . . published in 1756, relates primarily to the forced ventilation of distilling water and also includes a description of several demonstrated advantages of his ventilators, while Hales's last publication was an explicit continuation of the *Description: A Treatise on Ventilators. Wherein An Account is given of the Happy Effects of the several Trials which have been made of them* . . ., published in 1758.[14] In addition, the majority of Hales's surviving letters from at least as early as January 1741/42 refer to ventilators or ventilation. This includes a remarkable series of nearly a dozen letters to the millwright engineer Thomas Yeoman, written between 1743 and 1746, relating to design, improvement,construction and installation of ventilators, and also encompasses, sometimes by implication, his foreign correspondence with De Nemours, Duhamel de Monceau, Mazeas, etc., about their installation in France.[15] It is not unreasonable to suggest that Hales's image as a public benefactor after 1743 was primarily the result of his persistent campaign for the adoption of ventilators, which it should be noted, he specifically regarded as an application of science to practical ends. The preface to the *Description of Ventilators*, of 1743, contains the statement:

We have here an Instance, that the Study of Natural Philosophy is not a meer trifling Amusement, as some are apt to imagine: For it not only delights the Mind . . . But it is also the most likely means, to make the Gift of kind Providence, this natural world, the more beneficial to us, by teaching us how, both to avoid what is Hurtful, and to pursue what is most Useful and Beneficial to us. [vii–viii]

Postponing, for the moment, consideration of the role of science (or natural philosophy) in the enterprise, to what degree can it be said that it was, in fact, of practical value? The evidence seems clear that it was, though that value must have been derived from something other than the theoretical basis. Hales was prompted to design the ventilator by news of an epidemic of typhus (known variously in the eighteenth century as ship, gaol and hospital fever) among embarked soldiers awaiting transport to North America in 1740. The first installation, however, appears to have been in a granary where the forced ventilation of the grain encouraged drying and helped prevent mould and putrefaction. This application of the ventilator was perhaps its most widespread. It prompted Hales to adapt the principle to preservation of grain in sacks by blowing air from kitchen bellows through perforated tubes, was a major aspect of its adoption and imitation in France and Holland, and was one of the factors which ensured that the device retained its usefulness into the second decade of the nineteenth century.[16]

In its application to the purpose for which it was originally designed – i.e., installation on ship-board to replace bad, 'disease-causing', air with good air – Hales had more trouble. At the instructions of the Lords of the Admiralty, his ventilator was tested on a ship, to the satisfaction, according to Hales, of officers and men, but he met the usual resistance by military officialdom to civilian suggestions; Sir Jacob Ackworth, Surveyor of the Navy, was not interested. Hales then used his influence as a Trustee for the colony of Georgia to have his ventilators installed on merchant ships and he appealed to the public, through his *Description*, which he chose to dedicate to the Admiralty Lords. Between 1742 and 1749 the use of ventilators, particularly on slave and transport ships, appeared so successful in reducing illness and death that the Board of Trade and Plantations officially adopted their use. A law was even proposed to the Assembly of Pennsylvania to penalize ships entering the Philadelphia harbour that did not possess working ventilators. In 1751 and in 1754 the Admiralty again tested the ventilators and again rejected them, but their success in merchant ships, hospitals and gaols became so evident that the Navy eventually capitulated in 1756, with an order 'to fit ventilators into all His Majesty's ships'. Hales's friend, Thomas Yeoman, was appointed to be in charge of naval installations and at least as late as 1765 was still acting as 'Chief Marine Superintendent of H.M. Navy' and designing windmill-driven Hales's ventilators for installation into men-of-war.[17]

The extraordinary success of ventilating ships (for fresh air is not, after all, a curative agent for typhus) was paralleled by successes in ventilating hospitals and prisons. Though the Navy had been reluctant to install ventilators in its ships, they were soon placed in naval hospitals at Portsmouth, Gosport and Plymouth. In 1744 one was placed in a hospital at Hyde Park Corner; in 1747 another was installed in the Middlesex small-pox hospital, of which Hales was a governor, and by the time the *Treatise* was written in 1758, Hales could report their use in several London and county hospitals. Sir John Pringle included a section on the 'Use of ventilators in hospitals' in his famous *Observations on the Diseases in the Army*, of 1752, and Hales designed a portable ventilating system for temporary army hospitals which he described in the *Gentleman's Magazine* for the following year.[18]

84

It is possible, however, that Hales had a particular interest in the use of his ventilators in gaols, for his brother William had died in prison, in 1729, probably from gaol-fever.[19] Certainly this use of the Hales's ventilator was its most dramatic. A poem by William Hayley, celebrating the prison reforms of John Howard and published in 1780, contains a stanza reflecting the continuing popular esteem for Hales's contribution:

> I see the hallow'd shade of Hales
> Who felt, like thee [Howard], for human woe,
> And taught the health diffusing gales
> Thro' Horror's murky cells to blow.[20]

The first major prison installation was made in 1749 when Henry Fox, Secretary of State for War, requested a ventilator for Savoy Prison. The subsequent drop in prisoner deaths was so marked as to prompt installations in a number of county prisons, but the most dramatic adoption was that for Newgate Prison. The then Lord Mayor of London, Sir Richard Hoare, appears to have ordered an installation in Newgate in 1747, but the device was ignored until a later Lord Mayor, two judges, an alderman, several lawyers, an under-sheriff and five members of a Middlesex jury were affected by gaol fever spread from Newgate prisoners brought to trial in 1750. Hales and Sir John Pringle were appointed on a commission to correct the situation and a ventilator, operated by a windmill, was installed in 1752. Once again Hales was able to report a substantial drop in prison deaths following use of the ventilator and shortly thereafter Gate-House Prison, Westminster, New Prison and Clerkenwell Prison each had a ventilator installed. Hales also engaged in protracted negotiations, through his French correspondents, Duhamel de Monceau, the Duc de Noailles and the Abbe Mazeas, to have ventilators installed in prisons and ships in which British prisoners-of-war were held captive and remarked, with self-complacency, that he hoped no one would inform against him for corresponding, in this connection, with the enemy.[21]

The importance of ventilation had, of course, been recognized long before Hales and the idea of forced ventilation had also been discussed. One predecessor, notable chiefly because he is mentioned by Hales in the preface to the *Description*, was Nathaniel Henshaw whose *Aero-Chalinos: or, A Register for the Air*, published in 1677 by order of the Royal Society, describes an air chamber in which the quality and quantity of air was to be controlled for the 'better preservation of Health and cure of Diseases'. Hales denies having heard of Henshaw's device until after he had completed his own, but he can hardly have remained as ignorant of the work of a number of his contemporaries. For the ventilator provides yet another example of near-simultaneous invention. In 1735 Hales's friend, J. T. Desaguliers, published 'An Account of an Instrument or Machine for changing the Air of the Room of Sick People . . .' in the *Philosophical Transactions.*[22] The year that Hales read his first ventilator paper to the Royal Society, Martin Treiwald, Military Architect to the King of Sweden, independently developed a ventilator which was adopted by the Swedish and French navies having been demonstrated before the Royal Academies of Sciences in Stockholm and Paris and described in a paper published in 1742.

However, the only contemporary alternative which, in Britain at least, provided any competition to Hales's ventilator was that of Samuel Sutton. Sutton, a London brewer, was inspired to invention by the sailors' plight in the same epidemic that had inspired Hales. Like Hales, Sutton attempted to get his device installed in naval vessels and, like Hales, appealed to the public for the support he had failed to get from naval officials. A description of Sutton's method was read before the Royal Society in January 1741/42 and shortly thereafter Dr Richard Mead and Dr William Watson read papers approving Sutton's method and its results.[23] Sutton felt that his device, making use of the fire in a ship's galley and a system of pipes drawing draughts from the hold and discharging air up the galley chimney, was simpler and better than that of Hales, who, he felt, was using his social and political influence to impede the adoption of the better ventilator. Indeed, he implies that Hales's invention was a consequence of his own and complains that Hales has ignored him. Comparison of publication dates makes clear that Hales's invention was prior to Sutton's and surely Hales's failure to advertise a rival's invention requires no justification. Nor need Sutton's ultimate failure to get his ventilator adopted be blamed entirely on the use of personal influence. That Hales used such influence is clear, but Sutton's device, though simpler in conception, poses problems in execution – even deliberately designed fire places frequently fail to draw – in potential fire hazards on ship-board, and in fuel consumption.

Hales's ventilator was a manually operated device based on the design of organ bellows. A large, long, air-tight wooden box was bisected horizontally with a flat midriff centrally hinged at one end. The other end of the midriff was moved freely, through the arc of the box-depth, by a vertical rod fixed to the midriff and passing through the cover. As the rod was raised and lowered, air was alternately drawn in or expelled through valves at the hinged end of the ventilator. Two such boxes, fixed side-by-side, could be worked simultaneously by a pumping lever, centrally pivoted, and fixed to the vertical rods so as to raise one midriff as the other was lowered. Valves and air passages from the ventilators were to be kept large and light, central midriffs were light and loosely fitted, to ensure easy working of the ventilator, though Hales suggests that for land use, in mines, granaries, etc., it might be driven by horse or waterwheel. With an instrument the size used by Hales – 10 feet long, 5 feet wide and 2 feet deep – an optimum rate of 60 strokes a minute moved air at a rate of 3,000 feet a minute, better than the rate produced by 'another ventilating Machine, composed of a Wheel with Fans, in a Drum, such as is described in *Agricola de Re Metallica,* and in the *Philosophical Transactions*' [i.e., by Desaguliers]. According to the arrangement of channels leading to and from the valves, one could either convey good air to a place (driving out bad) or withdraw bad air (drawing in good).

Given the differences in the various ventilators proposed, it is clearly useless to look for a common theory of design. All, in fact, would seem to have resulted from an extrapolation of common, empirical, experience. Yet the nearly simultaneous appearance of competing ventilating systems, and particularly the two intended to cure the same epidemic, shows that the inventors shared some part of the common belief that the disease was caused by bad air. The nature of Sutton's belief is revealed in the naive commonplace, 'the sailors . . . were so dangerously ill, for want of fresh air, that they were put ashore to recover their health, and the ships to which they belonged stunk to such a degree that they infected one another'. That commonplace was, however, restated in more sophisticated terms by William Watson, whose support of Sutton shows an affinity between seventeenth century iatro-chemistry and a reviving materialistic chemistry and physiology. Foul air is loaded with malignant poisons and fumes. Numbers of uncleanly people, stowed too close together: '. . . heat the air, make it replete with noxious *effluvia,* destroy the particles therein adapted to cool the lungs, particularly the acid nitrous gas . . . Air robbed of this valuable property, and replete with hurtful ones . . . must produce the most putrid if not pestilential fevers.' Richard Mead, not yet wholly recanted of his increasingly old-fashioned mechanistic physiology, has a different explanation:

87

. . . it is that property of the air which is called its elasticity or springiness which makes it so useful to our life. When any part of it is enclosed . . . it expands itself, and, in proportion to the closeness of the place, loses its spring; and if any heat or moisture comes to it, the elastic force may be quite lost and destroyed. And . . . if it happens to be impregnated with noxious *effluvia*, either from unwholesome substances . . . or from the infectious breath of diseased bodies, it will become quite poisonous and deadly, in a manner suitable to the original cause.[24]

Now Mead's understanding of the elasticity of the air is obviously deficient, but his explanation of the effect of air in disease clearly derives from the work of Hales. Hence the irony, in which Sutton is supported by arguments drawn from a scientific theory, respecting the physiological significance of the dynamic activity of air, which were the source of Hales's own convictions that led to the invention of a ventilator.

Indeed Mead need not have gone to the original statement of Hales's theory, in the *Vegetable Staticks* and *Haemastaticks*, for his description of the nature of foul air. If he attended that May 1741 meeting of the Royal Society when Hales read his paper on ventilators, he must have heard what Hales was subsequently to publish in the *Description* – a justification for ventilation which is greater in detail but the same in substance as that which Mead was to repeat in his letter to the Society of nearly a year later: '. . . when the air we breath is loaded with Vapours which either render it too warm, or destroy its Elasticity, or both, it becomes unfit for Respiration . . .'.[25]

Respiration is best carried on, when the Air we breathe is perfectly elastick, and cooler than the Vapours in the Lungs . . . the oftner therefore we breathe the same air . . . it will not only be more and more loaden with Vapours which, we find by Experience, destroy its Elasticity; but it will also come nearer and nearer to the same degree of Warmth with the Air in the Lungs, and consequently will lose more and more of those Properties, Coolness and Elasticity, upon which the Circulation of the Air in the Lungs depends . . . [47]

Both of these observations are, it is true, quoted as from the 'ingenious *Lectures on Respiration*' of 'Dr Hoadly', but why Benjamin Hoadly should be so invoked is far from clear. Perhaps it was because Hoadly was a physician. Certainly an inspection of his *Three Lectures on the Organs Of Respiration* will reveal that everything that Hales cites from that work was originally, and explicitly, derived from the *Vegetable Staticks* or the *Haemastaticks*.[26]

By 1743 Hales had also been influenced by the rising tide of iatro-chemical, materialistic physiology, as can be seen in the *Description*, when he mentions the 'corruptible' vapours which arise from human bodies and, in prisons, often produce 'mortal Distempers' [42]. The same influence is more obvious in Hales's explanation of the anti-pestilential quality of vinegar, because there is a ferment between it and 'the too alkaline rancid Air, which may thereby be reduced . . . to a neutral, more wholesome state: as alkaline and acid mixtures frequently produce neutrals' [46]. Even in this connection the data of the *Statical Essays* are used to show the magnitude of the problem and the quantity of air which must be moved, as when the observations of James Keill and experiments of Hales show that 'a close confined Air, in which there are many Persons, is filled not only with the Vapours arising from their Breath, but also with what perspires off their Bodies; which Respiration and Perspiration both together, are equal to the Quantity of half the Meat and Drink which we take in Daily; which is estimated to be about thirty-nine Ounces in England, and is much greater in hot Climates' [42-3].

The explanation of why air, loaded with effluvia, moisture and rancid vapours, is harmful is, however, for the most part, still in the mechanical mode first followed in the *Vegetable Staticks* and continued in the *Haema-staticks*. Air particles, absorbed by the blood in respiration, 'supply the active Principles, so necessary to the Warmth of the Blood, and the Cohesion of its Parts'. If that air should be impaired of its activity, through inelastic combination with attracting impurities, the blood also becomes unfit 'for the Purposes of Life: So that by degrees . . . it is only fit to choak up and clog the Vesicles, and capillary arteries . . . Hence, 'tis no wonder that when we breath Air, thus loaded with Vapours, it should be apt to cause what are called Gaol-Distempers . . .' [44-5]. '. . . dry Air being in a more strongly repelling state' than damp, it will better dilate the small vesicles of the lungs, in respiration, thus allowing for freer circulation [106].

Even in its non-medical applications, Hales finds a mechanistic justi-fication for his ventilators, though the activity of the air comes to have an electrical explanation. The motion of air carries off 'the great Quan-tity of Vapour, which perspires from all kinds of Vegetables, which . . . would suffocate them and produce Mildews, &c. But it also greatly con-tributes to the gentle drying of the Substance of growing Vegetables, whereby they are not only enabled to attract vigorously fresh Nourishment, but also grow thereby gradually more and more firm and hard'. Desaguliers has shown dry air to be electrical, 'by which property it attracts Moisture strongly. . . . No wonder then, that air in passing up thro' Gun-Powder, for a Continuance, should dry it so perfectly well' [126–7]. And no wonder that fresh electrical air should so strongly attract the putrid, volatile, sulphureous particles of stinking water, as to contribute so markedly to processes for making sea-water wholesome [74].

This last reference is to the researches which Hales had begun at least as early as his *Philosophical Experiments* of 1739 and continued through the *Description* into such later work as his 'Account of some Trials to cure the ill Taste of Milk', his 'Account of the great Benefit of blowing Showers of fresh Air up through distilling Liquors', and particularly his *An Account of a Useful Discovery to distill Double the Usual Quantity of Sea-Water, by Blowing Showers of Air up through the Distilling Liquor* of 1756.[27] This last pamphlet is, perhaps, Hales's most complete, and impressive, technological achievement. Not only does he describe a device by which a stream of air is kept ascending through the distilling liquid, he develops an elaborate time and fuel study to demonstrate that with his device it is more economic to carry coal and distil fresh water from the sea than it is to carry the weight of fresh water as ship's stores. Given the improved efficiency of distillation per ton of coal, the possibility of pre-heating the water in a worm-pipe in the cook's stove, and the amount of time required to empty, clean and refill the stills, distil four-fifths of water content, and repeat, it appears that sufficient time is available each day to distil an adequate supply of fresh water, with an amount of coal that still leaves more space and weight of stowage for other uses than would be available if fresh water were carried – water which, moreover,would become putrid and stinking during the voyage and produce such distempers as the scurvy.

The method was originally suggested through a related device Hales learned of through the secretary of the Society of Arts, John Ellis, but again the rationale of the technique is provided by the concept of attracting, elastic air. He notes that 'It is a well known Property of moving Air, to carry along with it a considerable Quantity of adjoining Vapour . . .' He also adds, as an explanation for the apparent fact that sea-water, distilled by this new process, is less acidly bitter than that distilled by the old method:

90

The continual Streams of ascending fresh Air, not only in some Degree abating the Heat of the Water; but also incessantly carrying off the more rarefied Particles of the Water, which, when expanded into a repelling State, do thereby cause the overflowing Ebullition of the Water. On which Account it is probable, that less Spirit of Salt is formed and raised by Ventilation than without it.[28]

But though the mechanistic theory survives, Hales also shows that he retains the ability to observe with some objectivity, as in his experiments on keeping fish alive in water by blowing air through it.

Whence we may reasonably infer, how requisite it is, in order to keep the Blood in a salutory State, to have almost constant Supplies of . . . fresh Air, to mix with it. For if the principle Use of the Gills were only to cool, and churn, and comminute the Blood, Water devoid of Air could as well perform that office . . .[71]

Of all Hales's technological work, the highest value, retrospectively, is assigned to his technique to improve the efficiency of distillation. We are too out-of-sympathy with temperance movements to value his arguments against the drinking of drams, even if the theory behind them were to be accepted. We know too well that typhus is not caused by foul air to credit Hales's reports of the success of ventilation to the theory which lay behind its adoption.[29] But the distillation process works, today as it did in Hales's day, and the reason for its working can, without too obviously ignoring specifics, be reconciled with Hales's interpretation. Nonetheless, evaluation of Hales's activities in applied science must not be based on modern acceptance either of his techniques or of his theories. Judgment of the nature and significance of his work must depend upon the contemporary importance of the problems to which he addressed himself, the extent to which he deliberately and self-consciously applied theory commensurate with the scientific thinking of his time to the definition and/or solution of those problems, and the evidence of the effectiveness of those solutions at the time. In nearly all of Hales's technological achievements, those three criteria: importance, intent to apply scientific theory, and effectiveness, combine, in varying proportions, to justify his contemporary reputation as an eminently successful and public-spirited scientist and projector. Perhaps his continued efforts in the design of a farm implement, 'the Back-heaver', winnowing and cleaning grain, though useful and effective, contain too small an element of theory to qualify as applied science; the same is surely true of his methods to regulate the heat in melon-frames and greenhouses, or to control the spread of fires.[30] Yet the use of theory is evident enough in the agitation for the Gin-laws and the introduction of ventilators, while the technique for salting beef carcases by injection of brine through the arterial system, described in the *Philosophical Experiments* of 1739, is clearly related to the experiments, at least, of the *Haemastaticks*; and the long series of experiments on the use of lime and lime water to keep water and fish fresh, first alluded to in the *Philosophical Experiments* and reported at length to the Royal Society in 1754, has a theoretical connection, worthy of analysis, with Hales's discoveries of the chapter on air of the *Vegetable Staticks*.[31] The clearest example, however, of an optimum combination of social value, conscious use of theory, and apparent contemporaneous success is, ironically, in that area of Hales's concern least credited by modern commentators – the attempt to find a dissolvent for vesicle calculi.

The social problems represented by vesicle calculi were, perhaps, of less significance than those of excessive drinking or typhus, but the appearance of countless articles on the nature, cause, and cure of the stone, in the *Philosophical Transactions* and medical journals of the eighteenth century, attest to their importance.[32] And, as the standard surgical remedy nearly exceeded, in pain and danger, the ailment itself, the possibility of finding an alternative cure was a practical concern of major interest to eighteenth century physicians. There was, therefore, ample justification for Hales's investigations of the stone, apart from any personal concern that he may have had.[33]

Hales's interest in finding a dissolvent for the stone lasted at least from 1727 to 1756, but his publications on the subject essentially culminate in his pamphlet: *An Account of some Experiments and Observations on Mrs. Stephens's Medicines for Dissolving the Stone* of 1741.[34] In her own day Mrs Stephens was the centre of controversy; her 'remedy' for the stone, consisting mainly of burnt vegetable matter, calcined shells, soap and honey, was made public in 1739 on the award of £5,000 from Parliament and immediately was denounced as a fake. As lithodialysis is not highly regarded by modern urologists and, in any event, the ingredients of Mrs Stephens's medicine are unlikely to be generally useful for the purpose, she is today described as one of the more successful quacks of the eighteenth century, while her supporters, including Hales, are dismissed as dupes.

This disdain for Hales's association with Joanna Stephens's nostrums has spread to all of his work on the stone and occasioned such judgments as: 'Dabbling with medical problems would seem to have brought to the fore an amazing degree of naivety in this great scientist.'[35] Hales's contemporaries would not have agreed. His experiments, 'towards the discovery of medicines for dissolving the stone in the kidnies and bladder' were instrumental in his obtaining the Copley Medal of the Royal Society in 1739 and they were also, no doubt, responsible for his appointment the same year as one of the twenty-nine Parliamentary trustees to evaluate Mrs Stephens's medicines. The wisdom of hindsight makes it easy to criticize the judgment of those trustees, but should not obscure the fact that Hales did not pass on the medical virtues of the recommended remedy – this he accepted on the judgment and experience of the physicians and surgeons of the group.[36] He reported on its efficacy in dissolving the stone *in vitro*. In this regard he may well have been overoptimistic, but that optimism stemmed from his previous investigations of lithontriptics, and from the mechanical theory which had prompted those studies.

Calculi from the bladder and kidneys had been among the many substances subjected to 'distillation' and 'fermentation' for the chapter on analysis of the air in the *Vegetable Staticks* of 1727. On heating such stones, Hales obtained more air, bulk for bulk, than from any other substance; nearly four-fifths the weight of a stone appeared as air. 'Fermenting' processes were less effective, though mineral acids did, in time (sometimes twelve to fourteen days), manage to dissolve small pieces of stone with the production of air. Because of the amounts and solubility of the air 'released' by heating or dissolution, Hales believed that vesicle calculi were 'animal tartars', and, within the frame of his corpuscular dynamic chemistry, concludes:

From the great quantities of air that are found in these Tartars, we see that unelastic Air particles, which by their strongly attracting property are so instrumental in forming the nutritive matter of Animals and Vegetables, is by the same attractive power apt sometimes to form anomalous concretions, as the Stone, &c, in Animals, especially in those places where any animal fluids are in a stagnant state, as in the Urine and Gall Bladders . . . This great quantity of strongly attracting unelastic air particles . . . should rather encourage than discourage us, in searching after some proper dissolvent of the Stone in the Bladder, which . . . is found to be well stored with active principles, such as are the principal agents in fermentation. [110]

Encouraged 'by the greatest and most knowing chemists', and aware

93

that it was 'a Matter of . . . great Importance, to the Ease and Welfare of a considerable Part of Mankind', Hales returned to the problem, for an appendix to the *Haemastaticks*: 'An Account of some Experiments on Stones in the Kidnies and Bladder. With an Inquiry Into the Nature of those anomalous Concretions.'[37] The first eight pages of this appendix are essentially a repetition of the relevant passages from the *Vegetable Staticks*, with, however, slightly more detail on the presumed dynamic, cohesive mechanism of formation of animal and vegetable tartars. Hales then continues with experiments, 'to try by a Variety of fermenting Mixtures, whether the brisk Action . . . [of "fermentation"] might not possibly so shake and rouse these Air Particles, as to make them fly off into an elastick State, and thereby dissolve the Union of the Parts of the Stone' [197], for this, he believes, is the dissolving action of nitric acid. Initially his experiments were performed *in vitro* and he did not confine himself to solvents mild enough to inject into animals, for he argued that an effective solvent might reveal the nature of the stone and also be sufficiently dilutable to become practically useful. In his efforts he was to remain unsuccessful. Of the various solutions, chosen almost at random and ranging from hot water through such oddities as 'spirit of rye bread' and pulped onions and horse radish, none were conspicuously successful, though some seemed, at least, to soften the surfaces and might, therefore, be useful in smoothing rough, abrasive, edges.

One solution, of 'sal tartar' and 'oil of sulphur' (i.e., potassium carbonate and concentrated sulphuric acid) appeared more successful than the others in dissolving vesicle gravel and, for a time, softening the exterior of harder calculi. But the solution had 'no Effect on the Calculus after the ferment is over' – i.e., when the ebullition accompanying its production had ceased. Indeed stones soaked in the quiescent solution for over a year were not dissolved. Hence the effect, consistent with Hales's dynamic principles:

. . . seems not to depend on the Fitness of the Particles of the Menstruum to enter the Pores of the *Calculus*, but rather to certain harmonic Proportions between the Vibrations of the fermenting Liquor and the Tone or Degree of Tenseness of the Parts of the *Calculus*. . . .

For, as strings or organ pipes may vibrate in harmonic sympathy so 'we may not unreasonably suppose' that if a harmonic proportion existed between parts of the stone and the vibrating, fermenting liquid, then 'The *Itus* and *Reditus* of these Vibrations, increasing . . . each other's Force, some parts of the *Calculus* are thereby thrown off into elastic Air' [204–5]. In confirmation of his theory, Hales notes that an optimum range of proportions of acid and alkali existed, at which the most air was released from the 'fermenting' stone.

Although this solution seemed mild enough – it was slightly astringent in the mouth and was injected (using an ingenious double catheter of his own design), into dogs without significant uneasiness – it could not really be recommended for use on humans, for too many repeated injections would be required to dissolve even the softer stones, and some evidence suggested that it might harden and contract the fibres of the bladder. Nonetheless, its discovery was an indication that progress was being made toward finding a safe dissolvent. No other dissolvent seemed as promising, and that one being inapplicable, Hales turned to the possibility of preventing or discouraging the growth of calculi. He concludes, from his reading, that mucilaginous beverages (e.g., milk, barley-water, soft ale) are good preventatives. He supports this conclusion with an observation that the 'Cohesion of the tartarine Air particles' of toasted breads or meats which are less mucilaginous than when boiled, are more apt to breed the stone, because heating has broken the particles to such a degree 'as to leave them more at liberty to form [a stone] in this their detached unelastic State'. [221]. Perhaps it was this association of mucilaginous materials with calculi which later encouraged the writing of his paper 'A Proposal to bring small passable Stones soon and with Ease out of the Bladder'.[38] Here the intention is not the prevention of the stone, but the more efficacious removal of fragments through injection of mucilaginous liquids into the bladder. The advantage was achieved partly by the greater flushing force (carefully measured by comparing times of descent of a stone through columns of water, urine, oil, etc.), but also because of the greater slipperiness given the urethra if such fluids as olive oil or barley-water were injected.

Hales continues his study with considerations of the effect of season (amounts of perspiration, alternation of heat and cold), posture and diet on formation of the stone. The latter, particularly, emphasizes the tartarine concretions to be obtained from beverages and leads to a set of experiments performed on various samples of water, the incrustations obtained in their distillation, the air released from such incrustations on heating or dissolutions, and the relation between such incrustations and the nature of the soil matrix out of which the water comes. These experiments were the subject of much correspondence with Mickleburgh

95

and other chemists in Britain and on the continent and may, in their turn, have led to Hales's more general studies of well, spring and mineral water.[39] By 1735 he was corresponding with Dr Robert Nesbitt (later a fellow-trustee examiner of Joanna Stephens's medicine) on medicinal waters and the preservation of their properties. In 1738 he transmitted a paper to the Royal Society on 'steel waters', and in 1739 included that paper as an appendix to his pamphlet *Philosophical Experiments: containing useful, and necessary instructions for . . . long voyages at sea.*[40] In 1750 he published 'An Examination of the Strength of several of the principal purging Waters, especially that of Jessop's Well . . .' and, the same year, wrote a letter to Martin Clare on an analysis of Malvern water, which was subsequently published in 1756. His technique of analysis was essentially that employed in the *Haemastaticks*. Samples of water were evaporated to dryness, the remaining deposit was examined, and measured samples were heated or dissolved to determine if air would be released.[41] Hales assumed that the releasing of air gave some indication of medicinal activity and, therefore, the quantity of deposit was a measure of the strength of medical virtue, but he did not, himself, declare these waters to have such virtues – a judgment he left to professional, medical opinion.

When such opinion was not available he was, in fact, inclined to be something of a sceptic. In 1746, for example, he warned the public against an advertised remedy for the stone in 'Some Remarks on the boasted Liquid Shell', published in the *Gentleman's Magazine*, and in 1753 he published, through a London newspaper, a denial that the waters of a well at Glastonbury and of another near Godstone, in Surrey, possessed any properties other than those of common spring water.[42] When he had a respected authority he was, perhaps, inclined to be too credulous. A case in point would seem to be his *Account of some Experiments and Observations on Tar-Water.*[43] Bishop Berkeley's wide claims for the medical virtues of tar-water excited much attention and controversy during the 1740s (and the 'remedy' was still advertised a century later as 'Dr. Berkeley's aromatic tar-pills'). Although Hales claims at the beginning of his pamphlet that he is not interesting himself 'either in Favour or Disfavour of a Medicine that is under the inspection of the proper Judges' [2], the efforts he exerts in its examination imply a commitment which is explicitly revealed in his conclusion that 'it has . . . undoubtedly proved an efficacious Remedy in many Cases and Instances' [28–9]. Yet his studies are not directed to proving its efficacy.

Instead, he investigates the amounts of various kinds of tar which dissolve in water under different conditions, the nature and amounts of residue when the water is evaporated, and processes by which reproducible strengths of tar-water might be made. Repeatedly citing Boerhaave in connection with vegetable oil and acid remedies, Hales identifies 'whatever Virtue Tar-water has' with a 'subtile, volatile Acid' of tar and a fixed alkaline salt together making a 'penetrating, detersive Soap'. Clearly he starts with an acceptance of Berkeley's claims; all that he really leaves to 'the proper Province of the Physician, which I am no ways qualified to meddle in' is 'the adapting the due Proportions of acid and oily Principles, to different Cases and Constitutions', on the basis of his researches [29–30].[44]

This, too, is the nature of Hales's involvement with Mrs Stephens's lithontriptic. 'Mrs. Stephens's Medicines having been found by Experience to have been very effectual . . . [by] several Persons, who have persevered in taking them', Hales saw his task to be that of discovering 'wherein the principal Virtue and Efficacy' lay in order to render the remedy less nauseous and more efficacious. He was 'acting the part of a Naturalist', while the physicians, 'whose proper Province it is', were to make the improvements in the medicines and determine how they might be used with safety.[45] Hales performed dissolving experiments *in vitro* as continuations of similar studies by David Hartley and by the physician-chemists S. F. Morand and C. J. Geoffroy for the Royal Academy of Sciences in Paris. He boiled stones, or parts of stones, in solutions of Mrs Stephens's soapy medicine and of soap-lye. As the stones dissolved in the latter, he concludes that the active ingredient in the former (which, however, did not dissolve the stone) must be the soap-lye and that, in turn, depends upon 'the Energy which the fiery Particles of the Lime give to the lixivious Salts of the Pot-ash, whereby they acquire a Power of penetrating and intimately mixing with Oils, which are a principal Bond of Union of solid Bodies, and thereby dissolve them' [3]. He reasons that this must occur by giving to the salts some kind of 'lancinating Polarity', and be related to that 'prodigious Force' of nature, the 'strong Attraction of Cohesion', which for example enables particles of water to penetrate and expand the sap-vessels of wood. Hales also examines the lime-water part of Mrs Stephens's medicines, that made of calcined shells, and finds that limewater 'is a most powerful Dissolvent', though different limewaters made of different kinds of preparations of lime act somewhat differently [29]. Here combined, in a

97

single set of remedies, were, therefore, the two most powerful active agents in the universe: the attraction of cohesion, through lancinating polarity to dissolve the animal oils of the stone and the repulsive elasticity of air released in fermenting lime destroying the bonds of fixed inelasticity.

With his usual attention to quantitative data, Hales also examines the concentration of soap-lye necessary, in his experiments, for the dissolution of the stone. He then computes, on the basis of James Keill's statical studies of fluid taken into the body per day (equally the amount lost daily in urine, perspiration and respiration), that the recommended dosages of Mrs Stephens's soap medicine would produce the necessary concentration in the body [17–22], even without the concurring assistance of the lime powder.

But did experiments *in vitro* prove anything *in vivo?* Hales concludes that they did. His observations of dissolution of the stone were matched by clinical evidence that patients taking the medicine were cured. There was, that is, the 'concurring Evidence of the happy Effects' corroborating his experiments, 'even to the degree of a full Demonstration' [26]. It is true that Hales had long expected such a medicine to be found, and the fact that it seemed to depend upon the 'fiery particles of quick-lime' – those particles which he had identified with the particles of air released from inelasticity to activity – must have made the proposition all the more convincing.[46] Nonetheless, his approbation of the medicine did not depend simply on his experiments. By the time Hales's pamphlet had appeared, David Hartley had published accounts of 155 cases in which the medicine had succeeded, the Parliamentary trustees had studied four additional cases in detail, from initial determination that the stone was present, administration of the medicines, and subsequent conclusion that the stone was no longer there (in one instance the patient had been examined by 13 physicians and surgeons), and 40 more cases had been described in the studies of Morand and Geoffroy. Now clinical studies are notoriously deceptive and some of Hales's contemporaries found reason to question the results of these investigations. Nonetheless, a couple of hundred successful examples of its use might well be sufficient to persuade even an investigator with less *a priori* convictions than Hales and it is hardly surprising to discover that, in the end, he leaves to physicians, not the decision as to the value of the remedy but simply the problem 'how best to mix the medicine and how to deal with so Caustic a Quality' [45].

Given the nature of Hales's theoretical preconceptions and the 'happy concurrence' of clinical verification, his investigations and conclusions appear less the product of naivete than they might, while Arthur J. Viseltear has argued convincingly that critical examination of Joanna Stephens's lithontriptic 'helped to create an "atmosphere" that facilitated the search for other lithontriptics, which eventually culminated in an understanding of the chemistry of the various varieties of calculi and of the drugs themselves, by the end of the eighteenth and beginning of the nineteenth centuries'. The evidence is at least clear that the search for lithontriptics continued for more than a century beyond the publication of Hales's researches and was conducted by men of eminence in medicine and medical research.[47]

Was this not, however, a small return for the time and skill of so distinguished a scientist as Hales? If this were all the return, the answer must surely be that it was, for clearly the talents of lesser men would have been sufficient for this. But there is more to the story than the establishment of an 'atmosphere'. Of still larger, and more scientific, importance was the immediate chain of influence of Hales's work. His identification of lime as an active principle in Mrs Stephens's remedy inspired the Scottish physicians Charles Alston and Robert Whytt to a further study of lime water as a dissolvent for the stone.[48] Their investigations were continued by Joseph Black, who discovered that magnesia alba did not form an alternative 'lime water', but that the active principle in it and other 'alcaline' substances was a variety of air fixed in them. This discovery, a distinct reminiscence of Hales's earlier declaration respecting fiery particles of air fixed in quick-lime, led to the identification of a variety of airs and the explication of the constituent role of gases in chemistry. Whatever the immediate medical value of Hales's studies on the stone, they combined with his theoretical conception of the dynamics of aerial activity to flower, in another student's time, as pneumatic chemistry.[49] Theory had led to attempted practice in dissolution of the stone which, in turn, led to further development of theory. What more can be meant by a fruitful relationship between science and technology?

CHAPTER VIII

Founding Member and Vice-President
of the Society of Arts

A corollary of Hales's interest in practical invention and the application of science was his concern in the foundation and workings of a new London institution – The Society for the encouragement of Arts, Manufactures and Commerce. The chief source for the history of the foundation of that Society is Thomas Mortimer's *Concise Account*.[1] In it, Mortimer traces the evolution in the mind of William Shipley, a Northampton Drawing Master, of a scheme to stimulate artistic and scientific skills by competitions for prizes, and states that he was advised to try it out in London, though his contacts there were limited to three acquaintances who might be 'capable of forwarding his design': Henry Baker, the distinguished naturalist, Husband Messiter, a prosperous surgeon and Nicholas Crisp, a public-spirited pottery manufacturer; 'He had also a recommendation to the Reverend Dr. Stephen Hales of Teddington'.[2]

This introduction was crucial. For Hales had wide experience in the workings of philanthropic societies and had several influential friends concerned with the encouragement of inventions. He was on the Council of the Royal Society and was an honorary member of the Royal Academy of Sciences at Paris and of the Bologna Academy of Sciences, and thus in the main stream of scientific academies. He was also familiar with the work of the Dublin Society,[3] which since 1740 had been awarding premiums for 'promoting husbandry and other useful arts' on the lines now suggested by Shipley.

Hales's work on the ventilation of ships had led to an association with Lord Halifax, the President of the Board of Trade who, from his Northamptonshire seat, encouraged Shipley with his scheme. Another Northamptonshire acquaintance of Hales was Thomas Yeoman, the millwright who manufactured the Hales ventilators, and to whom Hales had written: 'Philosophical researches require the united Efforts of many to make even but a small Progress therein.' In the same letter he stated what was to be the essence of Shipley's purpose: 'I cannot', he wrote, 'keep useful secrets.'[4] Hales also knew Henry Baker. Clearly there were a number of links between Shipley's circle and Hales's, which helped to bring the two together; these links were strengthened by correspondence and personal contact between the principals.

In July 1751 Shipley wrote to Baker from Northampton, saying his:

. . . proposals are much approved by Gentlemen of Fortune and taste. Whenever, Sir, you do me the favour to oblige me with material from the Dublin Society for a Scheme to put them in execution, I'll immediately follow your advice in applying to Dr. Hales.

I believe if there should not be money enough collected to make this Scheme General, a beginning might very well be made by encouraging some things that shall be thought of the greatest consequence to the Nation. Dr. Hales particularly recommends Naval Improvements I believe. As this is a maritime nation no improvements can be of greater consequence than those of that kind.[5]

Baker's reply has not been preserved, though evidently he sent Shipley the material he required, for a correspondence was begun between Shipley and Hales, as may be seen from a further letter written by Shipley to Baker on 12 August 1753. In it Shipley reported that he had received two letters from Hales giving him 'the greatest encouragement to proceed' with his plans. Hales had shown his 'Proposals' to 'many of our Nobility and from their general approbation of them, he thinks it very probable that a scheme for putting them into execution may take place next winter'. But he had advised Shipley 'not to print the scheme as yet, lest the Gentlemen to whom it was shown might forget it by the time that they came to London'. Shipley followed Hales's advice and did not publish his scheme until 7 December, by which time he had left Northampton.[6]

Although he may not have realized it at the time, when Shipley set out for London in the spring of 1753 he already knew the names of four of the ten men who, with him, would attend the first meeting of the Society of Arts. That two of the unknown six were to be noblemen of wealth, whose credit would be pledged in support of the Society, transforming a vision into reality, was not to be revealed to him until he met Dr Hales. Mortimer continues the story: 'On his arrival he waited on the doctor and communicated to him the intent of his journey: this public spirited and most ingenious gentleman readily concurred with him in the undertaking.' Shipley's analogy that 'Encouragement is much the same to Arts and Sciences as culture is to vegetables' must have had an especial appeal to Hales, the author of *Vegetable Staticks*.

There was also a resemblance of character between the absorbed and modest artist from the provinces and the eminent scientist whose humility was 'so prevalent'. Considering their shared associations, common characteristics and similarity of interests, it is not fanciful to imagine that a rapport immediately sprang up between these two important figures in the history of the Society of Arts.

At their first interview Hales told Shipley that two influential peers, Lord Folkestone and Lord Romney, 'had expressed to him an ardent desire to seeing some such plan carried into execution, and had promised if any such should take place, that they would become subscribers thereto'.[7] Lord Romney was the nephew of Sir Thomas Hales (III), and also served on the court of St George's Hospital at Hyde Park Corner, where one of the Doctor's ventilators had been installed. Viscount Folkestone had been a benefactor and Trustee of Georgia in company with Hales and was married to Elizabeth Marsham, Lord Romney's sister. They abandoned their own scheme to encourage arts and sciences in favour of Shipley's *Proposals for raising by subscription a fund to be distributed in Premiums for the promoting of improvements in the liberal Arts and Sciences, Manufactures etc.*, which he had printed on the advice of Hales after their first meeting.

Although Folkestone and Romney signed a paper sanctioning Shipley 'to apply to the nobility and gentry for the promises of their subscriptions and interest', during three months of heavy canvassing only fifteen persons promised support 'and none had signed the above-mentioned paper except the Bishop of Worcester'.[8]

The Bishop shared Hales's abhorrence of spirit drinking and was his colleague on the governing body of the Middlesex County Hospital, where another of the Hales ventilators was installed. Most probably Hales recommended Shipley's scheme to the Bishop. In view of the poor response it had received, Shipley was urged 'to get a few Gentlemen of his Acquaintance to contribute in Order to make a beginning, which Mr. Shipley had said he believed he could do if their Lordships would be so good as to give them a Meeting'. Thus was arranged the first meeting of the Society of Arts at Rawthmell's Coffee House in Henrietta Street, Covent Garden, on 22 March 1754, 'where Mr. Shipley brought the following gentlemen to consult with their Lordships [Folkestone and Romney], ... viz. the Rev. Dr. Stephen Hales, F.R.S.; John Goodchild, Esq.; Mr. Henry Baker, F.R.S.; Mr. Nicholas Crispe (Sic.); Mr. Charles Lawrence; Mr. James Short, F.R.S.; and Mr. Messiter'.[9]

Nicholas Crisp, Husband Messiter and Henry Baker were known to Shipley when he came to London in 1753. Gustavus Brander and James Short would have known Dr Hales and Baker through the Fellowship of the Royal Society, and Brander and Baker were also linked as Fellows of the Society of Antiquaries. Charles Lawrence appears to have been a family connection of the Shipleys. John Goodchild, who was to be elected the Society's first Treasurer, was a prosperous wax chandler, well known to Hales as his neighbour at Teddington and as the father of his curate. If, as seems more than probable, Hales introduced him to Shipley, then the Doctor's role in the Society's foundation may well be regarded as decisive, for it was the wealth of Goodchild and of course, of Folkestone and Romney, together with the prestige of these two peers and that of the Bishop of Worcester (to say nothing of Hales's own fame) which ensured the success of the Society in the months following its first meeting.[10]

Hales attended the first and second meetings of the Society of Arts held on 22 and 29 March 1754, and was then absent for a period of nearly two years. The Society's Minutes do not record the attendance of members other than chairmen of meetings after 14 December 1757, but down to that date Hales's name is listed as having attended meetings on only four occasions. He was elected a Vice-President of the Society when officers were first chosen in 1755 and was re-elected each year until his death in 1761. It is possible that he was present on other occasions,[11] but some explanation is required for his lack of attendance, as it contrasts so markedly with the perseverence he had shown in assisting in the Society's foundation, and is at odds with the interest in its work and wellbeing he expressed in his correspondence. It seems likely that at the age of seventy-six Hales could not bring himself to add to the burden of his already busy programme of scientific research and public work. The enlargement of the church at Teddington, his duties as Clerk of the Closet to the Princess at Kew Palace and at Leicester House; the preparation of papers to be read to the Royal Society, as well as the routine of experiments which he carried on in his private laboratory, all consumed his time during this period. He nevertheless did assist the newly-founded Society a great deal by written communication.

At the first meeting of the Society of Arts a discussion took place on the advisability of awarding premiums to encourage the home production of cobalt and madder, both important materials in the manufacture of dyes for glass making and for textiles. During the course of the second meeting Hales 'produced two Abstracts' on the quarrying of cobalt and the cultivation of madder, and it was decided to offer premiums for both products. The campaign for madder lasted for some twenty years and cost the Society over £1,500.[12] By March 1755 specimens of supposed cobalt had been received and sent for analysis to Dr William Lewis of Kingston, a well known practical chemist. Lewis reported the results of his experiments to the Society through his neighbour Dr Hales, who was in consequence again brought into the orbit of the Society's affairs.[13]

In April 1755, Hales wrote a letter suggesting that the Society of Arts might assist in the publication of a treatise, on silk production, for use in the North American Colonies. The Society had already considered the possibility of encouraging colonial seri-culture and the Georgia Trust had been much concerned with the matter. Hales had himself been stimulated to collect mulberry seeds at Teddington in 1752 by the Rev Samuel Pullein, an Irish authority of silk cultivation. He now came forward and asked the Society of Arts to sponsor Pullein's methods. In his letter, Hales told the Society that Mr Pullein had 'many rational thoughts, and improvements' relating to silk production.[14] The letter was read to the Society on 9 April but consideration of its contents was postponed. Although a year or so later Hales was still writing in hopes that he 'could contrive by means of the Premium Society, to get the ingenious Mr.Pullein's book published', by then the Society had begun to offer premiums for silk growing in the colonies and in 1758 Pullein published his *Culture of Silk: or an Essay on its rational practice and Improvement* without a grant from the Society.[15]

For the ten months from April 1755 to February 1756, Hales does not appear to have communicated directly with the Society of Arts; but in a paper read to the Royal Society on 18 December 1755, he referred to 'our Society for the Encouragement of Arts, Manufactures and Commerce', which implied that he had by no means forgotten the junior organization. On 4 February 1756 he was once again present at a meeting of the Society of Arts, and three weeks later he forwarded a letter on cobalt which he felt might interest the Society. Although approaching his eightieth year, he had begun a further period of correspondence with the Society which was to last until the year before his death.[16]

The Society received two communications from Hales in June 1756. Both were contributions to discussions and investigations which the Society was undertaking at the time. The first was a comment on a suggested method of food preservation and the second concerned the work of the Dublin Society. His communication on food preservation, which was prompted by a proposal sent to the Society in May, was read to the Society on 16 June. At the same meeting the arrival of a set of the Dublin Society's publications was reported and, later in the month, Hales forwarded a letter which he had received containing a full account of the Dublin Society's proceedings. In both instances the 'Thanks of the Society were returned to Dr. Hales'.

In August, the Society's Treasurer, John Goodchild, 'having acquainted the Society, that Dr. Hales had received a letter from Admiral Boscawen's Secretary concerning the great advantage experienced in the Admiral's Ship by Use of the Ventilator, whilst other Ships for want of it were sickly', it was unanimously agreed 'That the doctor, for whom the society have the greatest Honour, be requested to favour the Society with a Copy of the said letter to be preserved in their Guard Book'. Hales agreed to this request.

In November the President, Lord Folkestone, drew the Society's attention to the experiments in fire-fighting which Dr Hales had asked him to communicate. A member of the Society was deputed to return their formal thanks to the Doctor. Clearly Hales was anxious to be of service. Even if he was unwilling to attend the Society's meetings on a regular basis, he would appear to have been always glad to share his discoveries with its members and to keep them informed of his opinions by means of written or verbal communications.[17]

In 1757, as in 1756, Hales's association with the Society was begun with a personal attendance at a meeting in the month of February. It was a year of high bread prices and the bakers and millers were suspected, as was usual in times of dearth, of exploiting the situation for their own advantage. Hales held strong views on the dietary benefits to be derived from wholemeal bread and published his opinions in the newspapers which were also printing unpleasant stories about bread adulteration. The Society appointed a committee in May, of which Hales was a member, to consider giving a premium for a hand-worked corn mill to assist the poor in avoiding the 'Imposition of Millers in grinding corn'. The Committee recommended a premium of fifty pounds, and the advertisement was approved by the Society on 1 June. By 30 November enough hand-mills had been received to warrant the appointment of a further committee to judge the entries. Hales was also a member of this committee; the premium was divided between two of th e candidates, both of whose mills could 'grind corn in a proper manner for the poor'. Another fifty pound premium was offered for 1758. A full award was made at the end of 1758 and Hales was again appointed to the judging committee.[18]

For the years 1758 and 1759 the Society offered a premium for a composition that could be used to mark sheep without spoiling the fleece for manufacturing purposes (the annual national loss from pitch stained and tarred wool was estimated at £40,000). Hales 'warmly recommended' the problem to Dr Lewis of Kingston 'as an object of very great importance to the woollen manufactory'. Lewis 'went through a set of experiments', and discovered a mixture which appeared to be suitable when applied to blankets. Hales preferred what he called 'Dr. Lewis's happy discovery . . . for which he desires no reward' to those submitted for the Society's premium, and he communicated it to the Society in February 1760.[19]

In the same month he sent to the Society a letter on the subject which had absorbed his interest for twenty years. Hales proposed that the Society of Arts should install in its Meeting Room in the Strand the system of ventilation which he had advocated through his numerous articles and in two full length books, his *Description of Ventilators* (1743) and its sequel a *Treatise on Ventilators* (1758). In the *Treatise* he had again referred to the success his method had had on board Admiral Boscawen's ship. Slave ships as well as men-of-war, prisons and hospitals had all benefited from Hales's ventilators. In his letter he told the Society that Christopher Pinchbeck, one of the Members, used the ventilators to refresh his assembly room at Tunbridge Wells and that 'they are also at the House of Commons, the Court of King's bench, in Westminster Hall, at the Play House in Drury Lane, [and] they are found also most salutary to the numerous French prisoners which are here'. He concluded his letter:

The Expence of these Air Trunks is very inconsiderable, and if the Society shall think proper to have them, Mr. Yeoman who lives in Little Peter St. Westminster, is the properest Person to give Directions for fixing them, He having been the Director in fixing them in the above Mentioned Places, and in many other Work-Houses, gaols and Hospitals.[20]

Thomas Yeoman was elected a Member of the Society in April 1760, and was to be active in its affairs for many years. A committee which was appointed in July 'to consider of a Method to Air the Great Room' and to take notice of 'Dr. Hales's Letter relating to Ventilators', made frequent use of his opinion. However the Minutes of the committee and of the Society do not make clear how much of Hales's system was actually installed and, after much discussion, the problem of ventilating the meeting room seems to have been put in abeyance until August 1761 when the making of 'Circular openings' in the floor was sanctioned by the Society. By then, of course, Hales was dead, but Yeoman, who became Chairman of the Society's committee of Mechanics in 1763, had made a fine scale model of the ventilator which he presented to the Society in 1768. It was placed in the Repository amongst the other mechanical improvements which the Society hoped to bring into use through public display. Ten years later Hales's portrait was included in James Barry's painting for the Society's Adelphi Meeting Room, 'The Distribution of Premiums in the Society of Arts', where it can still be seen, a reminder of the many services rendered in his time by 'Dr. Stephen Hales, Vice-President'.[21]

CHAPTER IX

Princess's chaplain;
the closing years

In 1751, four years before his election as a Vice-President of the Society of Arts, Hales – to his own surprise – had received the honour of an appointment as Chaplain to the Princess Dowager of Wales. By this date, of course, he had come before the public eye on many occasions and had met, and corresponded with, an ever-growing circle of acquaintances. His scientific books were widely read and he had written numerous articles for magazines and newspapers on his inventions and the evils of dram-drinking. He had preached publicly before the Georgia Trustees and attended at the House of Lords to certify Mrs Stephens's remedy. His work for Georgia and the Bray Associates had brought him into contact with eminent politicians, religious zealots, sea captains and American Indians. In his campaign for ventilation he had been obliged to argue with hospital governors and naval officers. Yet this varied experience had done nothing to alter what Peter Collinson called his 'native innocence and simplicity of manners'[1] or to awaken in him ambition either for honours or preferment. When he was created a Doctor of Divinity in 1733 he had been, as Henry Newman wrote to Jean Vat 'on his living in Hampshire not expecting any such honour', and his appointment as a royal chaplain was made, according to Dr Birch, 'without any sollicitation of his own or even knowledge of such intention'.[2]

Hales received £200 a year as the Princess's Chaplain, a substantial increase to his income and useful for such purpose as the enlargement of the church at Teddington, but otherwise, it seems, hardly welcomed. For Birch says 'his self denial had always been such that he was perfectly satisfied with his small preferments . . . and even when his late Majesty [George II] nominated him to a Canonry of the Church of Windsor [which would have meant a further £450 a year], he was under the greatest perplexity imaginable till he engaged the Princess to persuade the King to recall his nomination'.[3] Birch's reference to Hales's 'self denial' and 'small Preferments' raises the question of how far he was in fact dependent on his stipends from Teddington and Farringdon – the latter largely absorbed, as would soon be the former, by the payment of a curate. The answer is, perhaps, hardly at all. His wife's considerable legacies were probably spent long before 1759, for there is no trace in his own will of the 190 acres in Hertfordshire which she had bequeathed him in 1721. They may have been sold to help Robert Hales who had died in 1735 greatly in his brother's debt. Nonetheless he was able to bequeath an unspecified residue of 'Money, Goods and Chattels' to Robert's daughter, Sarah Margaretta, after £270 had been paid to various deserving causes and cases, and 'to each of my two servants, who shall be such at the Time of my death . . . fifteen pounds'.[4] Evidently he had sufficient means to live simply and comfortably. To the owner of Strawberry Hill he might appear poor, but he did not think of himself as belonging to that category: 'I have for more than 50 years thought *if I was poor*, I would feed my family with bones shaved, or rasped, where with to make good Jelly,' he told a correspondent in 1757.[5] For his health's sake he 'always began dinner with plain pudding', and yet enjoyed the delicacies produced by his syllabub machine, 'pies and tarts' cooked so the syrup would not boil over and wine, 'Nature's cordial', preserved in cool cellars. Very hot tea he avoided and he was sparing with ice cream. He believed in moderation but was not compelled to it by circumstance.[6] Of his general simplicity and humility there can be little doubt. To the young Charles Wesley who met him in 1736 he seemed, in spite of his high office as a ruler of Georgia, a 'truly pious, humble Christian full of zeal for God and love to Man'. The poet of the age, who was his friend and neighbour in Middlesex,[7] had characterized him as 'Plain Parson Hales', nearer to God than the Bishops of the Church:

> If Queensberry to strip there's no compelling,
> 'Tis from a Handmaid we must take a Helen,
> From Peer or Bishop 'tis no easy thing
> To draw the man who loves his God, or King:
> Alas! I copy (or my draught would fail)
> From honest Mah'met, or plain Parson Hale.[8]

His neighbour Gilbert White preserved a vivid impression of 'the good old man' which he put down on paper in later years for the benefit of his friend and fellow naturalist, Robert Marsham:

Dear Sir,

It was elegantly remarked on our common friend, and my quondam neighbour Doctor Stephen Hales, by one who has written his character in Latin, that – 'scientiam philosophicam usibus humanis *famulari* jussit.' The observation was just, and the assertion no inconsiderable compliment: for undoubtedly speculative enquiries can bear no competition with practical ones, where the latter profess never to lose sight of utility.

As I perceive you loved the good old man, I do not know how I can amuse you better, than by sending you the following anecdotes respecting him, some of which may not have fallen within your observation. His attention to the inside of Ladies' tea kettles, to observe how far they were incrusted with stone (*tophus lebetinus* Linnaei) that from thence he might judge of the salubrity of the water of their wells: – his advising water to be showered down suspicious wells from the nozzle of a garden watering pot in order to discharge damps, before men ventured to descend; – his directing air-holes to be left in the out-walls of ground rooms, to prevent the rotting of floors and joists; – his earnest dissuasive to young people, not to drink their tea scalding hot; his advice to water-men at a ferry, how they might best preserve and keep sound the bottoms or floors of their boats; – his teaching the house-wife to place an inverted tea-cup at the bottom of her pies and tarts to prevent the syrup from boiling over, and to preserve the juice; – his many though unsuccessful attempts to find an adequate succedaneum for yeast or barm, so difficult to be procured in severe winters, and in many lonely situations; – his endeavour to destroy insects on wall-fruit-trees by quicksilver poured into holes bored in their stems; – and his experiments to dissolve the stone in human bodies, by, as I think, the juice of onions; – are a few, among many of those benevolent, and useful pursuits on which his mind was constantly bent. Though a man of a Baronet's family, and of one of the best houses in Kent, yet was his Humility so prevalent, that he did not disdain the lowest offices, provided they tended to the good of his fellow creatures.[9]

Horace Walpole affected amused surprise at Hales's appointment as a royal chaplain. In a letter to Sir Horace Mann dated 11 December 1752 he wrote of 'Dr. Hales, the old philosopher, a poor, good primitive creature, whom I call the Santon Barsisa; do you remember the hermit in the Persian tales, who after living in the odour of sanctity for above ninety years, was tempted to be naught with the King's daughter, who had been sent to his cell for a cure? Santon Hales, but two years ago accepted the post of Clerk of the Closet to the Princess, after literally leading the life of a studious anchorite till past seventy.' Obviously

Walpole exaggerated the uncourtly qualities of Hales in order to give point to a good story. The Princess had wanted to reward Hales for his friendship to her late husband. The association of Hales and the profligate Frederick may seem surprising at first sight, yet Frederick had an unquenchable thirst for knowledge, and his interest in Hales's experiments is on a par with his well known encouragement of artists and his passion for gardening. According to Thomas Birch, Frederick 'from his neigbouring Palace of Kew frequently visited him [Hales] and took a pleasure in surprising him in the midst of those curious Researches into the various parts of Nature in which his time was almost wholly employed'. Though we may wonder if Hales liked these interruptions in view of the constant attention required by his various experiments and investigations. Perhaps to be surprised by the Prince of Wales was a welcome opportunity to show off his latest enthusiasm and to find a willing auditor whose high birth and august rank he so profoundly respected. There was also a social side to Hales's character which makes nonsense of Walpole's conception of him as 'a studious anchorite'.[10]

When Bishop Wilson's son 'Went to pay Dr. Hales a visit at Teddington in 1733', he 'found him at home and very civil' and Wilson made this entry in his Diary for 17 November 1735:

At the house of the Speaker of the House of Commons Arthur Onslow Esq. . . . Dr. Hales came in, We dined . . . Talked of Mathematical Experiments, Imateriality of the Soul . . . the Gin Affair.

Wilson stayed the night with Hales at Teddington and on the following morning they went to Twickenham and waited upon Lady Blount and her two sisters. Lady Blount showed off her 'fine closet of Rarities' with 'Shells and Egyptian and English Pebbles' and her 'well chosen study of pious books'. Then he 'took leave of Dr. Hales'.[11] Lord Egmont noted many occasions in the 1730s and 1740s when Hales dined with the Georgia Trustees at the 'Cider House' or some other public eating place, and three times at least Lord Egmont 'brought him home to dinner'. These were excursions resulting from his public commitments. He also went abroad to see new and interesting sights, – such as the artificial marble wainscotting at Craven House, which he went to see with Stukeley in 1725, and 'Mr. Pope's house and gardens' where he walked with Charles Wesley in 1737, or the fantastic villa at Hammersmith belonging to Prince Frederick's Treasurer, George Bubb Dodington, which, noted Dodington in his diary, Hales came on purpose to see in 1750.[12]

Another diarist, John Baker,who became Hales's parishioner at Teddington after returning from the West Indies in 1758, recorded several
social exchanges with the Doctor: 'I went *voir* Dr. Hales'; 'Dr. Hales
called and sat 2 hours *apres midi*'; 'Went to Dr. Hales's . . . and . . . Saw
frog dissected . . . dined home Dr. Hales'; 'Found *chez nous* Dr. Hales';
and 'Dr. Hales came'. No doubt Hales would turn the conversation in
the direction of his own current interest – requiring Charles Wesley to
concentrate on a medical case involving a blood disturbance while
retailing the history of his Georgia experiences, or treating Pope's friend
Joseph Spence to the following pronouncement:

Each member of the House of Commons, in a full house, breathes in six
pounds of vapour in six hours, so that 'tis no wonder that they are so heated.[13]

Probably he accepted chaff over his 'hobbies' with the good nature
shown by Uncle Toby and only the subject of Drams could make him
warm.

'He used to say,' wrote Gilbert White, 'that the hogs of distillers were
more brutal than the hogs of other men; and that when drunk they used
to bite pieces out of each other's backs and sides!' Although he had
something of the catholicity of taste common in his time – history and
antiquities seem to have been occasional interests – yet as White put it,
'His whole mind seemed replete with experiment, which of course gave a
tincture, and turn to his conversation, often somewhat peculiar, but
always interesting.' Even the Princess of Wales would be required to
search the bottom of her tea cup for mineral sediment when the question
was uppermost in his mind.[14]

After her husband's death in 1751 the Princess continued to surround
herself and her family with persons who had been his friends, giving
particular encouragement to those who possessed serious religious and
moral commitments which were especially congenial to her at a time of
mourning. Hales was eminently qualified in this respect, for he brought
to his office the same devotional qualities which he had shown as a
parish priest. Nor was he unused to the role of spiritual adviser to ladies
of rank. Lady Denbigh developed a curious spiritual passion for him,
and many benefactions for Georgia and the s.p.c.k. were received by
him from ladies or gentlewomen 'unknown'. His religious character
must have been self evident and does not require emphasis. He was also
acceptable to the Princess and her family because of his political neu-
trality. For his appointment may be seen as a part of the general re-

establishment of good relations between the King and his daughter-in-law which took place at this time. Though Hales had been befriended by the late Prince, yet his well-known books still bore their dedications to His Majesty and the Ministry can have had little to fear in the way of opposition and intrigue from so unpolitical a figure as Hales. Nonetheless the friction which seemed inevitable between the Court and the heir's household in the Hanoverian period was not long in re-appearing, and Hales's name figured on the periphery of the conflict.[15]

The sixteen year old Prince of Wales was given a new Governor in the person of Lord Harcourt, one of the King's Lords of the Bedchamber, whose 'high rank and low abilities' wrote R. R. Sedgwick, the modern authority on the affair, 'were considered to qualify him' for the post. 'A new Preceptor,' continued Sedgwick, 'was provided in the person of Dr Hayter, the Bishop of Norwich, a typical eighteenth-century ecclesiastical careerist . . . The only survivor of the former educational staff was George Lewis Scott, a mathematician, a Fellow of the Royal Society, and a man of high character and ability, who had recently been appointed on the recommendation of Lord Bolingbroke to be Sub-Preceptor, and was continued in his post at the request of the Princess of Wales.'[16] From the beginning, however, these arrangements did not work smoothly. Lord Harcourt and the Bishop of Norwich aimed at being the sole directors of the young Prince and when the Princess objected they accused her household of Jacobite connections and Tory principles, and Scott, as Lord Waldegrave put it 'was moreover pronounced an atheist on the presumptive evidence of being a philosopher and a mathematician'. The King made light of the charges when he returned from Hanover in November 1752, and Harcourt and the Bishop resigned in pique. Rumours continued to circulate and the Opposition claimed that the Prince was being brought up to believe in the principles of arbitrary power. This was the 'Whig clamour' that Horace Walpole mentions in his letter of 11 December 1752:

Among the other candidates [as Preceptor] they talk of Dr. Hales, the old philosopher . . . If he does accept the preceptorship, I don't doubt but by the time the present clamours are appeased, the wick of his old life will be snuffed out . . .[17]

Though Hales was not appointed to the preceptorship he did have, as Masters put it, 'some share in the instruction of her [the Princess's] illustrious children'. According to its author, Hales 'desired to have'

113

copies of a manual called *Youth's Friendly Monitor, being a set of directions, prudential, moral, religious and scientific* by James Burgh, for reading to 'the younger part of the children of Her Royal Highness'. *Youth's Friendly Monitor* takes the form of a moralizing sermon with an especial warning against the 'cursed Effect' which 'Strong Liquors' have 'upon the best and wisest of Men, [so] that they must certainly become foolish and wicked in some degree'. Burgh was something of a disciplinarian and in a later work called *Crito* he criticized Rousseau's views and the contemporary tendency to indulge youth for its own sake. He also wrote a thesis on the origin of evil after what he claimed had been an inspiring 'interview with the Princess Dowager of Wales [and] Dr. Hales her clerk of the closet'.[18]

In his *The dignity of Human Nature* (1754) Burgh doubted if, at a time when the 'liberal science of Card Playing' was thought to be a necessary part of a child's training, the Princess had 'influence enough to change the Fashion in Favour of virtue and Religion'. Hales, however, had more confidence in the efficacy of the royal example. He persuaded his friend Griffith Jones, the Welsh educationalist, to mention in the 1755 edition of his *Welch Piety*, 'the excellent example of the Princess in educating her Children, an example that ought to be much known in this careless age'. Jones was suitably eloquent; he begged 'leave to approach, with awful Regard, so near the Throne' and to 'point to the View of all Parents, the Noble *Exemplar* of prudent and pious Education', who 'with laudable and studied care' nursed her children 'in the *sincere milk of the Sacred word*, that they may grow thereby in the Grace of God . . . instilling into them principles of true Religion . . . as well as instructing them farther in every useful Knowledge for their high stations, as they advance in years'.[19] 'Every useful knowledge' would have embraced an extensive range of scientific subjects. 'Natural Philosophy, Astronomy, Optics, Chemistry' were listed in Burgh's *Monitor*, and would therefore have formed part of the curricula indirectly recommended by Hales 'for the younger part of the Royal Children'.

The Prince of Wales, himself, developed an interest in science which he retained even after assuming the burdens of the throne. Hales ministered to the Prince's taste for botany, which was also a favourite study for both his mother and Lord Bute, his friend and mentor, as well as for his brother and sisters. When Hales presented the Princess Dowager with specimens of sea moss made up into landscape pictures by John Ellis, she was, he told Ellis in a letter dated 3 February 1752, 'much pleased', desiring 'the favour of you to procure her some varieties of Sea Mosses'. A month later he again wrote to Ellis:

I carried the collection of Red Sea mosses, which you sent me, to the excellent Princess, for which she was thankful and well pleased. And this day I showed her the method of spreading them, which she soon practised herself, and liked very much . . . As the Princess designs to put several ladies on this agreeable amusement, it will be well to furnish her with plenty of these mosses.

The 'agreeable amusements' of the Royal household encouraged Ellis to make a systematic study of British corallines and sea mosses, which he published in 1755 in a book dedicated to the Princess.[20] One of the plant specimens that Ellis collected from all over the world was a shrub found in Carolina by Dr Alexander Garden, who suggested it should be given the name 'Halesia'. Ellis obtained the approval of Linnaeus for the classification, and arranged for the new plant to be most beautifully drawn and engraved. He attached the following dedication to the engraving:

To the Revd. Dr. Stephen Hales F.R.S. etc. etc. the Author of the incomparable Vegetable Staticks:
This rare Shrub lately sent over by Alexander Garden M.D. of Charles Town from Saluda in the N.W. part of S. Carolina is humbly dedicated by his most obliged Friend and Servt.

John Ellis

Presumably it was copies of this engraving that Hales referred to as 'drafts' in an undated letter to Ellis:

I received the drafts of the Carolina Plant and am obliged to you for the honour done me therein. I sent one of them immediately to the worthy Lord Bute; but, as I am named in it, I cannot well convey one to the Princess, but may probably take an opportunity to give one to one of my young pupils.[21]

The development of the gardens at Kew which interested both the Princess and Lord Bute, was carried on with Hales's advice. In November 1758 he wrote to John Ellis:

The Princess will build a hot greenhouse, 120 feet long, next spring, at Kew, with a view to have exotics of the hottest climates, in which my pipes, to convey incessantly pure warm air, will probably be very serviceable. And as there will be several partitions in the green-house, I have proposed to have the glass of one of the rooms covered with shutters in winter, to keep the cold

115

out, which will make a perpetual spring and summer, with an incessant succession of pure warm air. What a scene is here opened for improvements in green-house vegetation![22]

The office of Chaplain to the Princess of Wales was said to involve 'great honour' and 'small duty', but Hales was not of the temperament to accept a sinecure and was to perform his duties conscientiously. He was expected to do for the Princess what the Royal Chaplains did for the King, that is 'to attend at the right hand . . . during Divine service; to resolve such doubts as May arise concerning spiritual matters . . . to preach . . . and to say grace'.[23] In January 1752 he told a correspondent, 'My attendance on the Princess obliges me now to be much in London'. Hales had taken modest lodgings, conveniently near the Princess's town residence, and gave as his address 'Duke's Court, near St. Martin's Church', which was one he would often use during the next five years.[24] Except in high summer, he seems to have spent most weekends in town. In April 1753, he wrote to Serjeant Wynne from 'Duke's Court, Nr. St. Martin's Church, Where I am every Saturday, Sunday and Monday to wait upon the Princess of Wales'.[25] On 28 September 1757 Hales wrote to David Hartley: 'Tomorrow I enter My 80th year; and not only live but continue to enjoy life with a relish.'[26] A year later he anticipated a further season of service in town. He wrote to Stukeley on 25 September 1758 from Teddington:

If, when the Princess comes to reside in town, you should have a call towards Duke's Court, St. Martin's Lane, on a Saturday, after twelve o'clock, I should be glad to see a Fellow Collegiate old acquaintance. With what a number of years have we been blessed beyond those of many of our contemporaries! The infirmities of age will not permit me to visit you.

It seems the meeting did not take place, for a month afterwards he reported to Ellis: 'Having been ill lately, tho' I thank God, well recovered, I shall not venture to come to London this winter for fear of exposing my self to the ill Consequences of cold, to me who am 81.'[27]

It may be that he did not again attend the Princess in London though as we have seen he was much interested in the greenhouse she planned in 1759 at Kew. Old age and illness – possibly the 'gravelly disorder' of which he had once complained – seemed to have kept him at Teddington for the rest of his life. Early in 1759 he had again written to Ellis saying he had been ill. He made his will in October but at the end of December he was writing in a cheerful vein to his old friend Stukeley.[28]

January 1760 saw his urging the authorities to use ventilators on transport ships going to Germany, and in February there took place his correspondence with the Society of Arts about marking sheep and the installation of ventilators in the Society's Great Room. By early June he had completed a paper for the Royal Society on protection from exposure to night dews in hot climates. In October he wrote twice to the s.p.c.k. ordering books and once, at considerable length, to Bishop Hildesley, recommending in a postscript the use of tar-water: 'You may take about one fourth of a pint, at four several times, at a due distance from meals . . . I took it thus in the early spring, with good effects, and intend to begin again in fourteen days.' His 'excellent constitution' seemed unaffected by such remedies.[29]

Towards the end of November he sent, at the desire of a neighbour, an unspecified proposal to Dr Bradley, the Astronomer Royal, which he humorously describes as being 'on a subject, on which, I make no doubt you are often teased. And in which, and on a perpetual motion, I am sometimes a sharer'. Yet by early December writing at length was evidently becoming something of a strain for him. On the 8th of that month he asked Peter Collinson to forward to Connecticut a letter which he said was 'long for one of my age to write'. Seven days later he sent 'two folio pages close wrote' to Bishop Hildesley, apparently containing no complaint of indisposition, though including the phrase 'this is a long letter from one in his 84th year'. Within three weeks he died after a 'very slight illness', and Hildesley, Collinson and many others mourned the passing of 'This best of men', this 'Christian Philosopher'.[30]

He died at 'his parsonage house' at Teddington and was buried at his own request under the Church tower which he had built. A simple inscription recorded that he had been 'minister of this parish fifty-one years' and there can be little doubt that he left behind him many affectionate memories amongst his parishioners. 'His merits as an active minister', and, perhaps, stories of his eccentricities, remained even at the beginning of the nineteenth century 'traditionally vivid' in the recollection of the people of Teddington.[31] For the nation at large, there was to be the constant reminder of a monument in Westminster Abbey, carved by John Wilton, the King's sculptor, and paid for by the Princess. On it the figures of Religion and Botany support a medallion portrait of the dead philosopher, two cherubim blow winds (freshly ventilated?), and there are plants growing from the ground beneath the feet of the images. A Latin inscription concludes:

Anglia Te Primis in Sertum Jactat Alumnis,
Anglia, Newtono, Terra Superbo, Suo.[32]

The hyperbole beloved of the age has, in Hales's case, not seemed inappropriate to later generations.

CHAPTER X

Scientific reputation
and influence

The popular reputation of most scientists is evanescent and that of Stephen Hale was no exception. During the decade immediately following the completion of his *Statical Essays*, Hales's work was sufficiently known to the educated public, even on the Continent, to be used as a casual example in Voltaire's advices to a journalist on the handling of scientific topics.[1] Soon, however, the nature of his popular reputation began that shift which becomes manifest in published references to Hales after his death. A characteristic example is that of Archibald Campbell's 1767 satire, *The Sale of Authors . . . In Imitation of Lucian's Sale of Philosophers*, where Hales is admiringly described, in contrast to the pretensions of contemporary writers, as: '. . . one who has spent a long life in Philosophical and natural enquiries, not to satisfy an idle and empty curiosity, nor to acquire the vain and specious character of a learned and ingenious Person, but . . . to the benefit and advantage of his fellow-creatures . . . I will venture to say, that he has been the means of preventing more diseases and saving more lives by his ventilators alone, than . . . [other doctors] have occasioned or destroyed by their Quackeries.'[2] Although further editions of the *Statical Essays* were still to appear – in English (1769), Italian (1776) and French (1779–80) – the popular view of Hales as a clergyman-inventor was to persist into the early years of the nineteenth century. William Hayley's 'Ode to John Howard' of 1780, also celebrates Hales's ventilators, which were retained in public awareness by Rees's *Cyclopaedia* as late as 1819. Until the recent reprinting of the *Vegetable Staticks* and the *Haemastaticks*, the last of Hales's works to be republished was the *Friendly Admonition* against dram drinking, which appeared as late as 1807, under the auspices of the s.p.c.k.

Philanthropy and inventiveness provide no surer foundation for a lasting popular reputation than science does, however, and Hales was gradually forgotten. Within a century of his death a query could be raised as to the identity of Pope's 'plain Parson Hale', and the respondent declare, 'Dr. Stephen Hales . . . has been immortalized by a single line in Pope, rather than by the scientific works he himself published'.[3] So far as the general public was concerned, this statement was very nearly true. The question was raised again, a quarter-century later, and obtained a response more adequate to Hales's merit, but the line from Pope and the praise of Hales's ability to combine religion and philosophy, published in successive editions of John Wesley's *Journal*, were the major popular reminders of Hales's existence.[4]

Among the scientists, Hales's reputation and influence had a different, or at least more complicated history. Within the year of its publication, the *Vegetable Staticks* received a long and enthusiastic review by J. T. Desaguliers in the *Philosophical Transactions* and, by the time of Hales's death, had been published in two more English editions (1731, 1738) and been translated into French by Buffon (1735) and German by Christian Wolff (1748).[5] There was, perhaps, less excitement over the *Haemastaticks*, but it too was republished in English (third edition 1769) and translated into French, Italian, German and Dutch.

The value of Hales's scientific achievements had been officially recognized by the organized scientific community. He was a Fellow of the Royal Society from 1718 and, after publication of the *Vegetable Staticks*, was chosen to sit on the Society's Council. Of more significance, however, was the awarding to Hales of the Society's Copley Medal in 1739. Presented annually for the most important scientific discovery or contribution to science of the year, the Copley Medal is the most distinguished recognition for achievement that the Royal Society gives. In 1753, on the death of Sir Hans Sloane, Hales was chosen to replace him by the Academie Royale des Sciences as one of its eight foreign associates, the highest honour that academy could pay to a foreigner. (Hales, incidentally, was succeeded by Leonhard Euler.) And, in the fashion of the age, at least one other national scientific society, the Academy of Sciences of the Institute of Bologna, was proud to name Hales an honorary member.

A casual survey of the scientific literature of the mid-eighteenth century will reveal how widely Hales's works were read, on the Continent as well as in Britain, among lesser as among the more important scientists, and even by men not particularly interested in the specific subjects which Hales had made so much his own. Some of the more significant readers, and the nature of Hales's influence on them will be discussed shortly, but as an indication of the spread of his ideas, it can here be noted that James Logan, writing from Philadelphia in 1735, refers to the

Haemastaticks in a paper on lightning, Carl Linnaeus is known to have used the *Vegetable Staticks* in his lectures on dietetics for classes at Upsala, while, from St Petersburgh, Georg W. Richmann wrote to criticize Hales's experiments, described in an Appendix to the *Haemastaticks*, on the contraction of air in freezing water.[6]

It is an historical commonplace that the experiments a scientist performs are remembered long after his reasons for them and his interpretations are forgotten. Julius von Sachs, a distinguished plant physiologist of the nineteenth century and, himself, something of mechanist, notes bitterly that this had happened to Hales, whose successors 'quoted and repeated Hales's experiments, but forgot that which in his mind bound all the separate facts together'. By the early years of this century, the name as well as the theory was gone. The experiments are described as classic, pedagogical examples, without reference to their designer.[7] A man's scientific influence may therefore continue (even though anonymously) while his reputation changes and ultimately vanishes. This is particularly true during periods of conceptual uncertainty, for the process is not a simple one of forgetfulness but rather an active reinterpretation of old data into a new theoretical framework. This is what happened to Hales, although, in fact, his personal scientific reputation lasted longer than might have been expected. While the subjects of his investigations were not entirely neglected, they were not the most popular of his age, and the completeness of his approach and ingenuity of his experiments combined to give his work an appearance of finality. Like Newton on optics or physical astronomy, Hales on animal and vegetable physiology was thought by many to have ended the need for investigation. There was some contemporary study of minor aspects of these problems, but this was primarily as a filling-in of interstices. The first really significant continuations of Hales's work were delayed over a period of years and his direct reputation, in consequence, was more enduring than might have been the case had he had immediate successors.

Even so, his reputation suffered a major transformation. One of the first responses to the collapse of any theoretical system is a denial of all theoretical systems. And when the new conceptual framework being built to replace the old, under that protective cover of empirical protestations, is one of taxonomic materialism, the claims of Baconianism are exaggerated even to the point of retroactive identification with the more distinguished exponents of the old school. During the latter part of the eighteenth century, Isaac Newton's *Hypothesis non fingo* became a phrase by which this ultimate architect of the mechanical philosophy was turned into a Baconian. During the same period, Stephen Hales, one of the more successful Newtonians, was transformed into a standard example of the experimental inductivist. By the end of the century, Giambattista Beccaria was citing Galileo, Newton and Hales as masters of experimental enquiry, producers of a multitude of useful and interesting data which had created a physical science whose best ornament was observation and experiment.[8]

There were other pressures acting to transform Hales's scientific reputation, to bring it in line with changing views. He managed to survive as a standard authority, though the particles and forces he employed as explanation were replaced by imponderable fluids and vital spirits. Desaguliers, in 1727, had understood Hales as placing 'past all Doubt', the truths of the corpuscular Queries of Newton's *Opticks*. By 1745 Benjamin Franklin could see in Hales's elastic air, fixable in solid substances, a prototype for his own electric fluid, self-repelling but attracted to other bodies from which it was released by suitable operations.[9] In 1750, John Pringle was re-interpreting Hales's work in terms of a revitalized iatro-chemistry. In his *Observations on the Nature and Cure of Hospital and Jayl Fevers*, Pringle transforms Hales's mechanistic instrumentalism of the air's elasticity in the animal oeconomy into air poisoned by the addition of putrid effluvia.[10]

But Hales had himself contributed to this transformation. The dual role of air, providing expansive activity to matter but also, in a fixed state, acting as substantial cement, was not easily understood. His work in the *Haemastaticks*, deliberately or inadvertently, had challenged iatrophysical conceptions; his speculations on the role of electricity in muscular motion, on active principles in the blood and in the digesting of food, and his references to corruptible vapours and to fermenting qualities of rancid air were all consistent with a revival of materialistic explanations.

To these must be added the tendencies of his last two scientific investigations, on electricity and on earthquakes. In 1747 the *Gentleman's Magazine* reported on some electrical experiments performed at Hales's request by 'Mr. King' and 'Mr. Yeoman', to determine if electrification had any influence on vegetation. These experiments, and others, were later discussed in a paper for the *Philosophical Transactions*, where Hales refers to 'the active electric Fluid' as 'a great Agent, in Conjunction with the Air, in the Production of Fire' and expresses his hope that Mr King will electrify a frog to observe if this will accelerate the circulation of its blood.[11] The change in Hales's thinking to a consideration of essential qualities of substances is continued into his *Some Considerations on the Causes of Earthquakes*, of 1750.[12] Concerned to show that earthquakes are explicable by natural causes (which need not exclude the agency of God, who works through such causes), Hales's *Considerations* is an ingenious attempt to show that earthquakes are the result of effervescences and concussions at the surface of the earth as sulphureous fumes rising from pyrites in the earth on a hot day combine with pure air and suddenly reduce its elasticity. These sulphureous fumes are, perhaps, the same as those described in the *Statical Essays*, where aqua fortis and Walton pyrites combine to raise, by fermentation, fumes which mix with pure air to produce a reddish vapour, a violent effervescence, and a decrease in elasticity.[13] Hales goes on to conjecture that a mixture of these substances in the atmosphere is responsible for the production of lightning, while the agitation produced either in earthquakes or lightning storms puts into rapid motion a quantity of the 'Electrical Aetherial Fluid' causing the rumbling of thunder and that 'usually heard in Earthquakes'. There is an evident relation here to the mechanical, elastic-air, explanations of the *Vegetable Staticks*, but the assignment of chemical qualities to sulphureous fumes and the equivocal introduction of electrical aetherial fluid provide other instances through which Hales can be transformed from a mechanist to a supporter of material causes.

For each of the three areas in which Hales earned a reputation in science, and exerted an influence: pneumatic chemistry, vegetable physiology and animal physiology, the same pattern developed. First there was the initial, almost uncritical, acceptance of his work, then followed a re-interpretation or transformation of his discoveries, and finally a use of those discoveries in a new context to continue the development of science and the identification of Hales as an empiricist.

The area in which Hales was earliest and, in the final analysis, most influential, was that of chemistry, for the long chapter on analysis of air in the *Vegetable Staticks* was the theoretical if not the experimental foundation of pneumatic chemistry in the eighteenth century.[14] Probably the earliest use of that chapter in relation to chemistry was that of John Mickleburgh, third professor of chemistry at Cambridge (1718-56), a personal friend of Hales and Fellow of Corpus Christi. At least as early as 1731, Mickleburgh, in his chemistry lectures, was presenting Hales as the only person effectively to experiment from the chemical principles of Isaac Newton and John Freind. Making use of Hales's concept of repulsive forces between particles and accepting Hales's 'accurate experiments' as demonstration of the influence of elastic air in chemistry and the mechanical nature of heat, Mickleburgh's lectures probably come closest to presenting Hales's work as the author himself saw it.[15] But Mickleburgh never published his lectures and his interpretation of Hales can have reached few persons beyond the limited attendance at his classes, which ended about 1741. The first significant transmitter of some of Hales's ideas about the air was to be Herman Boerhaave.

Boerhaave's lectures in chemistry at the University of Leyden, prior to 1727 (if the unauthorized edition of those lectures in 1724 is to be credited) treated the role of air in chemistry, in the then standard mode, as an instrument of activity but not a constituent. The authorized version of those lectures, published by Boerhaave in 1732 as the *Elementa Chemiae*, attempts to incorporate Hales's work. There is a manifest inconsistency between retained discussions of the air as a 'mechanical pestil' and the new treatment of elastic air serving, in an unelastic state, to cement particles of matter together, while Boerhaave's conclusion that air is not concreted, coagulate or altered in bodies, only being concealed in them, is clearly not a full acceptance of air as a chemical constituent. Nonetheless, such a constituent view of air was derivable from Boerhaave's text, which was to be one of the most influential of the eighteenth century.[16]

The spread in Britain of Hales's notions respecting factitious airs can be exemplified in the references made to them by Benjamin Robins in his *New Principles of Gunnery* of 1742. Robins, the inventor of the ballistic pendulum, was not a chemist but was interested in the nature of gunpowder explosions, and he notes that Hales has identified as 'real air, endued with all the properties of that we breath' the elastic fluids released by burning, distillation, etc.[17] But it was Joseph Black who did more than any other person to transform Hales's studies on air into a new direction for chemistry. Black had studied at Glasgow under William Cullen (who was an admirer of Boerhaave as well as of Stahl and the Stahlians), but he also studied under Charles Alston and Robert Whytt, Edinburgh admirers and correspondents of Hales, and may have learned of Hales's work through them. Black's MD thesis, *de Humore Acido a cibis orto et Magnesia Alba*, of 1754, was initially intended as a further investigation of Hales's proposal of alkaline solutions as dissolvents for urinary stones. In this connection the work was a failure; but as developed and extended for Black's classic paper of 1756, 'Experiments upon Magnesia Alba, Quicklime and some other Alcaline Substances', it introduced an era of chemical researches to identify different species of air, involved as constituents in chemical processes and traceable, through those processes, by the material parameter of weight.

Neither of these views is explicit in Hales, but Black found, in the *Vegetable Staticks*, implications which helped lead to them. Black cites Hales's discovery that alkaline salts contain a large quantity of air fixed in them. There is no reference to the conjecture that the causticity of lime was related to the sulphureous and elastic particles of air trapped in it, but for all the ambiguity of Hales's statement of this theory, it is hard to believe Black was unaware of it.[18] Both the concept and the technique by which Black identified a particular kind of air as the precisely measurable constituent carrier of a causticity-affecting quality were well beyond Hales, but their ultimate origin is obvious enough to make the Halesian name 'fixed air', given to the newly identified gas, entirely appropriate.

Black's references to Hales in the magnesia alba paper and his chemical lectures (though these latter were to remain unpublished until 1803) presented a view of Halesian 'pneumatic chemistry' which was shortly to be reinforced by continental chemists. It was this view which Frederick Accum, and, following Accum, Samuel Clegg Jr were to follow into the mid-nineteenth century when they each credit Hales with observing the presence of an inflammable gas in coal.[19] Neither Henry Cavendish nor Joseph Priestley, Black's contemporary rivals as British chemists, adopted that materialist interpretation. Cavendish continued Black's identification of different kinds of air, but appears to have done so, initially at least, in connection with mechanist investigations of heat. In this, as in his other mechanistic predilections, Cavendish would find the unmodified view of Hales particularly congenial and his awareness of Hales's work is clear from references made in the unpublished Part IV of his *Experiments on Factitious Airs*.[20]

The influence of Hales's interpretation of pneumatic phenomena is manifest in Joseph Priestley's experimental techniques, his vocabulary and his explanations of the experimental results. In 1770 Priestley wrote to a friend, Theophilus Lindsey, that he was about to take up 'Dr. Hales's inquiries concerning air'. From that time his experiments made use of Hales's methods of producing airs from various substances and, in addition to his frequent references to Hales throughout his chemical works, Priestley's use of such expressions as: 'releasing' air, 'diminishing' it, changing its elasticity, and his persistent dependence upon volumetric parameters all reveal the Halesian origin of and influence on his basic pneumatic concepts.[21]

The mechanical view of nature is continued in James Hutton's *Dissertations on Different Subjects in Natural Philosophy* (1792), where a distinction is made between body and matter (the latter to be identified with force) and in which the insistence that both attractive and repulsive forces are necessary to an active universe is reminiscent of Hales. Hutton's ideas are continued in the early work of the young Humphry Davy, but on the whole mechanism in chemistry was, by that time, not in fashion. Ironically, the greatest impulse to the change in chemical theory came from continental chemists who used the pneumatic chemistry discoveries of Hales in achieving their purpose.[22]

From its earliest reception in France, Stephen Hales's *Vegetable Staticks* was understood to be an important contribution to pneumatic chemistry. Indeed, Charles DuFay, best known for his electrical studies, referred to it, in 1734, as 'the book on the analysis of the air by Mr. Hales', and Buffon's translation, the following year, was called *La Statique des végétaux et l'analyse de l'air*.[23] Buffon was so intrigued by the concept of forces in Newton's *Opticks* and Hales's *Vegetable Staticks*, that he returned to the notion to explain elective affinities in chemistry in volume thirteen of his *Histoire Naturelle*. The approach was, however, an anomaly to the French, never receptive in the eighteenth century to Newtonian force concepts. To the majority of French chemists, starting at least with Guillaume-François Rouelle, the importance of Hales's work was his demonstration of the constituent role of air in chemical composition. Rouelle was the leader in modifying the theories of Georg Ernst Stahl and establishing them in French favour. In his lectures Rouelle developed an instrument-constituent theory which held that the various elements of the Stahlians, previously divided between instruments of and constituents in chemical combination, each participated in both ways. Rouelle used Hales's *Vegetable Staticks* to show this role for air and repeated many of Hales's experiments for his students to see.[24] One of Rouelle's students, Pierre Joseph Macquer, continued the development and diffusion of Stahlian chemistry and used Hales in the same way, in both his text, *Élémens de Chymie-practique* (1751), and his famous *Dictionnaire de Chymie* (1766).

Such an interpretation could result in routine repetitions of Hales's experiments, as in the case of the Italian scientist, Giovanni Francesco Cigna, whose 'Dissertation . . . sur les causes de l'extinction de la lumière d'une Bougie, & de la mort des Animaux renfermes dans un espace plain d'air', of 1760, quotes frequently from Hales and offers very little beyond the results of Hales's experiments.[25] It could, however, lead to what eventually was to be a chemical revolution. The nature of that influence can first, perhaps, be more keenly appreciated in figures of less importance than the creator of that revolution. In August 1771, the French statesman (and occasional dabbler in science) A. R. J. Turgot wrote to his friend M. J. de Condorcet explaining that the increase in weight of the product of combustion was the result of air, which combined with or entered into the composition of the hardest bodies, contributing to their cohesion and hardness. For his authority in this explanation, Turgot cites the experiments of Stephen Hales.[26]

The person who put the ideas and discoveries of Stahl, Hales, Rouelle, Black, Priestley and Cavendish together with his own experiments and interpretations to form the chemical revolution of the eighteenth century was, however, Antoine Laurent Lavoisier. Henry Guerlac has convincingly demonstrated the importance to Lavoisier of Hales's work. By 1777 (and again in 1789), Lavoisier could refer to Hales as an historical curiosity, but it is clear that his first introduction to British pneumatic chemists had been to Hales, whom he early cites with admiration. Lavoisier had attended the chemistry lectures of Rouelle and later asserts that he saw Rouelle repeat Hales's experiments a number of times; he owned a copy of the *Statique des végétaux* and, prior to 1773, the only pneumatic chemist he mentions by name is Hales. Guerlac best illustrates the influence of Hales on Lavoisier by pointing out that Lavoisier could think of no greater praise of Joseph Priestley's first important work on gases than to compare the author favourably to Stephen Hales.[27]

Hales's pneumatic studies, though most clearly illustrating the Newtonian origin of his ideas, must, however, be regarded as peripheral to the main line of his interests. Indeed, it is clear that the chapter on analysis of air was in the nature of an afterthought to his experiments on vegetable physiology. Yet evidence of any conceptual influence of the physiological part of the *Vegetable Staticks* is hard to find. The second half of the eighteenth and first half of the nineteenth centuries were singularly devoid of distinguished plant physiologists. The line which begins with

Malpighi and includes Grew and Ray breaks off with Hales and, with the exception of Dutrochet, scarcely resumes until the German reductionists of the mid- and late nineteenth century. The editors of the 1809 *Philosophical Transactions, Abridged* observed that an abstract of Desaguliers' review of the *Vegetable Staticks* was unnecessary, 'the work itself being in the library of every person who possesses the least taste for physiological inquiries'.[28] Yet the use of it seems primarily confined to the chapter on air or for the apparent practical consequences of its investigations.

This does not mean that the botanists were unaware of Hales's work; indeed every significant figure in botanical studies (other than pure taxonomic) into the early years of the nineteenth century mentions Hales and speaks admiringly of the *Vegetable Staticks* or of some of the experiments in it. Yet even they, in curious parallel to the popular emphasis on Hales as an applied scientist, tend to emphasize the application of his plant studies to agriculture. Given the rapid development, early in the nineteenth century, of scientific agriculture, this emphasis could last only a short time. Jethro Tull's *Horse-Hoeing Husbandry: or, An Essay on the Principles of Vegetation and Tillage*, first published in 1733, fails to refer to Hales; insofar as Tull departs from empirical observation and generalization, he does so in the direction of iatro-chemistry. And the first truly significant British work in scientific agriculture, Sir Humphry Davy's *Elements of Agricultural Chemistry* (1813), does not even include Hales in a list of 'the most enlightened philosophers who have studied the physiology of vegetation', and refers to him but twice.[29] Hales's name is, of course, entirely absent from Justus Liebig's *Chemistry in its Application to Agriculture and Physiology*, of 1840.

During the intervening years, however, Hales was to be a standard authority. He had used Philip Miller's *Gardener's and Florist's Dictionary* for the *Vegetable Staticks*; the editions (eight of them between 1731 and 1771) of Miller's *Gardener's Dictionary* contain frequent references to Hales's work. Erasmus Darwin's *Phytologia; or the Philosophy of Agriculture and Gardening* (1800) uses Hales, or the French agronomes influenced by Hales, more than any other sources for experimental justification of agricultural practice, though neither the *Botanic Garden* (1789, 1791) nor the *Temple of Nature* (1803), Darwin's didactic, philosophical, botanical poems, refer to Hales more than casually.[30] It was, however, among the French, increasingly influenced by English practice, that Hales becomes most celebrated. French agricultural works of the middle and late eighteenth century nearly all cite Dr Hales and almost always with the prefix 'worthy'. The Abbé Le Blanc, writing in praise of the English farmer in his *Letters on the English and French Nations* of 1747, commends Buffon for his efforts in translating the *Vegetable Staticks* of Dr Hales, '... the best author the English have on this subject'.[31] Now Buffon's translation was, of course, crucial to the influence of Hales on the French and, as will be seen, Buffon was, himself, strongly influenced by aspects of Hales's work, but the person most responsible for the presentation of Hales as a practical agronomist was Henri-Louis Duhamel du Monceau. Duhamel was translator and author of many books and papers on agriculture (some of which were reprinted in the *Gentleman's Magazine*). He translated Tull's *Horse-Hoeing Husbandry*, then expanded its ideas into other studies, one of them assimilating the investigations of Grew, Ellis, Miller and Stephen Hales in a six-volume *Practical Treatise on Husbandry*, translated into English in 1759. Best known for his observations on trees and wood, e.g., *La Physique des Arbres* (1758), it was primarily in this connection that he became interested in Hales's studies of plants, but he also was concerned with the ventilation of granaries and adapted Hales's ventilators to that purpose.[32]

The greatest general philosophical influence of the *Vegetable Staticks* was probably that on Georges Louis Leclerc, Comte de Buffon, for whom the work provided an example of Newtonianism, separated from physical astronomy and applied to living substances, and developed through ingenious experiments and observations. Save for a paper on probability theory, Buffon's translation of the *Vegetable Staticks* was his first published contribution to science. He indicates the impression that the work made on him in a letter of 8 February 1734, to President Bouhier, of the Academy of Dijon: 'I have the honour to tell you that I am, as soon as possible, to have printed a translation, with notes, of an English work on physics which has recently appeared and the discoveries of which are so far superior to any that I have seen of the type, that I could not refuse myself the pleasure of giving them to the public in our language . . .'[33]

Only recently, in the work of Lesley Hanks and of Jacques Roger, has there begun the analytical study of Buffon and his work necessary to an understanding of his significance to the science of the eighteenth and early nineteenth century. As his major work, the *Histoire Naturelle*, in its forty-six volumes, was to be found in every respectable library of that period, it is clear he must have had a considerable influence. The nature of Buffon's interest in the *Vegetable Staticks* and of his translation of it must therefore be of some importance for, according to Hanks, who has most closely studied the early career of Buffon, it was in this translation that he began to form that literary style which won the admiration even of his detractors, and it was from the *Vegetable Staticks* that he derived many of the themes, scientific and philosophic, developed in the course of the *Histoire Naturelle*.[34]

The translation appears to have been made from the second English edition (1731), with appendices from the *Haemastaticks* of 1733 added. Buffon assures the reader, in his translator's preface, that the 'translation is literal, above all in those places where the author gives details of his experiments', though he has taken a few liberties in places of less importance.[35] At first glance, this seems true. The translation is, on the whole, faithful to the original, but it is not completely literal. In some places phrases have been restructured to gain logical coherence, for Buffon intended not merely to translate, but also to render the whole truly accessible to the public. His annotations attest to his efforts to make the work clear and precise. One figure has been added to illustrate a difficult passage and another passage altered to bring it into closer conformity with a figure already present; an apparently faulty calculation has been corrected, measurements are given in French units, and plants, described by English names, have added references to Tournefort, Bauhin and Hermann. There are even indications that Buffon had consulted the originals of works cited by Hales (e.g., that by Musschenbroek).

Closer reading, however, reveals subtle variations which suggest some of Buffon's biases and also indicate the particular view of Hales which continental readers were likely to acquire by way of this translation. Buffon claims that it is the experiments and observations that most concern him; certainly there are changes which exaggerate that view of Hales as contemptuous of all systems, which the French most celebrated. Most of Hales's poetic turns of phrase are excised, those places where he glories in the marvels of nature, or personifies nature and then identifies that person with God, architect and master of a harmonious universe. The notion of final design, central to Hales's metaphysic, is underplayed, as are his repeated assertions of congruence with Newtonian concepts. The explicit emphasis is on the methodology, on number, weight and measure as a means of discovery.

Implicitly, however, there is evidence that Buffon was, in fact, most impressed with the general mechanistic view of nature supported by the *Vegetable Staticks*; it was this interest, derived also from Newton's *Opticks*, which led Voltaire to regard Buffon, in 1739, as a leader of the young Newtonians in France. Most of the modifications Buffon effects in Hales's *Vegetable Staticks* make explicit (even where Hales had left it implicit) the interaction of opposing forces, attraction and repulsion and, in the air, fixity and elasticity. The result is to blur distinctions between physical and 'living' atoms and between plants and animals, as where the confusion between air as a mechanically active agent and a chemical ingredient is compounded by Buffon's insertion of the term 'respiration' when speaking of assimilation of air by plants.

The effect of the modified Hales on the science of Buffon is not yet defined, to say nothing of the second-order effect on continental science in general. Clearly, however, the *Vegetable Staticks* had an influence. Buffon's work on sylvaculture, already in progress while he was engaged in his translation and on which, appropriately, he was joined by Duhamel du Monceau, is filled with inferences drawn from Hales. The emphasis on plants in early volumes of the *Histoire Naturelle* is surely a reflection of Hales's plant physiology. Buffon's programme of study, in the years immediately after the translation, appears to emphasize the authors most cited in Hales's chapter on air (e.g., Boerhaave, Mariotte and Boyle). A section in the *Histoire Naturelle* even cites Hales's pamphlet on earthquakes, while, forty years after his translation of the *Vegetable Staticks* was published, Buffon returns to that work for a discussion, published in a Supplement to the *Histoire*, on the role of fixed air in formation of solid bodies. Any study of the development of Buffon's attitudes in science should, then, include the impact of Hales's ideas on him, while the influence of Hales, as modified by Buffon, in defining the character of French 'Newtonianism' is surely worthy of examination.

The other major eighteenth-century philosopher-biologist to acknowledge an influence of the *Vegetable Staticks* was Charles Bonnet. It is, however, difficult to specify any effect that work might have had on Bonnet's nature philosophy, which was less mechanistic than Hales's and appears to depend more on the work of Réaumur and on his own discovery of parthenogenesis and work on regeneration. In fact, the *Vegetable Staticks* seems rather to have complicated Bonnet's interpretation of plant nutrition.

As early as 1747, Bonnet, already suffering from the bad eyesight and hearing which ultimately forced him to employ assistants to do his research for him, began his change from microscopic examination of insects to the grosser examination of plants. Combining some observations of Malpighi on the anatomy of leaves with a suggestion of his friend Calandrini on the 'hidden purpose' which the different leaf surfaces must have, Bonnet commenced a study of *L'Usage des Feuilles dans les Plants*, which he published in 1754. Hales is cited several times in *L'Usage*, particularly in connection with the insensible transpiration of plants and its relation to the number and size of leaves. In his autobiographical sketches, Bonnet also refers to the 'profound' researches of Hales's *Statique Végétaux* and their proof that the leaves are provided for the raising, distributing and preparing of nourishing juices. 'But this excellent man, whose name will always be dear to the friends of humanity and true philosophy' had not attempted to discover the proper uses of the different surfaces of leaves.[36]

Unfortunately, in his effort to discover those uses, Bonnet conceived the notion that the important function of leaves was to absorb dew and this had to be brought into congruence with Hales's demonstration of transpiration. His arguments, supported by poorly designed and executed experiments, contribute relatively little to an understanding of plant nutrition, though *L'Usage des Feuilles* was to receive lavish praise for many years. In the long run, it is probable that Bonnet's greatest contribution to plant physiology was his establishment, by way of his assistant, Jean Senebier, of a 'school' of Swiss botanists, which contributed largely to an understanding of the chemistry of plant nutrition. This work, associated with the phenomenon of photosynthesis, is connected, through Joseph Priestley and Jan Ingenhousz, with that other influence of Hales's *Vegetable Staticks*, on pneumatic chemistry.[37]

Ingenhousz avowedly commenced his researches as a continuation of Priestley's discovery of the influence of growing plants on the purity of air, but his *Experiments upon Vegetables*, published in 1779, also reveals his awareness of the work of Hales, particularly the demonstration that 'air enters the composition of bodies' and even contributes to the cohesion of the parts of such solid substances as vegetables.[38] There were two superposed phenomena involved in Priestley's discovery, which had confused the issue, complicating reproduction of experimental results and leading Carl Wilhelm Scheele to deny the effect of plants on the air's purity. Ingenhousz managed to separate these phenomena, demonstrating that plants evolve dephlogisticated air (oxygen) in sunlight, but vitiate the air (or emit bad air) in darkness. He suggests that plants purify bad air by extracting the impure part, which is retained as food, and releasing the pure part as excrement. Before the confusion of some of his explanations could be unravelled, through use of the new chemistry of Lavoisier, Jean Senebier entered the picture with further discoveries relating to photosynthesis.

Senebier was clearly aware of the work of Ingenhousz, but, as his experiments were in continuation of those he had performed under Bonnet's direction, it is probable that his discoveries were, as he claimed, largely independent. Examining the action of leaves immersed in carbonated water, Senebier found that evolution of pure air from them bore a quantitative relationship to the amount of carbon dioxide dissolved in the water. Although he failed to recognize the nocturnal emission of carbon dioxide by healthy plants, Senebier insists that the carbon in plants is entirely derived from atmospheric carbon dioxide. Von Sachs describes Senebier's book, *Physiologie Végétale*, published in 1800, as 'tediously prolix', but concedes that it brought together all that contemporary literature afforded for the understanding of plant nutrition. Among the authorities cited, Stephen Hales's name appears frequently, in connection with the constituent role of the air, the influence of the sun on vegetative processes, and, unfortunately, in support of Senebier's curious explanation that the carbon extracted by the leaves from carbon dioxide is distributed through the plant by sap ascending from the roots.[39]

The next, and perhaps the greatest, physiological chemist of the 'Swiss school' was Nicholas T. de Saussure, whose *Recherches chimiques sur la Végétation*, of 1804, completes the discovery of photosynthesis with a sophisticated, quantitative, and 'statical' handling of plant intake and output, including water, gas and soil constituents. De Saussure may be said to have brought the study of plant nutrition as far as it could be taken without further development of organic chemistry and cytology and before the reflowering of reductionist physiology in the second half century. Unfortunately this, and some later work of almost equal importance, was presented by de Saussure in a non-vitalistic form which hindered its acceptability. Von Sachs writes: 'The *Recherches chimiques* have this in common with Hales's "Statical Essays", that the statement of facts which they contain have been made use of again and again for theoretical purposes, while the theoretical connexion between them was constantly overlooked . . .' It is only to be expected, therefore, especially in view of the equilibrium techniques adopted in his experiments, that de Saussure's *Recherches* give repeated evidence of his acquaintance with the work of Hales.[40]

An example of the unhappy influence of the concept of vitalism in plant physiology is to be seen in the work of Augustin P. de Candolle, whose work in establishing a natural system of plant taxonomy was of major importance, but whose *Physiologie Végétale*, of 1832, fails chiefly in its substitution of vital forces for an investigation of natural causes in plant nutrition. De Candolle does present a summary of previous work on plant nutrition, including an historical section naturally involving Hales who, according to the author, always deserves attention.[41] An earlier example of vitalism in vegetable physiology appears in the persistent neglect of Hales's mechanism of sap movement and its influence on plant growth. Even among Hales's contemporaries there continued attempts to study plants analogously to animals. In order to retain the analogy, they had to ignore Hales's denial of sap circulation. Duhamel du Monceau, for all his admiration of Hales's work, insisted on circulation. In 1785, nearly fifty years after publication of the *Vegetable Staticks*, John Walker, Regius Professor of Natural History of Edinburgh, was to declare that the circulation of sap was still a controverted question and find it necessary to repeat and extend Hales's experiments to disprove it.[42] Much of what might have been at least of suggestive value in Eramus Darwin's *Phytologia* is vitiated by the repeated assumption of complete circulation of sap. Indeed, the only persons, prior to 1837, who seemed interested in the mechanism of fluid motion in plants were physicists, like John Leslie, who discusses Hales's attempt 'to measure the force with which the sap mounts in . . . plants', as an example of capillary action and attractive forces in nature, for his *Elements of Natural Philosophy*.[43]

It was left to Henri J. Dutrochet to return to a study of the mechanism of fluid motion in plants. In his application of the concept of osmosis to sap movement and his treatment of turgidity as a factor in growth and movement, one can see signs of a continuing element of mechanism in plant physiology. It is the more remarkable, therefore, that Dutrochet does not appear to mention Hales in his *Mémoires pour servir a l'histoire . . . des végétaux* of 1837. The complete recovery of the spirit of Hales's plant studies was left to Julius von Sachs, who represented, in a finished form, the German flight to reductionism as a reaction against vitalism and German romantic *naturphilosophie*.

Von Sachs developed, in his own work, a micro-mechanical approach to many of the plant physiology phenomena for which Hales had earlier developed the macro-mechanics. This mechanical mode of explanation was adopted for all of his books and for most of these he drew on historical materials. His influential *Text-book of Botany* (1874) does not refer to Hales, as von Sachs did not feel 'the historical development of botanical views and theories' belonged in a text, but he had, by that time, already acknowledged the work of Hales.[44] In his *Handbuch der Experimental-Physiologie der Planzen* (1865), he uses Hales's measurements of sap and root-pressures and repeats some of Hales's experiments. In his *History of Botany*, from which many references have been taken for this chapter, von Sachs leaves no doubt that he regards Stephen Hales as among the most important contributors, in theory and experimental techniques, to the study of plant physiology. Finally, in his *Vorlesungen uber Pflanzen-physiologie* (1882), he calls Hales 'the founder of the mechanics of the movement of sap', identifies him as the first to note 'weeping of the root-stock', and accepts his measurement of extreme root pressures in vine roots.[45]

With the publication of von Sachs' work, the restoration of Hales's reputation as a major influential figure in the continued development of plant physiology was assured; histories of botanical studies would, henceforth, regularly praise Hales and trace his influence, although contemporary workers may still remain ignorant of that influence on them. Unhappily there has yet to develop the equivalent of von Sachs for the study of Hales and animal physiology. Major works in the history of physiology continue to be written which refer to Hales not at all or only with casual remarks.[46] The reasons are easy to understand. In the *Vegetable Staticks*, Hales was charting a new path to the understanding of plants; even when his modes of explanation became unpopular, the results of his experiments remained to be used and re-interpreted and, with the return of mechanism, the spirit of Hales could continue to inspire new directions. But the *Haemastaticks* marks the end of a tradition, not a beginning; the experiments in it are specifically designed to test the assumptions of iatro-physics. They are thus substantially less likely to inspire new investigations when a more sophisticated reductionist physiology develops, while they themselves contributed to the long, intermediate, period of anti-mechanistic physiology, which set in more rapidly for animals than for plants. The same edition of the *Philosophical Transactions, Abridged*, which declined to abstract the *Vegetable Staticks* because it was so widely available, declined to abstract an argument on

135

the mechanical power of the heart, estimated on mathematical principles, because 'Such calculations . . . are necessarily involved in much uncertainty, being founded on data taken from inanimate matter, the laws of which are not applicable to organs endowed with the principles of vitality'.[47]

The speed with which this change of attitude occurred in Britain can be seen in the various 'Croonian Lectures on Muscular Motion' published in the *Philosophical Transactions* between 1739 and 1745. In 1739, Alexander Stuart invokes the standard mechanistic parameters of particles, attractive forces, and hydrostatic pressures. By 1745, James Parsons inveighs against such explanations and substitutes an 'aura', filling the hollow nerves, whose property it is to inflate under impulse of the will. Parsons, in a work of 1722, *On the Analogy between the Propagation of Animals and Vegetables*, is even more explicitly anti-mechanistic. Insisting that plants and animals possess, in differing degrees, principles of animation and organization not given to inanimate objects, Parsons cites Hales's *Vegetable Staticks* as having demonstrated that plants rid themselves of substances not fitted to their growth and development.

It is true that the Croonian Lectures of 1747, by Browne Langrish, appear to return to mechanism, but the lecturer declares that his ideas have remained unchanged from 1733; and, moreover, the statement is untrue as his mechanism is tainted with materialism. Langrish's 'Lectures' were dedicated to Hales, from whom he had received 'many personal particular favours'. He uses the concepts of elasticity, corpuscular attraction, and antagonist forces to be found in the *Haemastaticks*, but he also introduces 'a nervous aether' which he likens to electricity, and he ends his Lectures with a cry of mechanist frustration, similar to that of Hales in the Appendix to the *Haemastaticks*, in which he declares that the agents of nature are too subtle to be the object of the senses. Arguments based on them cannot, therefore, be proved experimentally, but must be deduced from 'collateral proofs'.

Another example of electricity in physiological speculation is to be found in David Hartley's *Various Conjectures on the Perception, Motion, and Generation of Ideas* of 1746 and, still plainer, in his more famous *Observations on Man* of 1749. Hartley, a collaborator with Hales in promotion of Joanna Stephens's remedies for the stone, uses an electricity-aether-nervous fluid analogy in his doctrine of physiological psychology and cites Hales, in the *Conjectures*, as having demonstrated the electric virtue of blood globules.

Finally, Robert Whytt, distinguished for his investigations of the central nervous system and his discovery of the reflex arc, commits himself to an animate living principle in his *Essays on the Vital and other Involuntary Motions in Animals* of 1751, and others of his physiological writings. Not only does Whytt accept Hales's *Statical Essays* as authoritative and reliable sources of information on the vibratory motion of the capillaries in promotion of blood flow, the force of blood in the heart and arteries, and the speed of its motion, he explicitly credits Hales for the experimental observations which led him to the establishment of the central nervous system as the reflex centre of the body. It is the more remarkable, therefore, that Whytt shows no influence of mechanical arguments based on structure of parts, elasticity or action of fluids.[48]

On the Continent, the major medical figures who might have responded to the physiology of the *Haemastaticks* were Boerhaave and Albrecht von Haller. Boerhaave, whose mechanistic physiology dominated European medical education from his *de Uso Ratiocini Mechanici in Medicina* of 1702, probably died too early (1738) to have been influenced by the *Haemastaticks* which, in any event, was published too near the end of his career to have been effectively used in his teaching. It was von Haller, Boerhaave's sometime disciple, who set the pattern for modern physiology with his eight-volume *Elementa Physiologiae corporis humani* (1757–65). Von Haller, a pietist and romantic poet, was increasingly unhappy with the 'geometrical physicians', the 'medico-mathematical sect' and though his early *First Lines of Physiology* (published in Latin 1747, and several times translated into English) reveals strong affinities to Boerhaave's teaching, he tended to emphasize empirical, anatomical, descriptions with the typical naive materialism of the empiricist. The only explicit references to Hales in the Edinburgh edition of *First Lines* (1786) are in notes added by William Cullen and relate to the blood pressure measurements and to the uses of the air in the composition of bodies.[49] The *Elementa* makes repeated references to Hales, whom von Haller calls a 'college' of information, though he is critical of physical calculations of the Hales type when applied to medicine. As one might expect, it was the experimental details which von Haller found most useful, and particularly those on the velocity of circulation, blood pressure, etc., which might be taken as critical evidence against the mechanists.

Much of von Haller's use of the hydrodynamic data of Hales's work was conditioned by the studies of a physician-scholar who had found the

Haemastaticks of considerable importance. Daniel Bernouilli, better known as a mathematician and physicist, found the work of Hales to be his only source of experimental information on blood flow – angles between dividing arteries, thickness of vessels, forces of contraction, resistance to fluid flow, etc. – to be used in his work on hydrodynamics. In 1743 Bernouilli recommended that Leonhard Euler read the *Haemastaticks* as preparation for a study on pulsation of the arteries and, in 1753, he cited Hales on heart pressure in a report submitted to the Academie des Sciences.[50]

And von Haller must certainly have been encouraged in his use of Hales in criticism of the mechanists, by the continental version of the *Haemastaticks*, the French translation of which by François Boissier de Sauvages, published in 1744, became the source for the Italian and German translations. Like Buffon, Sauvages professes to be most impressed by Hales's experiments. In the *Haemastaticks*, he declares, one finds a 'complete physiology based on experiments and drawn from the most certain of principles'.[51] And, like Buffon, Sauvages contrives by his translation, but particularly by his notes and two appended memoirs: on the theory of inflammation and on the causes of fever, to work a transformation in the attitudes of Hales's text.

This transformation was a subtle one, for Sauvages was something of an anomaly – an animist addicted to the use of mathematical calculation as a primary method of research. In his translator's 'avertissement', he states that as the work is not one of 'esprit', he has not concerned himself with niceties of language, and only where it was a question of fact and geometrical reasoning has he attempted a precise rendering, for these were the 'door to all the world'. He adds to Hales's text notes from James Keill, George Cheyne and other British physiologists. In these additions to the *Haemastaticks*, and in other studies such as his *Dissertation où l'on recherche comment l'air, suivant ses différentes qualités, agit sur le corps humain* (1753) and his *Nosologia methodica* (1768), he discusses the animal 'oeconomy', and uses calculation and reasoning drawn from physics, mechanics and hydraulics to obtain results at variance with those of iatro-physicists.[52]

With physicians turning increasingly toward vitalism (the most distinguished of their physiologists, Albrecht von Haller, being explicitly anti-mechanist), and with the major avenue for the communication of the ideas of the *Haemastaticks* in the continental versions being rerouted through the animism of Sauvages, it is small wonder that Stephen

Hales's concepts lost impact. Only the experimental results remained effectively to impress themselves, and the mechanist matrix of these tended to conceal their importance. For a century, however, his experimental determination of blood pressure remained as the major source of this information. As late as 1819, Sir Charles Bell still regarded Hales's results with respect, though he sometimes also criticized the technique, in his *Essay on the Forces which Circulate the Blood*. Then J. L. M. Poiseuille developed an alternative method of measuring blood pressure. Poiseuille refers to Hales with respect as having achieved a major step in knowledge of blood pressure, he repeats some of Hales's experiments and cites the studies on perfusates and those on motion of sap in trees, but Hales's measurements, were, of necessity, relegated to the position of historical curiosities.[53]

What now can be said, in summary, of Hales's scientific career, his reputation and his influence? He was probably the most distinguished 'Newtonian' scientist of eighteenth century Britain and his reputation, in Britain at least, was second only to Newton's. In the particular areas of his investigation he had no real competitors for nearly half a century, and except in pneumatic chemistry, none for over a century. The nature of his influence is a more difficult matter to assess. During much of the eighteenth and early nineteenth centuries his investigations were adapted to conform to new views of the world. In three subjects, pneumatic chemistry, vegetable physiology and animal physiology, he devised research techniques, designed experiments and made discoveries which were to be of continuing importance whatever his own interpretations of his results might be. The tracing of Hales's scientific influence cannot, therefore, be a simple summing of explicit citations to his work over the years. One must, instead, identify his influence in his immediate successors who became the leaders in their various areas of research. Each of these successors became the sources of new influence, which was thus continued, explicitly or implicitly, through a succession of scientists down to our own day. The measure of Hales's scientific importance is the degree to which he was an essential link in the historical development of scientific understanding.[54]

In this view, Hales was a major figure of eighteenth century science. Every significant figure of pneumatic chemistry acknowledged his work, from Joseph Black, Henry Cavendish and Joseph Priestley, to Lavoisier and Davy. Every plant physiologist of note, from Duhamel du Monceau, through Buffon, Bonnet, Ingenhousz, Senebier, de Saussure and Dutro-

139

chet, and thence to von Sachs admitted the work of Hales in their considerations. And, for a hundred years, animal physiologists had to come to terms with the studies of Hales before proceeding with their own work. It is a record of which any professional scientist of the nineteenth or twentieth centuries would be proud. For an eighteenth-century amateur, incidentally trained in science and devoting major portions of his time to religion, public duties and public service, it was a phenomenal achievement. For Hales, religion and philosophy did indeed agree, and in their agreement he achieved results of enduring consequence.

Abbreviations used in the notes
and the bibliography

B.M.	British Museum (now British Library)
C.K.	A. E. Clark-Kennedy, *Stephen Hales, D.D., F.R.S.: an eighteenth century biography* (Cambridge, 1929)
D.A.B.	Dictionary of American Biography
D.N.B.	Dictionary of National Biography
G.M.	*Gentleman's Magazine*
R.C.P.	Royal College of Physicians
R.C.S.E.	Royal College of Surgeons of England
R.S.	Royal Society
R.S.A.	Royal Society of Arts
S.H.	Stephen Hales
S.P.G.	(United) Society for the Propagation of the Gospel in Foreign Parts
S.P.C.K.	Society for the Promoting of Christian Knowledge

Notes

CHAPTER I

1. See J. Debrett, *The Baronetage of England* . . . Vol. I (London, 1808), pp. 294–6; Dr Chapman suggested this was the book used by Sir Walter Elliot in *Persuasion* (R. W. Chapman, ed., *The Novels of Jane Austen*, Oxford 3rd ed., 1933, Vol. V, p. 270).

2. W. Betham, *The Baronetage of England*, Vol. II (London, 1802), pp. 112–17.

3. Betham describes Stephen as 'B.D.' although he mentions his being awarded a Doctorate in Divinity (*op. cit.*, p. 114).

4. Gilbert White to Robert Marsham, 25 Feb. 1791 (printed in *Transactions of the Norwich and Norfolk Naturalists Society*, Vol. II, 1875, pp. 152–4).

5. See K. V. Bligh, 'A descriptive list of part of the Bouverie collection: documents relating to the estates of the families of Pym, Hales and Bouverie in Kent and Somerset', typescript thesis for University of London. Diploma in Archive Administration, 1966, pp. 26, 27, 34, 35, 50–2. (We are indebted to Miss Bligh for kindly allowing us to quote from her thesis.)

6. Dr Everitt writes of the Hales of Dungeon as 'long since surpassed in wealth by the third branch' and as 'now extinct' in 1640. (See A. M. Everitt, *The Community of Kent and the Great Rebellion, 1640–60*, Leicester, 1966, p. 40.) Miss Bligh in her Hales Pedigree, however, shows Elizabeth, the daughter of James Hales of Dungeon, as marrying Sir Stephen Hales of Snitterfield in 1663 (see K. V. Bligh, *op. cit.*, table IIb).

7. A. M. Everitt, *op. cit.*, pp. 36, 45–8.

8. Sir George Sondes, *Plaine narrative*, 1655, quoted A. M. Everitt, *op. cit.*, pp. 50–1; Somerset House, Will of Sir Robert Hales, 20 Dec. 1693.

9. A. M. Everitt, *op. cit.*, p. 149; letters from Robert Hales to Mr Hodges, 11 April 1701, and Mr Lewis to Mr Chamberlayne, 10 May 1701. (S.P.C.K. Mss, printed. E. McClure, *A Chapter in English Church History . . . S.P.C.K. Minutes and Correspondence, 1698–1704*, London, 1888, pp. 330–6.)

10. G. E. Cockayne, ed., *Complete Baronetage*, Vol. II (Exeter, 1903), p. 79, notes he was 'admitted to the Inner Temple, Nov. 1654, and . . . presumably, matriculated at Oxford from Magdalen College 23 July 1656'; the registers of the parish of Beakesbourne record the baptism of twelve children between 1664 and 1683. They also record the burial in 1680 of 'Richard, the son of Thomas Hales Esq.', which may bring the total to thirteen instead of twelve. (Information extracted from C. H. Wilkie, *The Parish Register of St Peter's*

Beakesbourne, Canterbury, 1896, by Mr F. Higinbottom, City Librarian of Canterbury.)

11. Bligh, *op. cit.*, p. vii, and p. 34; letter from S.H. to Sir Hans Sloane, Howletts, 15 July 1732. (B.M., Sloane Mss 4052, ff. 147–8.)

12. See letters from S.H. to Sir Hans Sloane, 15 July 1732, in which S.H. informs Sloane 'Sir Thomas Hales who is now very well gives his service to you' (B.M., Sloane Mss 4052, ff. 147–8 printed, C.K., p. 115) and from Sloane to Sir Thomas n.d., containing medical information for 'Dr. Allen in Bridgewater' and sent c/o William Hales (*id.*, 4078, f. 280). S.H. witnessed the Hales-Marsham marriage settlement in company with his brother Thomas and the first Lord Romney, F.R.S., (K. V. Bligh, *op. cit.*, p. 26).

13. J. Venn and J. A. Venn, comps. *Alumni Cantabrigienses: a biographical list of all known students, graduates and holders of Office at the University of Cambridge, from the earliest times to 1900*, Vol. II (Cambridge, 1922), p. 282; 'Mem: Charles, son of Thomas Hales Esq., and Mary his wife. Died at Flushing in Zeeland. August 5 and was buried there.' (C. M. Wilkie, *Parish Register of St. Peter's Beakesbourne*, entry in Burials for 1747.)

14. Cockayne, *loc. cit.*; letter from John Chamberlayne to Robert Harley, 18 Aug. 1704 (B.M., Portland Mss 29, 191, ff. 196–7), partly printed in W. A. Bultmann, 'A Layman proposes Protestant Union: Robert Hales and the Helvetic Churches, 1700–1705', *Church History*, Vol. 27, 1958, pp. 32–45; Robert Hales was sworn in as Clerk to the Council in Ordinary on 6 April 1716, re-sworn on the accession of George II and was suspended on 8 Oct. 1728 (information supplied by the Privy Council Office). In 1718 he corresponded with Sir Hans Sloane about entertainment for the 'Emperor's envoy and others' (B.M., Sloane Mss 4078, f. 164).

15. Goldsmiths' Company records (information from these sources supplied through the courtesy of Miss Susan Hare, Librarian to the Company); F. G. Hilton Price, *A handbook of London Bankers* (London, 1890), p. 28.

16. E. McClure, *A Chapter in English Church History . . . S.P.C.K. Minutes and Correspondence, 1698–1704* (London, 1888), pp. 14, 85–7, 92, 110, 113, 116, 118–19, 122, 124, 130, 136–8, 159–61, 174, 179, 183, 198, 217, 241, 246, 250, 261, 267–9, 316, 323–4, 330, 339, 342, 355; L. W. Cowie, *Henry Newman, An American in London 1708–43* (London, 1956), pp. 13–14, 46; S.P.C.K., Abstract Letter Books, CR1/11, 7512; CR1/15, 10280; F. G. Hilton Price, *op. cit.*, pp. 452–3; 'L.L.', 'Dr. Stephen Hales', *Notes and Queries*, 2nd series, Vol. IV (1851), p. 343; P.R.O., State Papers Domestic, May 1729, S.P. 36/229; letter from Henry Newman to S.H., 6 Nov. 1735 (S.P.C.K. Mss, CN4.6, p. 42); S.H.'s will 30 Oct. 1759 (printed C.K., pp. 240–2).

17. W. Betham, *op. cit.*, Vol. II, p. 116; K. V. Bligh, *op. cit.*, p. 26; *Archaeologia Cantiana*, Vol. LIII (1941), p. 94. S.H. to Nathaniel Booth, Teddington, 12 Feb. 1741, printed *G.M.*, Vol. XLIX, ii (1799), pp. 551–2. (Nathaniel Booth

1709–70 was the eldest surviving son of Mary and her husband the Hon. Robert Booth, D.D., Dean of Bristol and Archdeacon of Durham, d. 1732. He succeeded to the title of Baron Delamere in 1758.)

18. C.K., p. 4; Robert Masters, *The History of Corpus Christi College, Cambridge*, Part II (Cambridge, 1755), p. 409.

19. In this connection it may be remarked that Dr John Tillotson, as Dean of Canterbury, witnessed the marriage settlement between Thomas Hales and Mary Pym, Nov. 1688 (K. V. Bligh, *op. cit.*, p. 34).

20. S.H., draft contribution to Dr Rawlinson's continuation of Wood's 'Athenae Oxiensis', 12 April 1742, printed *G.M.*, Vol. LXIX (1799), i, p. 267; Bishop Hildesley to Dr Tathwell, *c.* 1761 (letter printed in *G.M.*, Vol. LXXI, ii, 1801, p. 713). Mark Hildesley, D.D. (1698–1772) was the eldest surviving son of Mark Hildesley the Rector of Murston. After a long period of relatively minor preferments he was consecrated Bishop of Sodor and Man in 1755. Regarding his friendship with S.H., he wrote, 'The Doctor afterwards showed his regard to his first tutor, by transferring some share of it to his less worthy son.' (Bishop Hildesley. *loc. cit.*) In 1799 the *Gentleman's Magazine* noted the 'intimate acquaintance and friendship between Dr. Hales and the Bishop, which subsisted through life, and was cherished and kept up by a regular correspondence; of which, however, an unlucky accident has swept away all other traces than a single letter of Dr Hales preserved by the biographer of the Bishop'. (*G.M.*, Vol. LXIX, i, 1799, p. 9; see also W. Butler, *Memoirs of Mark Hildesley . . . Bishop of Man*, London, 1799, p. 368 and C.K., p. 228.)

21. W. Page, ed., *Victoria History of the County of Middlesex*, Vol. I (London, 1906), p. 163; Kensington and Chelsea Central Library (Local History Dept.), Ms Parish Poor Rate Book, 1683–1728, Cuttings file.

22. W. Page, ed., *Victoria History of Nottingham*, Vol. II (London, 1910), pp. 233–4; D. L. Edwards, *A History of the King's School Canterbury* (London, 1957), pp. 106, 201–4; *D.N.B.*; *European Magazine*, Vol. XXI (1791), p. 429; Richard Johnson, *Grammatical Commentaries: being an Apparatus to a New National Grammar: by way of Animadversion upon the Falsities, Obscurities, Redundancies and Defects of Lilly's System now in use . . .* (London, 1706), p. viii.

23. E. Hasted, *History of Kent*, Vol. II (London, 1782), p. 611; the *G.M.* (LXXI, ii, 1801, p. 713) in a note to Bishop Hildesley's letter states that Mark Hildesley was presented by 'Sir Thomas Hales Bt. and John Hales Esq., of the Inner Temple brothers of Stephen Hales'. John Hales certainly acted with Sir Thomas in the presentation but he was not one of his brothers. He was probably the son of Sir Edward Hales.

CHAPTER II

1. See above Chapter 1, ref. 23. Hildesley's suggestion that his father had noted philosophical interests in the young Hales was made too long after the event (more than three-quarters of a century) and in too close an agreement with Hales's subsequent fame to be taken very seriously.

2. See D. A. Winstanley, *Unreformed Cambridge, A Study of Certain Aspects of the University in the Eighteenth Century* (Cambridge, at the University Press, 1935), for a discussion of educational rules and practices there in the eighteenth century.

3. About half of Corpus's roughly sixty members were drawn from Norfolk and several of its twelve fellowships were tenable only by persons educated in certain Norfolk schools. Archbishop Parker, who had attended Corpus, left to it his library, endowed scholarships for graduates of King's School, Canterbury, and fellowships with Norfolk connections. Archbishop Tenison, also a graduate of Corpus, married the daughter of a master of Corpus. Two successive masters, Dr William Stanley (1693 to 1698) and Dr Thomas Greene (1698 to 1716), were known protégés of Tenison and the court. See Robert Masters, *The History of Corpus Christi College* (Cambridge, at the University Press, 1755), for a near-contemporary description of the College.

4. For a discussion of the college studies, and some of the texts used, see Christopher Wordsworth, *Scholae Academicae: Some Account of the Studies at English Universities in the Eighteenth Century* (Cambridge, at the University Press, 1877). During the fourth year the student would attend disputations in the 'schools', where he would keep his 'acts and opponencies' – i.e., defend three propositions in mathematics and philosophy against selected undergraduate opponents, and oppose twice against other disputants – and pass examinations in the Senate house, after which he was admitted B.A.

5. Robert Moss (1666–1729) entered Corpus from a Norwich school in 1682. He was A.B. in 1685, A.M. in 1688, B.D. 1696 and D.D. 1705. He became a fellow 'soon after his first degree' and 'engaged in the business of pupils' at least until the end of Easter term 1698, when he was chosen Preacher of Gray's Inn. In 1699 he was also elected assistant-preacher of St James's Westminster and by 1708 held so many preferments as to disqualify him for the college fellowship, which, however, he refused to resign until 1714, the year following his installation as Dean of Ely. See Masters, *History of Corpus Christi*, pp. 347–9.

6. See J. R. Tanner, *Historical Register of the University of Cambridge to the Year 1910* (Cambridge, at the University Press, 1917), p. 422. The list may include a few names not in strict order of merit, as the proctors, Vice-Chancellor and senior Regent might each place one candidate's name in the list anywhere they liked. An M.A. candidate was, by statute, supposed to keep five acts

145

(three against masters and two against fellow candidates) and two opponencies, but these were frequently 'huddled' – i.e., performed as mock exercises with ritualistic phrases in defence and opposition. No record can be found of propositions defended by Hales either for the B.A. or the M.A.

7. Richard Bentley (1662–1742) became master of Trinity College, Cambridge, in 1700 and made Trinity a centre of scientific studies. His *Eight Sermons* were reprinted at least six times between 1692 and 1735 and another edition appeared as late as 1809. I have used the fifth edition, *Eight Sermons* ... (Cambridge, Crownfield, Knapton and Knopstock, 1724). See also Perry Miller, 'Newton's Four Letters to Bentley and the Boyle Lectures related to Them', in I. Bernard Cohen, ed., *Isaac Newton's Papers & Letters on Natural Philosophy and Related Documents* (Cambridge, Mass., Harvard University Press, 1958).

8. See Michael A. Hoskin, ' "Mining All Within": Clarke's Notes to Rohault's *Traité de Physique*, *The Thomist* 24 (1961), pp. 353–63.

9. See L. J. M. Coleby, 'John Francis Vigani, first professor of Chemistry in the University of Cambridge', *Annals of Science* 8 (1952), pp. 42–60.

10. Roger Cotes (1682–1716) was a student of Trinity College, B.A. 1702, M.A. 1706. He edited the second edition of the *Principia* for Newton. See George Huxley, 'Roger Cotes and Natural Philosophy', *Scripta Mathematica* 26 (1961), pp. 231–8.

11. James Keill (1673–1719), M.D., brother of John Keill, educated at Edinburgh, Paris and Leyden. Said, e.g., by H. M. Sinclair and A. H. T. Robb-Smith, *Short History of Anatomy Teaching in Oxford* (Oxford, for the University Press, 1950), p. 19, to have lectured at both Oxford and Cambridge from about 1698 to some time after 1703. In 1705 he was made honorary M.D., *Comitia Regia*, at Cambridge and must therefore have been present there in that year. George Rolfe (*c.* 1674–*c.* 1730) is scarcely known, but with the aid of Dr Arthur Rook of Cambridge and E. H. Cornelius, Librarian of the Royal College of Surgeons, London, some information has been collected. Rolfe was probably the son of Francis Rolfe of King's Lynn, the son of Francis Rolfe, Gentleman. He was apprenticed to a surgeon of King's Lynn, and admitted to the freedom of the Barber-Surgeons on 9 March 1695. He probably served in the army, but at least as early as 1701 was privately teaching anatomy in London. George C. Peachey, *A Memoir of William and John Hunter* (Plymouth, for the Author, 1924), p. 24, concludes, from the evidence of newspaper advertisements, that Rolfe was 'the first definitely recorded private teacher of anatomy in London'. He may have assisted James Keill in the latter's anatomical lectures in Cambridge prior to 1707, when he was appointed first professor in anatomy. By December 1722 the Senate warned Rolfe that his chair would be declared vacant if he continued to neglect his duties and in April 1728 the professorship was officially

declared vacant. Kenneth Russell, *British Anatomy 1525–1800. A Bibliography* (Parksville, Victoria, Australia, Melbourne University Press, 1963), Nos. 725, 803, cites two works by Rolfe: *Syllabus Enterologias* . . . [title in Greek letter] (London, G. Sawbridge, 1704); and *Syllabus sive index omnium humani corporis* . . . (Cambridge, W. Thurlbourn, 1724).

12. William Stukeley, *Family Memoirs of the Rev. William Stukeley, M.D. and the Antiquarian and other Correspondence of William Stukeley, Roger and Samuel Gale, etc.*, ed. W. C. Lukis, Vol. 1 (Durham, for the Surtees Society, 1882–83), pp. vii, 21, 33, 41, 49.

13. Richard Davies, *The General State of Education in the Universities: With a particular View to the Philosophical and Medical Education: Set forth in An Epistle Inscribed to the Reverend Doctor Hales*, etc. (Bath, by M. Cooper, 1759), p. 44. The view of the senior-junior relationship of Hales and Stukeley is, in some measure, supported by the tone of Stukeley's own description for the memorial he wrote on 20 May 1763 for use in the *Éloge* for Hales of the Académie Royale des Sciences, Paris, see B.M., Birch Mss 4222.

14. Hales dated the experiments on animals in the preface (p. xxvi) to his *Vegetable Staticks* (London, Oldbourne Book Co., Ltd, reprint of the London, 1727 edition, 1961). Collinson's biography of Hales is to be found in the *G.M.* XXXIV (1764), pp. 273–8.

15. For the specific relation between the work of these men and that of Hales, see Chapter IV and V, below.

16. Note that Newton's 'real' beliefs are irrelevant here. Hales's attitudes were guided by what his contemporaries believed that Newton believed. Whether they were right or not is hardly germane to their influence on Hales. For a fuller treatment of early eighteenth-century Newtonianism, see Robert E. Schofield, *Mechanism and Materialism: British Natural Philosophy in an Age of Reason* (Princeton, Princeton University Press, 1970).

17. For Samuel Clarke, I have used his edition of *Rohault's System of Natural Philosophy*, done into English by John Clarke (London, for John Knapton, 1723); for John Keill, his *An Introduction to Natural Philosophy: or, Philosophical Lectures read in the University of Oxford Anno. Dom. 1700* (London, William and John Innys, and John Osborn, 1720).

18. See Coleby, 'John Francis Vigani'; Vigani's lectures are preserved in the University Library, Cambridge as Ms Dd.12.53 (A), ff. 1–57, 'Joan Francis Vigani (Veronens), Cours de Chymi'.

19. Boyle was a kinematic corpuscularian, as was Lemery; John Mayow was an iatro-chemist, not a mechanist; Geoffroy was an early disciple of Georg Ernst Stahl; and Wilson, like Vigani, was a practical chemist who lectured privately in London from about 1691 to 1711, to physicians and medical students on the compounding of medicines. His *Compleat Course of Chemistry*, first published in 1691 and republished and re-edited as late as 1746, was a

compendium of recipes. See F. W. Gibbs, 'George Wilson (1631–1711)', *Endeavour* 12 (1953), pp. 182–5.

20. The original article, as published in *Phil. Trans.* 26 (1708–09), No. 315, pp. 97–110, is translated as 'On the Laws of Attraction and other Physical Properties', in the Hutton, Shaw, Pearson, *et al.*, edition of *Philosophical Transactions, Abridged*, Vol. 5 (London, 1809), pp. 407–24.

21. The book is dedicated to Newton and acknowledges indebtedness to John Keill in its preface. A second edition was published in 1726 and there was an English translation, *Chymical Lectures: In which almost all the Operations of Chymistry are reduced to their True Principles and the Laws of Nature* (London, for Jonah Bowyer, 1712), from which my observations are taken. John Freind (1675–1728), F.R.S. was educated at Christ Church, Oxford, B.A. 1698, M.A. 1701, B.M. 1705, M.D. (diploma) 1707. He was named professor of chemistry at Oxford in 1704, but removed to London in 1705. He also wrote a treatise *Emmenologia* (1703) which may have influenced Hales's physiological experiments.

22. [Francis Hauksbee and William Whiston.] *A Course of Mechanical, Optical Hydrostatical and Pneumatical Experiments* (London, n.d. [1714]); *Memoirs of the Life of Mr. William Whiston*, Vol. I (London, for the Author, 1749), pp. 136–7, 235–6.

23. John Keill, 'On the Laws of Attraction . . .' p. 424; Roger Cotes, *Hydrostatical and Pneumatical Lectures* (London, for the editor, 1738), pp. 5, 123, 125, 202–3.

24. Letter of Stephen Hales to Charles Alston, 26 February 1754, Alston Papers, University Library, Edinburgh: '50 years since I knew most English plants, of which I have now forgot many.' Stukeley's Ms memorial for the Royal Academy, *op. cit.*, says that Hales taught him the taxonomic system of John Ray, in which classes were assigned by the flower. This is the sole indication of botanical taxonomy in Hales's career.

25. For Ray, see Charles E. Raven, *John Ray, Naturalist, his Life and Work* (Cambridge, at the University Press, 1950), pp. 181–201; though Raven sees more influence of Ray on Hales than we can find justification for. Grew's work has recently been reprinted, with an introduction by Conway Zirkle, *The Anatomy of Plants* (New York, Johnson Reprint Corporation, Sources of Science Series, No. 11, from the London 1682 ed., 1965).

26. Keill's *Anatomy of the Humane Body Abridged: or a short and full view of all the parts of the body. Together with their several uses drawn from their compositions and structure* was first published in 1698 as an epitome of Amatus Bourdon's *Nouvelle Description du Corps Humain* (1679); it was successively revised and enlarged in seven editions by Keill's death and, in all, appeared in eighteen English editions to 1771, and was translated into French, Dutch and Latin. The twelfth edition is used here (London, for John Clarke, 1759). The

Medicina Statica Britannica was first published as an appendix to the *Tentamina medico-physica* of 1718 which, in turn, was the third edition of Keill's *Account of Animal Secretion*, first published in 1708, again in 1717, as *Essays of Several Parts of the Animal Oeconomy* and still again, in a fourth posthumous edition, *Essays on . . . the Animal Oeconomy* (London, for George Strahan, 1738), which is the form used here.

27. These observations on Keill's system of physiology are selected from both the *Anatomy* and the *Essays*. For further discussion, see Robert E. Schofield, *Mechanism and Materialism*, Chapter III.

CHAPTER III

1. R. Masters, *History of Corpus Christi College Cambridge*, Part II (Cambridge, 1755), pp. 327, 347–9; H. P. Stokes, *University of Cambridge, College Histories: Corpus Christi* (London, 1898), p. 118; N. Sykes, *Edmund Gibson, Bishop of London, 1669–1748: a study in politics and religion in the Eighteenth Century* (London, 1926), p. 118.

2. See his own statement that he was 'nominated Feb. 21 to the donative of Teddington', *G.M.*, Vol. LXIX (1799), i, p. 267. There are entries in the Parish Registers in his hand under the dates 12 Feb. 1707/08, 19 May 1708 and 17 Jan. 1708/09, which may be retrospective or point to an earlier association with the Parish. (St Alban's Church, Teddington, Mss Parish Registers, Vol. A1/3, f. 9; made available through the courtesy of the Revd F. Bale, Vicar.)

3. Daniel Lysons, *Environs of London*, Vol. III (London, 1792–96), p. 507. S.H. was the fifth incumbent to be appointed since this arrangement, which comprised a settlement of fair farm rents (see list compiled by P. E. Towell and printed in H. T. Dade, *Parish Church of St. Alban the Martyr, Teddington, and the Old Parish Church of St. Mary, Teddington*, Teddington, 2nd ed., 1957, p. 16).

4. In 1753 he wrote to William Wynne, Serjeant at law, about the settlement and referred to Charles Longueville, then deceased, as 'his cousin', (B.M., Add. Mss 41843, f. 119); Longueville was a trustee of the rent settlement; Teddington Registers, A 1/4, f. 13. (See genealogical table for the Longueville/Hales relationship.)

5. S. Reynolds, ed. *Victoria History of the County of Middlesex*, Vol. III (London, 1962), p. 66 et seq.

6. C.K., p. 52; S.P.C.K., Abstract Letter Books (Ms), CR1/11, 7165.

7. References to these summer visits may be found scattered through S.H.'s correspondence (see for example S.H. to John Mickleburgh, 21 June 1729, 'I shall go the 7th July to reside for six weeks at Farringdon near Alton, Hampshire', Cambridge, Trinity College Mss, R4, f. 25 and S.H. to Thomas

Yeoman, 10 April 1744, 'I believe I shall go 14 Days hence to Farringdon near Alton, Hampshire, and continue there till the end of June,' London, Royal College of Physicians Ms Transcripts). For the beauty of the village see in W. Page, ed., *The Victoria History of Hampshire*, Vol. III (London, 1908), p. 20. See also S.H., 'Some Extracts from the Church Warden's Account Book for the Parish of Farringdon near Alton, Hampshire', which noted such customs as 'Shooting of the Cock' and gathering 'Hock Money' in 1557 and other years of the sixteenth century (B.M., Add. Mss, 38, 3330, ff. 244–51), and his notes inside front cover of the Farringdon Parish Register, (Winchester, Hampshire County Record Office: Vol. 2M, 70/4). In 1729 he complained to Mickleburgh that at Farringdon he was 'cut off from all Philosophical Experiments, having no Instruments there' (Trinity College Mss, *loc. cit.*), but by the 1740s he was making trials there of a reed cane to preserve corn (see below).

8. Statutes of Corpus Christi College, Cambridge, printed R. Masters, *op. cit.*, appendix pp. 11–12, and information supplied by Dr R. I. Page, Librarian of the College; Teddington Registers, A1/4, 20 October 1721; Record of S.H.'s marriage on 26 March 1720 (in J. W. Clay, ed., *The Registers of St. Paul's Cathedral*, London, 1899); Middlesex Record Office, Teddington Manor Court Book, 1764–71, f. 11, recording the succession to Hales's property of his heiress and niece Sarah Margaretta Johnson. (The Court Book for Hales's period is not extant so it is not possible to determine the date of his admission to the property.)

9. N. Sykes, *op. cit.*, p. 221; *The Book of Common Prayer*, Section 29. Henry Compton, Bishop of London since 1675 was 79 when he ordained Hales at Fulham on 7 July 1709. (Date given by S.H. in 'Rawlinson's Continuation', *G.M.*, *loc cit.*); S.H. lived under four diocesans.

10. Two of S.H.'s sermons are available in published form: (A) *A Sermon Preached before the Trustees for establishing the colony of Georgia in America; and before the Associates of the late Rev. Dr. Thomas Bray, for Converting the Negroes in the British Plantations, and for other good purposes; at their Anniversary Meeting in the Parish Church of St. Brides, Fleet-Street, on Thursday, March 21, 1734.* (London, 1734); (B) *The Wisdom and Goodness of God in the Formation of Man. Being an Anniversary Sermon Preached before the Royal College of Physicians, London, in the Church of St. Mary Le-Bow, on September 21st, 1751. According to the Institution of Dr. Croun, and his Widow the Lady Sadlier.* (London, 1751.) It is likely that his regular sermons stressed the same teachings, though no Mss have survived to tell us of their content. C.K. (p. 45) suggests that they were popular and that this necessitated the enlargement of Teddington Church in 1716.

11. *Sermon preached before the Trustees*, pp. 3–4, 6, 9.

12. *Wisdom and Goodness of God* . . . pp. 13, 15.

13. The services at Teddington, which were said to have been held monthly

before Sir Orlando Bridgeman endowed the living, were held twice on Sundays in Hales's time, with monthly communion services and weekly catechizing (S. Reynolds, *op. cit.*, p. 77). In 1741 S.H. calculated that there were '346 of Age to communicate' from which 17 Dissenters and Papists and 119 to stay at home (1 from each family) should be subtracted leaving 210 who might attend the Communion 'but there never was at once there above 100'; S.H., 'A Collection of Some Observations . . . etc.', 1741, B.M., Ad. Mss, *op. cit.*; W. K. Lowther Clarke, *Eighteenth Century Piety* (London, 1944), pp. 12–13; S.P.C.K., Abstract Letter Books (Ms), CR1/11, 7191.

14. S.P.C.K., A.L.B., CR1/16, 11204. The scope of the work was indicated by its title: *A Companion to the Altar; showing the nature and necessity of a sacramental preparation, in order to our worthy receiving the Holy Communion, wherein those fears and scruples about eating and drinking unworthily, and of incurring our own damnation thereby are proved groundless and unwarrantable; unto which is added, Prayers and meditations, preparative to a sacramental preparation, according to what the Church of England requires from her communicants*, 11th ed. (London, 1729).

15. S.P.C.K., A.L.B., CR1/13, 8324, S.H. to the Society, Teddington, 16 June 1725, 'That he has a sum of money in his hands to lay in Bibles and the Whole Duty of Man for the Use of the Poor and he desires . . . [£25] worth'; *Id.*, CR1/14, 9287, same to same, Teddington, 19 June 1727, 'has £25 to be laid out in Bibles, New Testaments and Common Prayers'; *Id.*, CR1/21, No. 15815, same to same, Teddington, 17 March 1740/41, 'desiring Bill of charges for 50 Catechisms'. The majority of the abstracts of Hales's letters to the Society simply refer to requests for packets of books without specifying their titles. See W. O. B. Allen and E. McClure, *Two Hundred Years: The History of the S.P.C.K., 1689–1898* (London, 1898), pp. 168–9; W. Lowther Clark, *op. cit.*, p. 16.

16. S.P.C.K., A.L.B., CR1/13; S.H. 'Collections of Some Observations on Bills of Mortality and Parish Registers', 1741 (B.M., Add. Mss, 38. 3330, f. 244–51); S.H. to David Hartley, Duke's Court, 18 April 1757 (Berkshire Record Office, D/E, Hy, F.79).

17. S.H., *A Friendly Admonition to the Drinkers of Brandy, and other distilled Spirituous Liquors*, 2nd ed. (London, 1734), p. 8; C. J. Abbey and J. H. Overton, *The English Church in the Eighteenth Century*, 2nd ed. (London, 1887) p. 474; J. Beresford, ed., *The Diary of a Country Parson, the Reverend James Woodforde 1758–81* (Oxford, 1926), p. 69; Teddington Parish Registers, Vol. A1/4, note by S.H. inside front cover (printed C.K., p. 49); Winchester, Hampshire County Record Office, Farringdon Parish Registers, Vol. 2M 70/4, f. 3 (printed C.K., p. 54); S.H. to Mark Hildesley, 16 May 1758 (B.M., Add. Mss, 19, 683, f. 61).

18. F. Bale, *Church of St. Mary Teddington* [Teddington n.d.], p. 1; Teddington Parish Registers, Vol. A1/3, f. 60, Vol. A1/4, f. 41; London Borough of Rich-

mond Offices, York House, Twickenham, Teddington Vestry Minutes, 8 April 1753.

19. S. Reynolds, *loc. cit.*; the Teddington Vestry Minutes are extant only for the years after 1739. They record some forty meetings between that year and 1755, twelve of which were attended by S.H.

20. Teddington Parish Registers, Vol. A1/3, f. 40, note by S.H.

21. S.H. to Thomas Yeoman, 11 March 1745/46 (Royal College of Physicians, Ms Transcripts); Gilbert White to Robert Marsham, 25 Feb. 1791 (printed *Transactions, Norwich and Norfolk Naturalists Society, loc. cit.*); R. Masters, *History of Corpus Christi College*, Part 2 (Cambridge, 1755), p. 305.

22. Robert Masters, *op. cit.*, p. 303; A. Dyce, ed., *The Works of Richard Bentley*, Vol. III (London, 1838), pp. 1, 55, 80. S.H., *The Wisdom and Goodness of God in the Formation of Man; Being an Anniversary Sermon Preached before the Royal College of Physicians, London, in the Church of St. Mary-Le-Bow, on September 21st, 1751, According to the Institution of Dr. Croun, and his Widow the Lady Sadlier* (London, 1751); S.H. preached on the text Job X, 11, 12 which he had previously cited in the *Haemastaticks*, p. 160. See also *Vegetable Staticks*, p. xxi.

23. See Samuel Johnson's comments (J. Boswell, *Life of Johnson*, ed. Hill, Revd Powell, Vol. V, Oxford, 1950, pp. 246–7, quoted M. Nicolson and G. S. Rousseau, *This Long Disease My Life: Alexander Pope and the Sciences*, Princeton, 1969, pp. 104—9), and Thomas Twining's verses (R. Twining, ed., *Recreations and Studies of a Country Gentleman of the Eighteenth Century: Being Selections from the Correspondence of the Reverend Thomas Twining, M.A.*, London, 1888, pp. 240–5), quoted M. Nicolson and G. S. Rousseau, *op. cit.*, p. 105. Nicolson and Rousseau appear to be mistaken in dating the poem *c.* 1744 and in thinking that the 'antique Pars'nage' and the 'Parson's spouse' refer to Hales's house and wife); S.H., *Haemastaticks*, pp. xvii–xviii, 63; William Stukeley, *Family Memoirs*, I, p. 33; J. M. Osborn, ed., *Joseph Spence: observations, anecdotes and characters of books and men*, Vol. I, Oxford, 1966, p. 118; S.H. to John Mickleburgh, 17 May 1733 (Trinity College, Cambridge, Mss R.4, 42, f. 29).

CHAPTER IV

1. Royal Society Journal Book, 1714–20, pp. xii, 289: quoted C.K., p. 59, although the date given there is 15 March 1718. S.H. had first attended a meeting of the Society on 14 March 1716/17 and was elected Fellow on 13 March 1717/18, on the nomination of William Stukeley who, oddly enough, was himself elected Fellow at the same meeting; see C.K., *Hales*, p. 58.

2. Collinson, 'Life of Hales', p. 274.

3. Stephen Hales, *Vegetable Staticks: Or, An Account of some Statical Experiments on the Sap in Vegetables: Being an Essay toward a Natural History of Vegetation. Also,*

a *Specimen of An Attempt to Analyse the Air, By a Great Variety of Chymio-Statical Experiments* (London, W. and J. Innys, 1727); I have used the 1961 reprint edition, published in London by Oldbourne Book Co. Ltd.

4. *V.S.*, p. xxvi.

5. Quoted by André J. Bourde, *The Influence of England on the French Agronomes, 1750–1789* (Cambridge, at the University Press, 1953), p. 8.

6. Richard Bradley, 'Observations and Experiments relating to the motion of the Sap in Vegetables', *Phil. Trans.* 29 (No. 349, for July, Aug. and Sept., 1716), pp. 486–90. A contributing factor in Hales's new interest in plants may also have been the acquisition, at about this time, of a copyhold property in Teddington.

7. See E. T. Renbourne, 'The Natural History of Insensible Perspiration: a Forgotten Doctrine of Health and Disease', *Medical History* 4 (1960), pp. 135–152, for a discussion of Sanctorius and also of the still earlier uses of the same concept.

8. His failure to include hair-roots in his estimate of root systems vitiated that part of his determinations, but the measured rate of transpiration is the same order of magnitude as that measured by von Sachs over a century later.

9. *V.S.*, p. 26. Keill had written, in his 'Laws of Attraction', etc., that the ascent of the sap in trees and plants was to be explained by the attractive force of capillarity, an opinion Cotes supports in his *Lectures* with the statement, 'It is very reasonable to believe this [capillary attraction] is also the cause of the ascent of the sap in trees, and of the various secretions of fluids through the glands of animals . . .' p. 125.

10. For a discussion of the spurious and official versions of Boerhaave's chemical lectures, see G. A. Lindeboom, *Herman Boerhaave, The Man and his Work* (London, Methuen & Co., Ltd, 1968), pp. 175–84, 340–54. See also Schofield, *Mechanism and Materialism*, p. 1218, for a discussion of the variations in the official version to accommodate Hales's discoveries.

11. The *Oxford English Dictionary* includes in its definition of 'wrought', the words 'worked into', 'spun', etc., making possible that sense of being held, trapped or imprisoned by the composition which is sometimes suggested in the text.

12. Book II, prop. XXIII, Theorem XVIII and Scholium of the *Principia*, where he derives Boyle's law from the proposition that air particles repel one another with a force inversely proportional to their distance, and extending only to adjacent particles, or not much beyond.

13. Roger Cotes, 'Lecture XVI. Air sometimes generated, sometimes consumed, – the nature of factitious airs; explosion in vacuo, dissolutions, fermentations, &c.', *Hydrostatical and Pneumatical Lectures*, ed. Robert Smith (London, for the Editor, 1738), pp. 185–206.

14. *V.S.*, pp. xxvii–xxviii, 176–8.

15. James Keill, *Anatomy of the Humane Body Abridg'd*, etc., 12th ed. (London, for John Clarke, 1759), p. 136; *Essays on Several Parts of the Animal Oeconomy* 4th ed. (London, for George Strahan, 1738), p. 167.

CHAPTER V

1. Stephen Hales, *Statical Essays: containing Haemastaticks*, etc. (London, for W. Innys and R. Manby, and T. Woodward, 1733). I have used the 1964 reprint edition, published, under the auspices of the Library of the New York Academy of Medicine, by Hafner Publishing Company, New York. My quotation from Hales is taken from the first sentence to his Preface of this work.

2. John G. McKendrick, 'On Physiological Discovery . . . Lecture I. The Circulation of the Blood: A Problem in Hydrodynamics', *British Medical Journal* 1 (1883), p. 654.

3. Archibald Pitcairne, *Philosophical and Mathematical Elements of Physick* [1st ed. 1718] (London, for W. Innys, T. Longman and T. Shewell, and Aaron Ward, 1745), p. 101.

4. For a general discussion of these iatro-physicists, see Robert E. Schofield, *Mechanism and Materialism*, Chapter 3. See also Theodore M. Brown, 'The Mechanical Philosophy and the "Animal Œconomy" – A Study in the Development of English Physiology in the Seventeenth and Early Eighteenth Century', unpublished Ph.D. Dissertation, Princeton University, Princeton, New Jersey, 1968 (University Microfilms 69–2727), which appeared after this chapter was written.

5. John Freind, *Emmenologia*, transl. Thomas Dale (London, for T. Cox, 1729), pp. 128–45, 160–7, 181–5, 199–204; first published in Latin in 1703. James Keill, *Essay*, pp. 42–9.

6. Percy M. Dawson, 'Stephen Hales, the Physiologist', *Bulletin of the Johns Hopkins Hospital* 15 (1904), p. 237.

7. Stephen Hales does not refer to the perfusate experiments of Freind and there is no need to suppose that he knew of Freind's *Emmenologia*, though he used Freind's Newtonian chemistry. Hales's experiments follow as naturally from his 'hydraulic' experiments as Freind's do from his mechanistic explanation of the menstrual cycle.

8. Hales's expectations of success may have been in reminiscence of his earliest reported physiological experiment, the successful casting, in lead, of the lungs and bronchi, see Chapter II, *supra* footnote 13.

9. See Schofield, *Mechanism and Materialism*, pp. 86, 143, 256.

CHAPTER VI

1. William Stukeley, *Family Memoirs*, I, p. 22.
2. S.P.C.K., Minute Books (Mss), Vol. 10, p. 42. 'A distinction was drawn between residing members, who living in or near London could be expected to attend meetings (Bishops with their town houses counted as such), and corresponding members who lived in the Country' (W. K. Lowther Clarke, *op. cit.*, p. 88). In December 1740 S.H. wrote to the Society 'Recommending Dr. Hartley Physician in Princes St. to be a Subscribery Member' (S.P.C.K., A.L.B., CR1/21, 15702. For David Hartley, F.R.S., 1705–57, see *D.N.B.* and Chapter VII below).
3. W. K. Lowther Clarke, *op. cit.*, pp. 88–9.
4. S.P.C.K., A.L.B., CR1/12, 7551, 7632; Lady Torrington was the widow of Lord Torrington, second son of the first Earl of Bradford. Mr Metcalfe was presumably the clergyman who contributed to Georgia through S.H. in 1736.
5. *Id.*, CR1/14, 9617; CR1/14, 10142; CR1/15, 10754. Luke Cotes was Dean of Middleham, 1719–41.
6. *Id.*, CR1/19, 13834; CR1/21, 16053. Presumably the Lady Blount who was visited by S.H. and Bishop Wilson's son on 18 Nov. 1735: when she showed them her 'well chosen study of pious books'. (See C. L. S. Linnell, ed., *The Diaries of Thomas Wilson D.D., 1731–37 and 1750: Son of Bishop Wilson of Sodor and Man*, London, 1964, p. 140.)
7. *Id.*, CR1/13, 8324, 8378, 16 June and 6 July 1725; the gifts totalled £50; *Id.*, CR1/15, 10356 (£20); CR1/19, 13760 (£10 10s).
8. *Id.*, CR1/12, 7191; the school had twenty-six pupils in 1726 (see M. Jones, *The Charity School Movement in the Eighteenth Century*, Cambridge, 1938, p. 368).
9. S.P.C.K., A.L.B., CR1/19, 14235, 17 Sept. 1737; CR1/20, 14672, 17 July 1738; CR1/21, 16002, 13 July 1741.
10. *Id.*, CR1/14, 9199, 21 March 1727–28 and M. Clement, ed., *Correspondence and Minutes of the S.P.C.K. Relating to Wales, 1699–1740* (Cardiff, 1952), pp. 138, 186, 289; Revd W. Watkins to William Stukeley, 18 Dec. 1755 (W. Stukeley, *op. cit.*, III, pp. 23–4).
11. S.P.C.K., A.L.B., CR1/11, 12133, 11 April 1733. S.P.C.K., Henry Newman's Salzburger Letter Books, printed G. F. Jones, *Henry Newman's Salzburger Letter Books* (Athens, Georgia, 1966), pp. 46–7.
12. Except in regard to areas outside North America and the West Indies. Hence we find S.H. sending funds to the Society for its 'East India Mission' (S.P.C.K., A.L.B., CR1/18, 26 Sept. 1734; W. Lowther Clarke, *op. cit.*, pp. 5–12, 59).
13. S.H. to the S.P.G., 23 April 1734 (S.P.G., Letter Book P.25/219); S.P.G.,

Journal of Minutes (Ms), Vol. 15, pp. 57–8. (The S.P.G. Mss are cited by kind permission of the Society.)

14. Central Council for the Care of Churches, *The Parochial Libraries of the Church of England* (London, 1959), p. 23, which speaks of the trust as a committee of the S.P.C.K. But see Henry Newman's letter of 1711 stating: 'The Design of the parochial libraries is not carried on by the Society . . . but by another body of men, most of whom are indeed of the Society, but are in this thing independently' (quoted L. W. Cowie, *op. cit.*, p. 53). In his will Bray bequeathed a box of books for a parochial library in 'a parish near Arundel in Sussex' which was to be 'of Lady Blount's or Mr. Stephen Hale's [*sic.*] nomination'. (*Parochial Libraries*, p. 64.)

15. H. P. Thompson, *Thomas Bray* (London, 1954), p. 98; J. W. Lydekker, *Thomas Bray 1658–1730; founder of Missionary enterprise* (Church Historical Society Publication No. 14, Philadelphia, 1943), pp. 12, 30. John, Lord Perceval (1683–1748), became Earl of Egmont in 1733. See Historical Manuscripts Commission, *Manuscripts of the Earl of Egmont; Diary of the First Earl of Egmont, Viscount Perceval*, 3 Vols. (London, 1920–23); (hereafter cited as *Egmont Diary*).

16. James Vernon (d. 1756), Member of the S.P.C.K., Commissioner of the Excise (1710) and Clerk to the Privy Council (1715). He was a close friend of Oglethorpe's. See *D.N.B.* under James Vernon (1646–1727).

17. Thomas Coram, 'Letters', printed *Mass. Hist. Soc. Proc.* LXI, pp. 20–1, and quoted H. P. Thompson, *op. cit.*, pp. 97–8. Coram was an ex-sea captain, philanthropist and founder of the Foundling Hospital. See *D.N.B.*

18. S.P.G., Bray Associates' Papers, Ms 'Assignment of Trustees of Mr. D'Allone's Bequest'; H. P. Thompson notes that 'the deed still remains in the keeping of the Associates and is, with Bray's will, their most cherished possession'. (H. P. Thompson, *op. cit.*, p. 99.) See also J. W. Lydekker, *op. cit.*, p. 32, and V. W. Crane, 'Dr. Thomas Bray and the Charitable Colony Project 1730', *William and Mary Quarterly*, 3rd series, Vol. 19, 1962, p. 53.

19. In his will, dated 15 Jan., Bray appointed 'William Belitha, Stephen Hales and Samuel Smith to be overseers . . . if Goditha Martin declines the burdensome duty'. He bequeathed to each of them 'a ring of one pound value'. (H. P. Thompson, *op. cit.*, p. 101.; S.P.G., Bray Associates' Papers, Original Will of the Revd Dr Thomas Bray.)

20. S.P.G., Bray Associates, Ms Minutes, *passim*. (Hereafter cited as Bray Minutes.)

21. J. W. Lydekker, *op. cit.*, p. 31; V. W. Crane, 'The Philanthropists and the Genesis of Georgia', *American Historical Review*, XXVII (1922), p. 64; *Egmont Diary*, I, pp. 44–6, 99; J. R. McCain, *Georgia as a proprietary province: the execution of a trust* (Boston, 1917), p. 23.

22. Bray Minutes, 30 Nov. and 2 Dec. 1730.

23. S.P.G., Bray Associates' Papers (Bray 9), Daniel Waterland to S.H., 5 Jan. 1730/31.

24. S.P.C.K., A.L.B., CR1/16, 11937.

25. Bray Minutes, 2 Nov. 1737; S.P.G., Bray Associates' Mss, American Papers, April 1735. He presented 250 copies on 4 Nov. 1734 (Bray Minutes).

26. Bray Minutes, 31 May 1733.

27. He agreed to preach at short notice. On 4 Feb. 1733/34 the Associates resolved to ask Dr Richard Bundy 'to preach the Anniversary sermon on 21st March'; on 4 March, however, the Minutes state, 'Captain Coram reported that Dr. Bundy was willing to preach the anniversary sermon in case Dr. Hales did not, but Dr. Hales had agreed to preach the same' (Bray Minutes). Lord Egmont noted in his diary for 4 March, 'We adjourned to the anniversary Meeting this month, when Mr. Hales promised to preach the sermon,' and for 21 'went to the anniversary Meeting of the Georgia Society to St. Bride's Church in Fleet St., where Mr. Hales, one of our Common Council, gave us an excellent sermon, Which we desired him to print'. (*Egmont Diary*, II, pp. 43, 66.)

28. S.H., *Sermon preached before the Trustees* . . . p. 11.

29. See E. L. Pennington, *op. cit.*, p. 348 et seq., citing M. W. Jernegan, 'Slavery and Conversion in the Colonies', *American Historical Review*, XXI (1916), pp. 504–27; *D.N.B.* article on S.H.; *Egmont Diary*, II, p. 66.

30. Bray Minutes, 3 Feb. 1734/35; *Egmont Diary*, II, pp. 146–7, 157, 170, 182; E. L. Pennington, *op. cit.*, pp. 325–6.

31. Bray Minutes, 3 March 1734/35; the '£100 from a gentlewoman Unknown to be applied to the support of a Missioner to the Indians' which Lord Egmont noted as being brought by Hales on 16 March 1736/37 (*Egmont Diary*, II, p. 370), was for the Georgia Trust.

32. E. L. Pennington, *op. cit.*, pp. 335–9; Bray Minutes, 16 March 1737–8, 6 June 1740, 19 March 1746/47. Garden should not be confused with the botanist mentioned in Chapter VIII.

33. E. L. Pennington, *op. cit.*, p. 328. Ottolenghi subsequently became head of the public filature at Savannah and corresponded with the Society of Arts over its premiums for American silk (see below Chapter VIII).

34. In the Charter, S.H. appears as 'our trusty and beloved . . . *Stephen Hales, Master of Arts*' (see A. D. Candler, *Colonial Records of the State of Georgia*, Vol. I, Atlanta, 1904, pp. 12–14; A. B. Saye, *Georgia's Charter of 1732*, Athens, Georgia, 1942, p. 21). For the powers of the Common Council and the Trustees in general, see J. R. McCain, *op. cit.*, pp. 102–4.

35. A. D. Candler, *op. cit.*, I, pp. 66–81, II, p. 4 (Lord Perceval noted S.H. as present at an unminuted meeting of the Trust held on 22 June 1732, when he found S.H. and others, 'busy setting down the names of the Aldermen of

London in order to apply to them for subscriptions to promote the colony', *Egmont Diary*, I, p. 282).

36. J. R. McCain, *op. cit.*, p. 40; *Egmont Diary*, II, p. 200; A. D. Candler, I, p. 82–6.

37. *Egmont Diary*, I, p. 342.

38. J. R. McCain, *op. cit.*, pp. 30, 110. S.H.'s attendances have been counted from the minute books.

39. *Egmont Diary*, II, pp. 472–3, 502, 511.

40. *Id.*, II, pp. 41, 230–4, 246, 373.

41. Obituary Notice reprinted in *G.M.*, LXIX, i (1799), p. 12; the notice continued 'he used to consider them only like those experiments which, upon trial, he found could never be applied to any useful purpose, and which he therefore calmly and dispassionately laid aside'.

42. A. D. Candler, *op. cit.*, I, pp. 222, 350–1, 394, 534–5; S.H.'s will, 30 Oct. 1759. For William Crowe, D.D. (d. 1743), see *D.N.B.*

43. A. D. Candler, *op. cit.*, III, p. 20, I, p. 312.

44. The demonstration took place on 17 April 1736. See S.H. *Treatise on Ventilators* (London, 1758), pp. 283–9.

CHAPTER VII

1. S.H. to John Mickleburgh, 17 May 1733, library, Trinity College, Cambridge, R.4.42f29. The correspondence with Mickleburgh began in connection with the pneumatic experiments of the *Vegetable Staticks*. For the influence of Hales on Mickleburgh, third professor of chemistry at Cambridge, see Chapter X.

2. *Vegetable Staticks*, p. 118; *Phil. Trans.* 35 (1727–28), pp. 559–62, plate; *Haemastaticks*, pp. 332–46.

3. Hales, 'A Description of a Sea Gage', *G.M.* XXIV (1754), pp. 215–19; 'An Account of the bucket Sea-gage to find the different Degrees of coolness and saltness of the Sea', *Phil. Trans.* 47 (1751–52), pp. 214–16. The bucket-gauge was a simple weighted bucket with valved cover and base permitting free flow of sea-water in descent, but closing as the bucket was raised. Ellis appears to have tested this device successfully.

4. Hales, 'A Method of conveying . . .', *Phil. Trans.* 43 (1744–45), pp. 20–1; Christopher Warwick, 'An Improvement . . .', *Phil. Trans.* 43 (1744–45), pp. 12–19; 'A Letter containing further accounts of the Success of injecting medicated Liquors into the Abdomen . . .', *Phil. Trans.* 43 (1744–45), pp. 47–8; and 'A Further Account of the Success of some Experiments of injecting Claret, &c. into the Abdomen, after Tapping', *Phil. Trans.* 49 (1755–56),pp. 485–9. (These last two, which incidentally refer to S.H., appear under the

158

names of Warren and Warrick respectively, but are clearly by the same man as the Warwick of the first.) S.H., *Haemastaticks*, pp. 163–4.

5. See, for example, W. E. H. Lecky, *History of England in the Eighteenth Century*, Vol. 1 (New York, D. Appleton and Company, 1878), pp. 518–22; Dorothy Marshall, *Eighteenth Century England* (New York, David McKay Company, Inc., 1962), pp. 159, 224–5.

6. See, for example, Joseph Blomfield, *St George's, 1733–1933* (London, The Medici Society, 1933), p. 26 for a reference to its distribution in hospitals. We are indebted to Dr George Edwards, Beaconsfield, Bucks, for this reference.

7. [Thomas Wilson], *Distilled Spirituous Liquors*, etc. 2nd ed., (London, J. Roberts, 1736), p. iv. C. L. S. Linnell, ed., *The Diaries of Thomas Wilson, D.D. 1731–37 and 1750; Son of Bishop Wilson of Sodor & Man* (London, S.P.C.K., 1969) makes clear that this pamphlet is by Wilson and not, as has sometimes been thought, by S.H.

8. 'Some Observations of the very Ingenious Dr. Hales, in his Treatise of Ventilators', *Gentleman's Magazine* XIII (1743), pp. 432–3; Hales, 'Some Considerations on the Causes of Earthquakes, etc.', *Phil. Trans.* 46 (1705), appendix, pp. 669–83, espec. p. 671; and Henry, *A New Year's Gift to Dram-Drinkers* (Dublin, 1762), preface.

9. S.H. to Bishop Hildesley, 16 May 1758, *Gentleman's Magazine* LIV (1794), pp. 689–91.

10. Hales, *A Friendly Admonition to the Drinkers of Brandy, and other Distilled Spirituous Liquors*, 2nd ed. (London, for Joseph Downing, 1734), 24 pp.

11. Herman Boerhaave, *A New Method of Chemistry*, transl. P. Shaw and E. Chambers, Vol. 2 (London, J. Osborn and T. Longman, 1727), pp. 210–16; S.H., *Haemastaticks*, p. 128.

12. Hales, *Friendly Admonition*, pp. 3–4, 6, 15–16; *Haemastaticks*, pp. 113, 128–9, 137. See also James Jurin, 'An Account of some Experiments relating to the Specific Gravity of Human Blood', *Phil. Trans.* 30 (1717–19), pp. 1000–14, for the effect of stagnation on the blood, and John Huxham, 'A Letter . . . Concerning Polypi taken out of the Hearts of several Sailors . . .', *Phil. Trans.* 42 (1742–43), pp. 123–6, for the origin of polypuses from stagnant blood, in persons with a history of long, continued consumption of distilled spirits.

13. Hales, *A Description of Ventilators . . .* (London, W. Innys, R. Manby and T. Woodward, 1743). The title is typically eighteenth century in length and continues with references to the usefulness of ventilators in preservation of grain and other goods and drying of substances such as corn, meal, hops and gun-powder. The pamphlet is roughly 200 pages long with two handsome folding plates.

14. Hales, *Treatise on Ventilators* (London, R. Manby, 1758). His articles in the *Gentleman's Magazine* and *Phil. Trans.* will be cited as appropriate; they are all listed in the bibliographical appendix.

15. See appended list of Hales's correspondence; also Eric Robinson, 'The Profession of Civil Engineer in the Eighteenth Century: A Portrait of Thomas Yeoman, F.R.S., 1704(?)–81', *Annals of Science* 18 (1962, publ. 1964), pp. 195–215.

16. Hales, 'A Method to keep corn sweet in sacks', 'Preserving of quantities of corn, &c. in graineries' and 'An Account of several methods to preserve Corn well by Ventilators', *Gentleman's Magazine* XV (1745), pp. 354–5, 640; 16 (1746), pp. 315–18 respectively. S. T. McCloy, *French Inventions of the Eighteenth Century* (Louisville, Univ. of Kentucky Press, 1952), pp. 120–1; and Abraham Rees, *Cyclopaedia* of 1819, articles: 'Granary', 'Gunpowder' and 'Ventilators', with a picture in the 'Pneumatics', plate xvii, on which see Robinson, 'Yeoman', *op. cit.*, p. 197n, 208.

17. The record of S.H.'s successes and failures in getting ventilators used on ships can be gleaned from his various published writings on the subject – the pamphlets, letters and notices in the *Gentleman's Magazine*, etc. – and from Admiralty Records. C.K., *Stephen Hales*, pp. 151–69 has, however, treated this subject so exhaustively that further investigation seems unnecessary for present purposes.

18. Hales, 'Some Considerations about means to draw the foul Air out of the sick Rooms of occasional Army-Hospitals, in private Houses in Towns', *Gentleman's Magazine* XXIII (1753), p. 173.

19. See previous chapter and Chapter I.

20. W. Haley, 'Extract from the Ode to John Howard . . .', *Annual Register* 23 (1780), pp. 206–7. There is a note appended to the extract presuming to explain the origin of the ventilator in an accidental placing of boards in Hales's barn. The story is improbable and, besides, is irrelevant to the more general consideration of explaining the impulse for use of ventilation. William Hayley's 'Ode Inscribed to John Howard, Esq., F.R.S.', was reprinted in his *Poems and Plays*, Vol. I (London, T. Cadell, 1785), pp. 123–37.

21. Again information about ventilator installation in hospitals and prisons may be extracted from S.H.'s publications and correspondence but is summarized by C.K., pp. 159, 168, 189–207, 232–3.

22. Desaguliers, 'An Account of an Instrument . . .', *Phil. Trans.* 39 (1735–36), pp. 41–3; this and two subsequent articles, to p. 49, also by Desaguliers, describe the machine (a turbine-type blower or fan), calculate the velocity of air moved by it, and discuss its usefulness.

23. Sutton obtained a patent for his ventilator, No. 602, 16 March 1744 and published *An Historical Account of a New Method for Extracting the Foul Air out of Ships, &c.*, reprinting the supporting accounts of Mead and Watson, in 1759. The *Historical Account* was republished by George Eyre and William Spotteswoode, London, 1858, which is the form in which we have seen it.

24. For the quotations from Sutton, Watson and Mead see Sutton, *An Historical Account*, pp. 164, 173 and 171 respectively.

25. Hales, *Description*, p. 44; bracketed numbers in following quotations are page references to the same work. One might note that Mead does not refer to S.H. in this connection.

26. Benjamin Hoadly, *Three Lectures* ... (London, W. Wilkins and J. Roberts, 1740). Hoadly adds a few of his own confirming experiments and may, perhaps, elaborate more of an anatomical or physiological interpretation than is to be found in his source, but everything so clearly depends initially on Hales that I shall treat the references to these lectures in the *Description* as S.H.'s own work, though it comes, second-hand, *via* Hoadly.

27. Hales, 'Account of some Trials . . .', and 'Account of the great Benefit . . .', *Phil. Trans.* 49 (1755), pp. 339–47, 312–32, respectively; *Account of a Useful Discovery* ... (London, R. Manby, 1756). These papers were, as usual, extracted in the *Gentleman's Magazine* XXVI (1756), pp. 78–9, 130–1.

28. Hales, *Useful Discovery*, p. 22; the quotation about moving air carrying vapour is from p. 10.

29. Careful inspection of his reports reveals, in almost every instance, an associated activity of cleaning and fumigation to which the reported successes can be ascribed. *The Description of the Ventilator* recommends fumigating with burning brimstone, in such quantity as to destroy 'Rats, bugs and other Insects', as well as washing the decks and sprinkling with vinegar [45, 51], while the 'Account of the good Effects of Ventilators, in Newgate and the Savoy Prison', *Gentleman's Magazine* XXIII (1753), pp. 70–1, which reports a drop in deaths to less than one-quarter pre-ventilator figures, also notes that the prison-masters now keep the prisons clean and fumigate with burning brimstone every six weeks.

30. See, for example, S.H., 'A description of a Back-Heaver, which will winnow and clean corn, both much sooner and better, than by the common methods of doing it', and 'A Description of a very great Improvement which is made to the Back-Heaver', etc., *Gentleman's Magazine* XV (1745), pp. 353–4; XVII (1745), pp. 310–12, respectively; 'Rational and easy methods to purify the Air and regulate its heat in Melon-Frames and hot Green-houses', *Gentleman's Magazine* XXVII (1757), pp. 165–6 (reprinted in Benjamin Martin's *General Magazine of Arts and Sciences* 6 (1757), p. 524); and 'A Proposal for Checking in some Degree the Progress of Fires', *Phil. Trans.* 45 (1748), pp. 277–80 (abstracted, *Gentleman's Magazine* XIX (1749), p. 554).

31. See Hales, *Philosophical Experiments: containing useful, and necessary Instructions for such as under-take long Voyages at Sea*, etc. (London, W. Innys and R. Manby, 1739), and 'An Account of some Trials to keep Water and Fish sweet, with Lime-water', *Phil. Trans.* 48 (1754), pp. 826–31 (reprinted in *Gentleman's Magazine* XXV [1755], pp. 310–21). This latter paper is notable

for its report of correspondence with the chemist, Charles Alston of Edinburgh, working with the same materials on the same problem.

32. Given the discomfort and danger of both the ailment and its cure, and the political and economic importance of some of the more prominent sufferers – including Robert Walpole and Benjamin Franklin – one might argue that the stone had considerable social significance.

33. A letter from S.H. to John Ellis, 7 January 1754, Linnean Society, London, Linnean Correspondence, Vol. XVII, mentions that he is suffering a 'gravelly' disorder, but this may have been an ailment of his old age.

34. There are references to the problem in the *Vegetable Staticks* and in a letter, S.H. to Hans Sloane, 4 January 1727, B.M. Sloane Mss 4049, while a letter, Hales to Charles Alston, 4 May 1756, Edinburgh University Library, La. III 375/41 expresses an interest in the latter's calculi experiments at that date.

35. By André Cournand, in his introduction to the reprint of the *Haemastaticks*, p. xii. C.K., p. 114, is scarcely less critical in his description of the work on the stone reported in the *Haemastaticks* as 'a hundred worthless pages'. Arthur J. Viseltear, 'Joanna Stephens and the Eighteenth Century Lithontriptics; a misplaced chapter in the History of Therapeutics', *Bulletin of the History of Medicine* 42 (1968), pp. 199–222, provides a recent, more balanced, appraisal of both Mrs Stephens's and S.H.'s work.

36. The basis for the award of S.H.'s Copley Medal is not recorded among the papers of the Royal Society, but is credited on the claims of Peter Collinson, 'Account of the Life of . . . Stephen Hales', *op. cit.*, S.H.'s friend and a contemporary fellow of the Society. Viseltear, *op. cit.*, note 11, lists the 29 trustees, including 10 who might reasonably be supposed to have medical knowledge of the problem.

37. Hales, 'An Account', *Haemastaticks*, pp. 187–252, espec. pp. 189–90.

38. *Phil. Trans.* 43 (1744–45), pp. 502–5.

39. E.g., a letter, 8 Oct. 1729, S.H. to Mickleburgh, Trinity College Library, R.4.42ff 25–30, asks if Mickleburgh has done the experiments on incrustations requested of him, and reports that similar experiments are being performed at Paris and in Holland.

40. Hales, *Philosophical Experiments*, etc. (London, W. Innys and R. Manby, 1739). S.H. to Nesbitt, 11 Sept. 1735, Hunter-Baillie Collection, Roy. Coll. of Surgeons, London (printed in *Post-Graduate Medical Journal* 22 (1946), p. 121) and S.H. to Hans Sloane, 5 Feb. 1738, B.M., Sloane Mss, 4056.

41. Hales, 'Examination . . .', *Phil. Trans.* 46 (1750), pp. 446–51; significantly, the title of the manuscript, preserved among the Letters and Papers, Decade II, 137, Library of the Royal Society, is 'Of the residues from Purging Waters'. Hales's analysis of Malvern water, on the other hand, found no residue, though possibly a 'subtle, volatile sulphur' vapour or oil rose from the liquid near dryness, and its medical virtue was attributed to its singular

purity – see J. Wall, 'An Essay on the Waters of the Holy Well at Malvern, Worcestershire', *Phil. Trans.* 49 (1756), pp. 459–68, espec. pp. 460–3.

42. Hales, 'Some Remarks . . .', *Gentleman's Magazine* XVI (1746), p. 520, reporting his failure to observe any dissolving power and his identification of the residue, after evaporation, to be lime and a small quantity of soap lye. Identification of Hales as the 'celebrated chemist' whose analysis of Glastonbury water, etc. was reported in the *Public Advertiser*, is that of Mark Hildesley, see C.K., pp. 216–17.

43. Hales, *Account of some Experiments*, etc., 2nd ed. (London, 1747). See T. E. Jessop, ed., *The Works of George Berkeley, Bishop of Cloyne*, Vol. 5 (London, Thomas Nelson and Sons Ltd., 1953), pp. vii–viii, 203–4 for further discussion of Hales and the Bishop on tar-water.

44. S.H.'s correspondence with Thomas Yeoman and Edward Cave during 1745 and 1746 (contemporary copies, Library, Roy. Coll. of Physicians, London) repeatedly asserts the usefulness of tar-water as a medicine and Cave apparently contemplated publication of an abridgement of S.H.'s treatise on the subject.

45. Stephen Hales, *An Account of some Experiments and Observations on Mrs. Stephens's Medicines for dissolving the Stone: wherein Their Dissolving Power is inquired into, and shown,* etc. (London, for T. Woodward, [1741]), pp. 1, 33.

46. See Chapter IV *supra*, p. 33.

47. Viseltear, *op. cit.*, p. 220. See also, e.g.: George Pearson, 'Experiments and Observations tending to show the composition and properties of Urinary Concretions', *Phil. Trans.* 88 (1798), pp. 15–46; William Brande, 'A Letter on the Differences in the Structure of Calculi . . .' and Everard Home, 'Some Observations on Mr. Brande's Paper . . .', *Phil. Trans.* 98 (1808), pp. 223–43, 244–8; Alexander Marcet, *An Essay on the Chemical History and Medical Treatment of Calculus Disorders*, 2nd ed. rev. (London, Longman, Hurst, Rees, Orme and Brown, 1819); S. Elliott Hoskins, 'Researches on the Decomposition and Disintegration of Phosphatic Vesical Calculi . . .', *Phil. Trans.* 133 (1843), pp. 7–16; and finally Henry Bence Jones, long-time secretary of the Royal Institution, conducted experiments on the subject and reported on them periodically at least between his book, *Gravel, Calculus, and Gout: the Application of Liebig's Physiology to these Diseases* (London, 1842) and his paper, 'On the Dissolution of Urinary Calculi in dilute Saline Fluids . . . by the aid of Electricity', *Phil. Trans.* 143 (1853), pp. 201–16.

48. The University Library, Edinburgh, contains six letters from S.H. to Alston (La III 375/36–41) many of which discuss lime-water, some mentioning the stone, and one, of 4 May 1756, referring to Black's essay on Magnesia Alba.

49. During the course of his investigations described in the *Haemastaticks*, S.H. also invented an instrument for physical removal of the stone without surgery

which proved sufficiently effective to be employed by many contemporary surgeons and seems to have been an early approach toward a lithontriptor. Consisting of a spring forceps within a catheter, the instrument was passed into the urethra until the stone was reached. The catheter was then withdrawn just far enough to release the jaws of the forceps and allow them to embrace the stone, and then slipped forward again, fixing the stone securely within the forceps. The instrument and stone were then withdrawn together.

CHAPTER VIII

1. The account which follows of S.H.'s association with the Society of Arts is a revised version of that already published in the *Journal of the Royal Society of Arts*, Vols. CX (1962), p. 855, CXI (1963), p. 53 and the *Middlesex Local History Council Bulletin*, No. 14 (1962), p. 17. Mortimer's book is entitled *A concise Account of the Rise, Progress, and Present State of the Society for the Encouragement of Arts, Manufacturers and Commerce, Instituted at London, Anno. MDCCLIV. Compiled from the Original Papers of the first Promoters of the plan; and from other authentic records. By a Member of the Said Society* (London, 1763). A copy in the Society's possession bears his signature on the title page. In the introduction (p. iv) he states that the 'substance' of his narrative was based on a Ms by James Theobald, deposited in the Society of Antiquaries; unfortunately this is no longer to be found (see Joan Evans, *A History of the Society of Antiquaries*, London, 1956, pp. 123–5).

2. D. G. C. Allan, *William Shipley; Founder of the Royal Society of Arts* (London, 1968; revised edition London, 1980), p. 49; Thomas Mortimer, *op. cit.*, pp. 5–8.

3. S.H. admired and possibly corresponded with Thomas Prior in the 1740s. (See letter from Bishop Berkeley to Thomas Prior, 19 Feb. 1746/47, printed A. A. Luce and T. E. Jessup, eds., *The Works of George Berkeley, Bishop of Cloyne*, Vol. VIII, London, 1956, p. 293.) Prior was Secretary of the Dublin Society from 1731–51. (See H. F. Berry, *A History of the Royal Dublin Society*, London, 1915, p. 9.)

4. E. Robinson, 'The Profession of Civil Engineer in the Eighteenth Century: a portrait of Thomas Yeoman, F.R.S., 1704(?)–1781', *Annals of Science*, XVIII, 4 (1962), p. 202; S.H. to Thomas Yeoman, 10 April 1744 (Royal College of Physicians, Ms Transcript, cited by kind permission of the College).

5. W. Shipley to H. Baker, 8 July 1751, Manchester, John Rylands Library, English Mss, 19, IV, 339, printed D. G. C. Allan, *William Shipley*, p. 180.

6. D. G. C. Allan, *William Shipley*, pp. 180–3.

7. Thomas Mortimer, *op. cit.*, p. 8.

8. *Egmont Diary*, Vol. II, p. 463. Thomas Mortimer, *op. cit.*, pp. 8–9, 18–21.
9. *G.M.*, Vol. XVII (1747), p. 270; R.S.A., Dr. Templeman's Transactions, Vol. I, p. 166. This is the opening of the Ms 'Historical Register' of the Society which supplements Mortimer, p. 21. (The R.S.A. Mss are cited by kind permission of the Society.)
10. See letter from Henry Baker to his Norfolk correspondent William Arderon, 16 Aug. 1754, mentioning that 'the Lords Folkestone, Romney . . . the Bishop of Worcestor, Dr. Hales, etc., are at the Head of' the new Society of Arts. (Victoria and Albert Museum, Forster Collection, Baker-Arderon Correspondence, III, p. 151.)
11. Henry Baker's constitution or 'Plan', which was adopted by the Society on 18 Feb. 1755, provided for the election of these officers (see D. G. C. Allan, *op. cit.*, pp. 192–3). S.H. sent 'several' copies of the 'Plan' to Dr Alexander Garden in America with a letter telling him of his (Garden's) election as a Corresponding Member of the Society. Garden was elected on 19 March 1755 (see Alexander Garden to Cadwallader Colden, 27 Oct. 1755, printed in New York Historical Society Collections, *Letters and Papers of Cadwallader Colden*, Vol. V, New York, 1919, pp. 32–3). On 22 Feb. 1758, S.H. proposed the Revd Dr John Thomas, a chaplain to the King, Prebendary of Westminster and future Bishop of Rochester. Thomas was elected on 8 March 1758 and remained a Member of the Society down to his death in 1793 (see *D.N.B.* and R.S.A., Ms. Subscription Book, 1754–63). He had become a perpetual subscriber in 1763. S.H. paid his own subscription on an annual basis. The Subscription book records payments by him on 12 March 1755, 3 March 1756, 31 January 1757, 27 Jan. 1758, 31 March 1759 and 29 Feb. 1760.
12. R.S.A., Society Minutes, 22 March 1754, *Id.*, 29 March 1754. The Minutes describe the abstracts as 'one from Mons. Geofery's treatise on Fossils, in which Cobalt is described and the places mentioned where it is found: the other from Mr. Miller's Dictionary when he mentions the cultivation of Madder.'
13. F. W. Gibbs, 'William Lewis, M.D., F.R.S., 1708–1781', *Annals of Science*, VIII, No. 2, pp. 122–48. 'Peter Shaw and the Revival of Chemistry', *Annals of Science*, VII, No. 3 (1951), pp. 211–37; R.S.A., Soc. Min., 12 and 19 March, 9 April 1755; R.S.A. G.B., III, 13.
14. S.H. to the Society, 'A Proposal for publishing a Book on Silk Worms', 8 April 1755, R.S.A., G.B., I, 16; R.S.A., Soc. Min., 24 April 1754; S.H. to John Ellis, 16 Sept. 1752 (Linnean Society, Linnean Correspondence, Vol. XVII, printed, Sir J. E. Smith, *op. cit.*, II, p. 29). Pullein, a graduate of Trinity College, Dublin (see *D.N.B.*), had published *Some Hints Intended to Promote the Culture of Silk-Worms in Ireland. Addressed to the Dublin Society* (Dublin, 1750). The young Prince of Wales also took an interest in the matter.

(See S. Pullein, *The Culture of Silk: or an Essay on its rational practice and improvement . . . for the Use of the American Colonies*, London, 1758; Dedication to His Royal Highness the Prince of Wales.)

15. S.H. to John Ellis, *c.* 1757 (Linnean Correspondence, Vol. XVII, printed Sir J. E. Smith, *op. cit.*, Vol. II, p. 37); (Premium List of the Society of Arts, *To the Publick*, 9 April 1755).

16. *Phil. Trans.*, XLIX (1756), p. 313. Dr Linden to S.H., 25 Feb. 1756. (R.S.A., G.B., I., 107.)

17. Revd William Henry to S.H. from Dublin, 13 June 1756; S.H. to the Society (on preserving casks of food on long sea voyages), 16 June 1756 (R.S.A., G.B., I, 121, 114); R.S.A., Soc. Min., 18 and 30 June 1756. See also S.H. to David Hartley, 13 July 1756 saying 'I received lately a letter from the Revd. Dr. Henry of Dublin, giving an Account of the great improvements in that Country from the encouragements of their premium Society; which letter I sent to our Premium Society' (Berkshire County Record Office, Reading, Berks., D/E HY F79); R.S.A., Soc. Min., 18 Aug. and 1 Sept. 1756; A. Macpherson to S.H. 3 Aug. 1756 (R.S.A., G.B., I, 127); Admiral Edward Boscawen (1711–61) was then engaged in the naval operations against France (see *D.N.B.*); S.H. to Lord Folkestone, 2 March 1756 (R.S.A., G.B. III, 51); R.S.A., Soc. Min., 3 and 17 Nov. 1756, Dr Templeman's Transactions, II, p. 282.

18. R.S.A., G.B., III, 39. (This is a contemporary copy of a letter from S.H. to James Stonhouse written in response to Stonhouse's 'Expedients for alleviating the Distress occasioned by the present dearness of Corn', *G.M.*, Vol. XXVIII (1758), pp. 17–20. For the controversy over bread adulteration 1756–58, see F. A. Filby, *A History of Food Adulteration and Analysis*, London, 1934, pp. 79–89); R.S.A., Soc. Min., 18 May 1757, 11 Jan. and 1 Nov. 1758; Loose Archives E1/23, 12 Dec. 1757. (On 15 April 1759 S.H. attended a committee meeting called to examine some English mill stones. This is the only time his name occurs in the Minutes of the Society's committees.)

19. F. W. Gibbs, 'William Lewis, M.B., F.R.S. (1708–1781)', *Annals of Science*, Vol. VIII, No. 2 (1952), pp. 139–40; W. Lewis, *Commercium Philosophico-Technicum* (London, 1763), p. 360; S.H. to the Society 19 Feb. 1760 (R.S.A., G.B., IV, 111).

20. S.H., *A Treatise on Ventilators* (London, 1758), p. 96; S.H. to the Society of Arts, read 20 Feb. 1760 (R.S.A., G.B., II, 20, entitled 'A Proposal for refreshing the Premium Society's large Meeting Room'). Pinchbeck was the second son of Christopher Pinchbeck, inventor of the copper and zinc alloy called after his name (see *D.N.B.*). From July 1759 the Society had been in occupation of the premises opposite Beaufort Buildings in the Strand which included a Meeting Room, eighty feet by forty feet, decorated by William Chambers. The premises were vacated by the Society in 1774 and subse-

quently demolished (see D. G. C. Allan, *The Houses of the Royal Society of Arts*, 2nd ed., London, 1974, pp. 3–6).

21. R.S.A., Soc. Min., 16 July and 1 October 1760, 26 Aug. 1761; Min. Comm. (Miscellaneous), 13 and 19 Aug., 6, 9 and 24 Sept. 1760; R.S.A. Soc. Min., 30 Nov. 1768; William Bailey, *The Advancement of Arts, Manufactures and Commerce* (London, 1772), pp. 289–91 and plate of S.H.'s ventilators; J. Barry, *An Account of a Series of Pictures in the Great Room of the Society of Arts* (London, 1783), p. 77. In this passage Barry wrote of S.H. as 'not less eminent for his piety and virtue, than for his ingenuity and great philosophical acquisitions'. James Barry (1741–1806), the celebrated Irish history painter, began his paintings for the Society's Meeting Room in 1777. The Society had moved into its present house in the Adelphi in 1774 (see D. G. C. Allan, *The Houses of the Royal Society of Arts*, pp. 13, 17).

CHAPTER IX

1. 'He possessed a native innocence and simplicity of manners, which the characters of other men, and the customs of the world could never alter'. Obituary in *Annual Register*, Vol. IV (1761), p. 46.

2. 'The University of Oxford in their late Public Act Complimented Dr. Hales with his degree of Doctor of Divinity while he was on his living in Hampshire not expecting any such honour.' Henry Newman to Jean Vat, 18 Sept. 1733 (printed G. F. Jones, *op. cit.*, p. 57). The degree was conferred on 5 July 1733. For the text of the diploma see R. Masters, *op. cit.*, Appendix LXXIV and C.K., pp. 117–18; T. Birch, 'Memoirs of the Life of Stephen Hales', *c.* 1761, B.M., Birch Mss 4222, ff. 167–8.

3. Royal Archives, Windsor Castle, Establishment Books 21–7. (Reference supplied through the courtesy of the Librarian of Windsor Castle); T. Birch, *op. cit.*, ff. 167–8.

4. The Revd Cecil Wray Goodchild was appointed to assist S.H. at Teddington *c.* 1753 (Teddington Vestry Minutes, 8 April 1753, note his presence and curacy). He was the son of John Goodchild, the Teddington linen draper and wax chandler, who became with S.H. a founder member of the Society of Arts. C. W. Goodchild served as curate at Teddington until March 1760 when the Revd William Johnson, husband of S.H.'s niece and former housekeeper, Sarah Margaretta, came to assist in the parish (Teddington Parish Register, from 30 March 1760); S.H.'s wife was the heiress of the Revd Dr Richard Newce, Rector of Hailsham, Sussex, and a member of a long established land owning family at Much Hadham, Hertfordshire. Under her will, proved 8 Nov. 1721, S.H. inherited the estate intended for the issue of their

167

marriage, of which there was none. Mary Hales also bequeathed £200 to the S.P.G. and £750 to other charities (Will of Mary Hales, 20 Sept. 1720). S.H. appears to have visited Much Hadham with some regularity, c. 1729–33. (See his statements, 'I have been this week at Hadham', letter to John Mickleburgh, 21 June 1729, Trinity College Mss R.4.42, f. 25, 'I have appointed to go to Hadham next Monday as I usually do the week after Whitsun week', letter to same 17 May 1733, Id., f. 29.); S.H.'s will, 30 Oct. 1759 (printed C.K., pp. 240–2).

5. S.H. to James Stonhouse, c. Nov. 1757 (R.S.A., G.B., III, 39, 'Copy of a letter from the Rev'd. Dr. Hales to Dr. Stonhouse'). This letter was a comment on Stonhouse's 'Expedients for alleviating the Distress occasioned by the present dearness of Corn' (see G.M. XXVIII, 1758, pp. 17–20).

6. S.H. to Mark Hildesley, 16 May 1758 (B.M. Add. Mss 19, 683, f. 61); E. Pyle to S. Kerrick, 1 Nov. 1758 (printed in A. Hartshorne, Memoirs of a Royal Chaplain, London, 1905, p. 313 and quoted C.K., p. 226. C.K. is possibly mistaken in thinking the palace whose housekeeper blessed Hales for his invention was Leicester House, more likely it was the residence of the Bishop of Winchester where Pyle lived from 1752–61); Transactions of the Norfolk and Norwich Naturalists Society, loc. cit.; S.H., Vegetable Staticks, p. 116; S.H. to John Ellis, 21 Nov. 1758, Linnean Society, Linnean Correspondence, Vol. XVII, printed Sir J. E. Smith, A Selection of the Correspondence of Linnaeus and other Naturalists, Vol. II (London, 1821), p. 42; S.H., Treatise on Ventilators, pp. 315–17.

7. T. Jackson, ed., The Journal of the Rev. Charles Wesley, Vol. I, p. 56. Wesley afterwards went to stay with S.H. at Teddington, 25—26 Jan. 1736/37, and they 'took a walk to see Mr. Pope's house and gardens'. (T. Jackson, op. cit., pp. 66–7); M. Nicolson and G. S. Rousseau, op. cit., pp. 108–9, wrote: 'Curiously enough, there is no reference to Stephen Hales in Pope's extant Correspondence, although he must often have seen him during the quarter-century they were neighbours. He referred to Hales twice in poetry, the first time by indirection in the Epistle to Cobham, written in 1733, the year of Hales's Haemastaticks . . .' His climactic couplet is an analogy between the moral and scientific worlds, based on his neighbour's experiments: "Like following life thro' creatures you dissect, You lose it in the moment you detect" (ll. 31–40). Pope's other poetic reference to Hales in the Epistle to a Lady was not to the scientist, but to the Curate of Teddington, the neighbour he knew so well that he was one of the two witnesses to Pope's will'.

8. A. Pope, Of the Characters of Women (London, 1734–5), C. C. 193–9. Catherine Hyde, Duchess of Queensberry (1700–77), was said to be one of the most beautiful women of her time; Mah'met was the king's faithful Turkish slave. (See E. Solly, 'Dr. Stephen Hales, not Hale', Notes and Queries, 6th Series, VII 1, 1883, pp. 352–3.)

9. John Burton, *Opuscula Miscellanea Metrico-Prosaica* (1771), p. 55; Notes by J. E. Harting to the edition of the White/Marsham correspondence printed in *Transactions of the Norfolk and Norwich Naturalists Society*; Gilbert White to Robert Marsham, 25 Feb. 1791. (*Transactions of the Norfolk and Norwich Naturalists Society*, Vol. II, 1875, pp. 152–4.)

10. W. S. Lewis, ed., *The Yale Edition of Horace Walpole's Correspondence*, Vol. 20 (London, 1960), pp. 346–7; A. Edwards, *Frederick Louis, Prince of Wales 1707–1751* (London, 1947), esp. Chapter IX, 'Frederick and the Arts'; T. Birch, *op. cit.*, ff. 167–8.

11. C. L. S. Linnell, *The Diaries of Thomas Wilson D.D. 1731–37 and 1750, Son of Bishop Wilson of Sodor and Man* (London, 1964), pp. 105, 118, 140.

12. *Egmont Diary*, II, pp. 479, 247; T. Jackson, *op. cit.*, p. 67; W. Stukeley, *Family Memoirs*, I, p. 76; J. Carswell and L. A. Dralle, eds., *The Political Journal of George Bubb Dodington* (Oxford, 1965), p. 54. Dodington had been appointed Treasurer to the Prince in 1749 and anticipated high office at his succession.

13. P. C. Yorke, ed., *The Diary of John Baker, Barrister of the Middle Temple, Solicitor-General of the Leeward Islands* (London, 1931), Aug. 1758, 10 and 16 Jan., 10 March, 11 June 1759, pp. 112, 119, 121, 124; T. Jackson, *op. cit.*, p. 56; J. M. Osborn, ed., *Joseph Spence: Observations, anecdotes . . .*, Vol. I, p. 401.

14. Gilbert White to Robert Marsham, 25 Feb. 1791 (*Transactions of the Norfolk and Norwich Naturalists Society, loc. cit.*); for S.H.'s antiquarian and historical interests see his transcripts from the Church Warden's Account Book at Farringdon (mentioned in Chapter Three, above) and a letter to William Stukeley asking for information about the inscription on a cup found at Littlecott (S.H. to William Stukeley, 15 May 1726, printed J. Nichols, *Illustrations of the Literary History of the Eighteenth Century, Vol. III*, London, 1817, p. 799). In view of S.H.'s friendship with Stukeley, it might be expected that his interest in these matters would have been more pronounced than this rather meagre evidence suggests and it is perhaps significant that unlike Stukeley or such other friends as Henry Baker, Thomas Birch, Peter Collinson and David Hartley he never joined the Society of Antiquaries or, as far as its records show, communicated to its proceedings; S.H. to John Ellis, 22 Aug. 1755 (Linnean Society, Linnean Correspondence, Vol. XVII; printed Sir J. E. Smith, *A Selection of the Correspondence of Linnaeus and other Naturalists*, Vol. II, p. 32).

15. E. S. Wortley, ed., *A Prime Minister and his son, from the correspondence of the 3rd Earl of Bute and Lt. General the Hon. Sir Charles Stuart, K.B.* (London, 1925), pp. 17–21; letter from the Earl of Buckingham to Lady Suffolk, 18 Nov. 1763 (printed in J. W. Croker, ed., *Letters to and from Henrietta, Countess of Suffolk, and her second husband, the Hon. George Berkeley, from 1712 to 1767*, Vol. II,

London, 1824, pp. 282–3); the Princess had living in 1751 the following children: (i) George William Frederick, Prince of Wales, b. 1738, ascended the throne as King George III on his grandfather's death in 1760, d. 1820; (ii) Edward Augustus, Duke of York, b. 1739, d. 1767; (iii) William Henry, Duke of Gloucester, b. 1743, d. 1805; (iv) Prince Henry Frederick, afterwards Duke of Cumberland, b. 1745, d. 1808; (v) Prince Frederick William, b. 1750, d. 1765; (vi) Princess Augusta, afterwards Princess of Brunswick-Wolfenbattel, b. 1737, d. 1813; (vii) Princess Elizabeth Caroline, b. 1740, d. 1759; (viii) Princess Louisa Ann, b. 1749, d. 1768; (ix) Princess Caroline Matilda, afterwards Queen of Denmark, b. 1751, d. 1775; R. Sedgwick; *Letters from George III to Lord Bute* (London, 1939), p. xxi; *Vegetable Staticks* (1727) had been dedicated to George II as Prince of Wales and *Haematicks* (1733) to 'The King's Most Excellent Majesty'.

16. R. Sedgwick, *op. cit.*, pp. xxi–xxii, citing Lord Waldegrave's *Memoirs*, p. 29. For Thomas Hayter (1702–62) and George Lewis Scott (1708–80) see *D.N.B.*

17. Lord Waldegrave's account, quoted R. Sedgwick, *op. cit.*, pp. xxii–xxiii; 'Memorial of Several Noblemen and Gentlemen of the First Rank . . . that books inculcating the worst maxims of Government and defending the most avowed tyrannies have been put in the hands of the Prince of Wales', B.M., Add. Mss 6271, f. 3 (1752); H. Walpole to H. Mann, 11 Dec. 1752 (printed W. S. Lewis, ed., *op. cit.*, Vol. XX, 1960, pp. 345–7). In his next letter Walpole was able to report the appointment of Dr John Thomas, the Bishop of Peterborough (*Id.*, p. 348).

18. R. Masters, *op. cit.*, p. 305; J. Burgh, *Youth's Friendly Monitor* . . . (London, 1754), pp.v., 22; J. Burgh, *Crito, or Essays on various subjects* (London, 1766), p. 143.

19. G. Jones, *Welch Piety, or a farther account of the circulating Welch Charity Schools* (London, 1755), pp. 22, 24; S.H. to David Hartley, 9 Dec. 1755 (Berkshire Record Office, Hartley Mss, D/E Hy, F79); J. Burgh, *op. cit.*, pp. v,64.

20. V. K. Chew, *Physics for Princes* (London, 1968) [p. 2]; John Ellis, *An Essay towards a Natural History of the Corallines and other Marine Productions of the like kind, Commonly found on the Coasts of Great Britain and Ireland* (London, 1755), Introduction, pp. v–vi; for Samuel Pullein or Pullen (*fl.* 1758) and Robert Whytt, M. D., F.R.C.P. Edinburgh, F.R.S. (1714–66), see *D.N.B.*; S.H. to John Ellis, 3 Feb. and 2 March 1752 (Linnean Correspondence, Vol. XVII, printed Sir J. E. Smith, *op. cit.*, p. 26).

21. Alexander Garden to John Ellis, 25 March 1755, printed Sir J. E. Smith, *op. cit.*, pp. 342–54; E. Berkeley and D. S. Berkeley, *Dr Alexander Garden of Charles Town* (Chapel Hill, N.C., 1969), pp. 37–9, 55, 97; letters from John Ellis to Linnaeus, *c.* 1756–57, printed Sir J. E. Smith, *op. cit.*, Vol. I, pp. 82–8;

Plate of *Halesia*, drawn by G. D. Ehret and engraved by C. H. Hemirich; S.H. to John Ellis, Teddington, n.d. (Linnean Correspondence, Vol. XVII, printed Sir J. E. Smith, *op. cit.*, Vol. II, p. 37).

22. S.H. to John Ellis, 21 Nov. 1758, (Linnean Correspondence, Vol. XVII, printed Sir J. E. Smith, *op. cit.*, Vol. II, p. 42). C.K., p. 224, notes that the hot house in question was erected by Sir William Chambers in 1761 and was demolished a century later.

23. Revd Edward Young to the Duchess of Portland, 20 Jan. 1761, accepting the appointment on S.H.'s death (Historical Manuscripts Commission, *Calendar of the Manuscripts of the Marquis of Bath preserved at Longleat, Wiltshire*, Vol. I, London, 1904, p. 326); W. J. Thoms, *The Book of the Court* (London, 1838), pp. 375–7. (Reference supplied through the courtesy of the Librarian of Windsor Castle.)

24. S.H. to Mr Joynes, 21 Jan. 1752 (Boston University, Newhall Coll. Mss); S.H. to John Ellis, 27 Jan. 1752 'from Mrs. Batchelor's in Duke's Court', Linnean Correspondence, Vol. XVII, printed Sir J. E. Smith, *op. cit.*, Vol. II, p. 25), of which little seems known beyond a reference in B. Lillywhite, *London Coffee Houses* (London, 1963), p. 718; S.H., *Considerations on the Causes of Earthquakes* (London, 1750), p. 9, where he writes 'As to the Affair of Earthquakes, particularly that which happened at *London, March 8,* 1749–50, about 20 Minutes before Six in the Morning, I being then awake in Bed on a ground Floor, near *St. Martin's in the Fields* Church in *London,* very sensibly felt the Bed heave'; Mary Batchelor's property in Duke's Court (South) was rated on a rentable value of £16 *p.a.* (see Westminster Reference Library, Ms Rate Books of the Parish of St Martin's-in-the-Fields, F520-540, 1745–59).

25. S.H. to William Wynne, 21 April 1754 (B.M. Add. Mss, 41843, f. 121); S.H. to John Ellis, 7 Jan. 1754, Linnean Correspondence, Vol. XVII (printed Sir J. E. Smith, *op. cit.*, Vol. II, p. 30); W. Stukeley, *Diaries and Letters*, Vol. III, p. 143.

26. S.H. to John Ellis, 22 Aug. and 22 Oct. 1755 (Linnean Correspondence, Vol. XVII, printed Sir J. E. Smith, *op. cit.*, Vol. II, pp. 31, 35); S.H. to David Hartley, 24 Feb. 1756, 18 April, 28 Sept. 1757 (Berkshire Record Office, D/E Hy F79); S.H. to Edmund Godfrey, 6 July 1757 (Trinity College, Cambridge, Mss R. 4.4.42, f. 30).

27. S.H. to William Stukeley, 25 Sept. 1758 (letter printed in J. B. Nichols, *Illustrations of the Literary History of the Eighteenth Century*, Vol. III, p. 810); S.H. to John Ellis, 21 Nov. 1758 (Linnean Correspondence, Vol. XVII, printed Sir J. E. Smith, *op. cit.*, Vol. II, pp. 30, 42).

28. S.H. to John Ellis, 7 Jan. 1754, 4 Jan. 1759 (Linnean Correspondence, Vol. XVII, printed Sir J. E. Smith, *op. cit.*, Vol. II, p. 42); Will of S.H., 30 Oct. 1759; S.H. to William Stukeley, 23 Dec. 1759 (Oxford, Bodleian Library, Mss Eng. C113, f. 227).

29. S.H. to Lord Barrington, 10 Jan. 1760 (Wellcome Institute of the History of Medicine, Ms 56474); letters to the Society of Arts cited in Chapter VIII above; 'A Proposal to prevent noxious Effects of Exposures to Dews at Night in Hot Climates', read 19 June 1760 (Royal Society, Letters and Papers, Decade IV, 20); S.H. to the S.P.C.K., 14 and 28 Oct. 1760 (S.P.C.K., A.L.B., CR1/24, 151, 152); S.H. to Bishop Hildesley, 25 Oct. 1760 (W. Butler, *Memoirs of Mark Hildesley*, pp. 362–27); Butler, *op. cit.*, p. 373.

30. S.H. to Richard Bradley, 25 Nov. 1760 (Bodleian Library, Ms Bradley, 16451, f. 56); S.H. to Peter Collinson, 8 Dec. 1760, f. 108; Linnean Society, Peter Collinson's Commonplace Book, f. 108); Bishop Hildesley to Dr Tathwell, n.d. (printed in *G.M.*, LXXI, ii (1801), p. 713), citing what was presumably the letter from S.H. to Hildesley, 14 Dec. 1760 (paraphrased in W. Butler, *op. cit.*, p. 370). The phrases 'very slight illness' and 'Christian Philosopher' occur in W. Butler, *op. cit.*, p. 373; Collinson noted in his Commonplace Book, *loc. cit.*, 'This Best of Men Died Saturday Jan'y 3, 1761, Lamented by all Men that knew Him and his Works'.

31. *G.M.*, XXXI (1761), p. 32; W. Butler, *op. cit.*, p. 376; J. N. Brewer, *London and Middlesex*, Vol. IV (1819), p. 490.

32. *G.M.* XXXII (1762), p. 444; W. Butler, *op. cit.*, p. 376; C.K., p. 246; A. R. Hall, *The Abbey Scientists* (London, 1966), p. 26.

CHAPTER X

1. Voltaire, 'Conseils a un Journaliste . . . Sur la Philosophie', dated 10 May 1737, in Louis Moland, ed., *Oeuvres Completes de Voltaire*, Vol. 22 (Paris, Garnier Frères, 1879), 'Mélanges', Tome 1, pp. 241–3.

2. [Archibald Campbell], *The Sale of Authors . . .* (London, printed and sold by the Booksellers in London and Westminster, 1767), p. 126. Campbell is probably paraphrasing the memoir by Peter Collinson, 'Account of the Life of . . . Hales', *op. cit.*, published also in the *Annual Register* 7 (1764), 'Characters', pp. 42–9.

3. 'L.L.', 'Dr Stephen Hales', *Notes and Queries* 4 (2nd Series, 1857), p. 343.

4. Edward Solly, 'Dr. Stephen Hales, not Hale', *Notes and Queries* 7 (6th Series, 1883), p. 352. Wesley's *Journal*, with the pertinent reference, dated July 1753, was extracted for Methodist publications and printed and reprinted at least eleven times by 1856. For the reference, see, e.g., Nehemiah Curnock, ed., *The Journal of the Rev. John Wesley, A.M.*, Vol. 4 (London, Charles H. Kelly, [1913]), p. 73. Wesley's view found a curious reflection in Adam Clarke's annotated *Holy Bible* (London, Joseph Butterworth and Son, 1825), where a passage from the *Vegetable Staticks* is cited to illustrate the curse on Adam; see Vol. 1, note to Genesis 3.18.

5. J. T. Desaguliers, Review of the *Vegetable Staticks, Phil. Trans.* 34 (1726–27), pp. 264–91, 35 (1727–28), pp. 323–31. There were also translations into Dutch (1750) and Italian (1765).

6. James Logan, '. . . concerning the crooked and angular Appearance of the Streaks, or Darts of Light'ning . . .', *Phil. Trans.* 39 (1735–36), p. 240; Norah Gourli, *Prince of Botanists, Carl Linnaeus* (London, H. F. & G. Witherby Ltd., 1953), p. 100; Georg Richmann, 'On the force of water in freezing', *Novi Commentarii Academiae Scientiarum Imperialis Petropolitanae* 1 (1747), p. 276.

7. Julius von Sachs, *History of Botany* (Oxford, Clarendon Press, 1890 [first German edition 1875]), p. 481. In a cursory survey of six plant physiology texts, dating from 1900 to 1938 and including a laboratory manual, only one, a text translated from the German and therefore probably influenced by von Sachs, refers at all adequately to the pioneer work of Hales.

8. Paraphrased from *Dell'elettricismo Opere del P. Giambattista Beccaria* (1793), as cited by I. Bernard Cohen, *Franklin and Newton* (Philadelphia, American Philosophical Society, Memoir 43, 1956), pp. 278–9.

9. For S.H.'s influence on Franklin, conceptual as well as experimental, see Cohen, *op. cit.*, pp. 278–9.

10. Pringle's *Observations* is discussed by Dorothea Waley Singer, 'Sir John Pringle and his Circle – Part II. Public Health', *Annals of Science* 6 (1950), pp. 229–61.

11. Note in *Gentleman's Magazine* XVII (1747), p. 200; S.H., 'Extract of a letter . . . concerning some Electrical Experiments', *Phil. Trans.* 45 (1748), pp. 409–11.

12. First read to the Royal Society in April 1750 and published in the *Phil. Trans.* 46 (1750), Appendix, pp. 669–83, the *Considerations* were also published in a pamphlet (London, R. Manby and H. S. Cox, 1750) which went through two editions that year. The pamphlet was then described in the *Gentleman's Magazine* XX (1750), pp. 169–71, was translated into French by G. Mazeas in 1751 and that translation republished in *Histoire des Tremblements de terre arriv's a Lima . . . et autre lieux* (La Haye, 1752).

13. The 'sulphureous' fumes Hales describes here are what Joseph Priestley was later to call nitrous air (our nitric oxide) and to use in his early approach to eudiometry.

14. James R. Partington essentially credits John Mayow and Robert Boyle for experimentally beginning pneumatic chemistry. Partington discusses S.H. as 'rather commonplace', and paying too much attention to Newtonian 'staticks' and too little to Mayow; see Partington, *A History of Chemistry*, Vol. 3 (London, Macmillan & Company Ltd, 1962), pp. 112–23. Mayow's iatro-chemistry, however, was totally different in spirit from the researches of eighteenth century chemists, who knew of his work and ignored it, while they refer to that of S.H. and develop from it. The best study of S.H.'s influence on

chemists is that of Henry Guerlac, 'The Continental Reputation of Stephen Hales', *Archives Internationales d'Histoire des Sciences* 30 (1951), pp. 392–404.

15. For a brief discussion of Mickleburgh and his chemical lectures, see Schofield, *Mechanism and Materialism*, pp. 47–9.

16. For Boerhaave's chemistry, see G. A. Lindeboom, *Herman Boerhaave* (London, Methuen & Co. Ltd, 1968), pp. 109–15, 323–54.

17. B[enjamin] R[obins], *New Principles of Gunnery, containing the Determination of the Force of Gunpowder*, etc. (London, J. Nourse, 1742), pp. 3, 5–6.

18. On S.H.'s conjecture, see Chapter IV, above. For Black, see particularly Henry Guerlac, 'Joseph Black and Fixed Air . . .', *Isis* 48 (1957), pp. 124–51, 433–56.

19. Black's *Lectures on the Elements of Chemistry*, Vol. I (Edinburgh, by Mundell and Sons, for Longman and Rees, London, and William Creech, Edinburgh, 1803), p. 239, cites S.H. as observing the absorption of part of the air surrounding burning bodies. Accum's reference to S. H. is in *A Practical Treatise on Gas-Light* (London, 1815), p. 56; Clegg's can be found in *A Practical Treatise on the Manufacture of Coal-Gas*, London, 1841), p. 3.

20. Cavendish's unpublished chemical studies were edited by Sir Edward Thorpe in Vol. 2 of *The Scientific Papers of the Honourable Henry Cavendish* (Cambridge, at the University Press, 1921); it contains at least one explicit reference to S.H. on p. 313. For a general discussion of Cavendish as a mechanist natural philosopher, with an interpretation of his chemical studies, see Russell McCormmach, 'Henry Cavendish: A Study of Rational Empiricism in Eighteenth-Century Natural Philosophy', *Isis* 60 (1969), pp. 293–306.

21. The letter to Lindsey, of 21 Feb. 1770, is printed in J. T. Rutt, *Life and Correspondence of Joseph Priestley*, Vol. 1 (London, R. Hunter, 1831–32), pp. 112–14. For Priestley as a mechanist, see Schofield, *Mechanism and Materialism*, pp. 269–73.

22. For the mechanism of Hutton and the young Davy, see Schofield, *Mechanism and Materialism*, pp. 275–6, 292–7 respectively.

23. Charles DuFay, 'Cinquième Memoir sur l'Electricité', *Memoires de l'Académie Royale des Sciences* (1734, Amsterdam 16mo. ed.), pp. 490–1. Buffon's translation will be discussed, later in this chapter, in the section on vegetable physiology.

24. For Rouelle, see Rhoda Rappaport, 'G. F. Rouelle: 18th-Century Chemist and Teacher', and 'Rouelle and Stahl – The Phlogistic Revolution in France', *Chymia* 6 (1960), pp. 68–101 and 7 (1961), pp. 73–102 respectively.

25. On Cigna and his dependence upon S.H., see Henry Guerlac, *Lavoisier – the Crucial Year* (Ithaca, Cornell University Press, 1961), pp. 77–8, 165.

26. Guerlac, *Lavoisier*, pp. 147–50. Turgot's citation is, in fact, to a 'Stales', but this can be no one other than Hales.

27. Guerlac, *Lavoisier*, p. 34.

28. Charles Hutton, George Shaw and Richard Pearson, eds., *Philosophical Transactions . . . Abridged*, Vol. 7 (London, C. and R. Baldwin, 1809), p. 191.

29. Tull, *Horse-Hoeing Husbandry*, etc., 4th ed. (London, A. Millar, 1762); Davy, *Elements of Agricultural Chemistry* (London, Longman, Hurst, Rees, Orme & Brown; Edinburgh, A. Constable and Co., 1813), see pp. 9, 208, 210.

30. Erasmus Darwin, *Phytologia* (London, J. Johnson, 1800), *passim*.

31. See André J. Bourde, *The Influence of England on the French Agronomes*, *1750–1789* (Cambridge, at the University Press, 1953), pp. 19–20, 25–26.

32. See Bourde, *op. cit.*, pp. 42–3, 123, 158–60; also two articles by Duhamel, each of which refers to S.H., in the *Gentleman's Magazine* XIX (1749), pp. 155–7, 259–61, and H.-L. Duhamel du Monceau, *The Elements of Agriculture*, transl. and reviewed, Philip Miller, Vol. I (London, P. Villant and T. Durham, and R. Baldwin, 1764), pp. 26, 32–3, 40–1, 45–6, 278, 382–3. Note that these last references are almost entirely related to theory of agriculture, two, only, relating to practice – one on 'smutty' grain and the other on the ventilator.

33. P. Flourens, ed., *Des Manuscrits de Buffon* (Paris, Garnier Frères, 1860), p.xv.

34. Lesley Hanks, *Buffon avant L'Histoire Naturelle* (Paris, Presses Universitaires de France, 1966), pp. 71–2, 223. Hanks's work is the source of the following discussion of Buffon and Hales.

35. Buffon, 'Preface du Traducteur', p. vii in *La Statique des Végétaux et celle des Animaux*, Première Partie (Paris, Theophile Barrois, 1779).

36. Raymond Savoiz, ed., *Memoires Autobiographiques de Charles Bonnet de Geneve* (Paris, Librairie Philosophique J. Vrin, 1948), pp. 90, 147. Bonnet had previously used Hales's *Vegetable Staticks* in his entomological studies; see Charles Bonnet, 'An abstract of some new Observations upon Insects', *Phil. Trans.* 42 (1743), pp. 458–87, where he refers to S.H.'s observations on the growth of animal bones.

37. I am indebted to the labours of Miss Nona Gilbert, in her unpublished M.Sc. dissertation, 'The Work of Stephen Hales (1677–1761) and its Influence on his Contemporaries and Successors', University College, London, 1957, for tracing many specific references to S.H. in the works of Senebier, de Saussure, de Candolle and other botanists and physiologists.

38. See Howard S. Reed, 'Jan Ingenhousz, Plant Physiologist, with a History of the Discovery of Photosynthesis', *Chronica Botanica* 11 (1949), pp. 285–396, including a reprinting of the *Experiments upon Vegetables*. Ingenhousz's explicit reference to S.H. is on p. 375.

39. Julius von Sachs, *History of Botany*, pp. 496–7. Gilbert notes Hales citations in Senebier's *Physiologie végétale* (Geneva, 1800), in Vol. 1, pp. 79, 120, 310; Vol. 2, pp. 301, 339; Vol. 3, pp. 24, 35, 66, 90; and Vol. 4, p. 57.

40. Von Sachs, *History of Botany*, pp. 498–504. Gilbert notes citation to S.H.

in de Saussure's *Recherches chimique sur la Végétation* (Paris, 1804), pp. 76, 77, 104, 120, 130, 275.

41. Miss Gilbert cites, from de Candolle's *Physiologie végétale* (Paris, 1832), references to S.H., pp. 89, 90–3, 107.

42. John Walker, 'Experiments on the Motion of Sap in Trees', *Transactions of the Royal Society of Edinburgh* 1 (1788), Part II, pp. 3–40.

43. See John Leslie, *Elements of Natural Philosophy* (Edinburgh, Oliver and Boyd, and Geo. B. Whittaker, London, 1829 [first ed. 1823]), p. 361.

44. Julius von Sachs, *Text-Book of Botany*, transl. Alfred W. Bennett and W. T. Thiselton Dyer (Oxford, Clarendon Press, 1875), Preface. Oddly enough, the English translators claim, in their preface, to have departed from von Sachs' 'rule of passing over authorities whose interest is now chiefly historical', but they also fail to refer to S.H. in their notes.

45. Julius von Sachs, *Vorlesungen*, transl. as *Lectures on the Physiology of Plants* by H. Marshall Ward (Oxford, Clarendon Press, 1887), pp. 283, 271, 274. Miss Gilbert, *op. cit.*, notes citations to S.H. in von Sachs' *Handbuch* (Leipsig, 1865), pp. 202, 234.

46. See, for example: Kenneth J. Franklin, *A Short History of Physiology* (London, Staples Press, Ltd, 1949); Thomas S. Hall, *Ideas of Life and Matter, Studies in the History of General Physiology, 600 BC–1900 AD* (Chicago, Univ. of Chicago Press, 1969); G. J. Goodfield, *The Growth of Scientific Physiology* (London, Hutchinson & Co., 1960); and Chandler McC. Brooks and Paul F. Cranefield, eds., *Historical Development of Physiological Thought* (New York, Hafner Publishing Co., 1959).

47. Hutton, Shaw and Pearson, eds., *Phil. Trans. Abridged*, Vol. 30 (1809), p. 375.

48. For the British physiologists of this non-mechanical school, see Schofield, *Mechanism and Materialism*, pp. 192–205.

49. Albrecht von Haller, *First Lines of Physiology* (New York and London, Johnson Reprint Corporation, *Sources of Science*, No. 32 from the 1786 Edinburgh edition, 1966), with an introduction by Lester S. King, 2 vols. in one, Vol. I, pp. 39n, 159n; Vol. II, p. 243n.

50. Heinrick Buess, 'William Harvey and the Foundation of Modern Haemodynamics by Albrecht von Haller', *Medical History* 14 (1970), pp. 175–82.

51. F.-B. de Sauvages, transl., Etienne Hales, *Haemastatique, Ou La Statique des Animaux. Expériences Hydrauliques Faites sur des Animaux vivans* (Geneva, les Herit. Cramer & Frères Philihert, 1744), 'Avertissement du traducteur', p. xii.

52. Mathieu Barbaste, *Etude Biographique, Philosophique Médicale et Botanique, sur François Boissier de Sauvages* (Montpellier, Isidore Tournel, 1851), particularly pp. 122–8.

53. On the use of Hales by Bell and Poiseuille, see Nona Gilbert, 'Stephen

Hales', *op. cit.*, where several page references in Bell and in Poiseuille's article in the *Journal de Physiologie Expérimentale et Pathologie* 8 (1828), pp. 274–305 and his *Recherches sur les Causes du Mouvement du Sang dans les Vaisseaux Capillaires* (Paris, 1836) are cited.

54. Since this chapter was written, an admirable summary of Hales's work and its importance has appeared in: Henry Guerlac, 'Hales, Stephen', *Dictionary of Scientific Biography*, ed. Charles C. Gillispie, Vol. VI (New York, Charles Scribner's Sons, 1972), pp. 35–48.

Calendar of correspondence
and writings of Stephen Hales

1708

Teddington, Middlesex; St Alban's Church, Parish Registers, Vols. A1/3 and A1/4:
Entries and notes by Hales, *c.* 1708–61.

1721

London, Society for Promoting Christian Knowledge (S.P.C.K.); CN2, CN4, CS2:
Letters from Henry Newman to Robert and Stephen Hales, 1721–43.

1722

London, S.P.C.K.; Abstract Letter Books (A.L.B.) CR1/11, 7070, 7165, 7191, 7220:
Abstracts of five letters to S.P.C.K., 17 and 18 May, 27 Sept., 6 and 27 Dec., ordering books.

1723

London, S.P.C.K.; A.L.B. CR1/12, 7409, 7512, 7535, 7549, 7551, 7632:
Abstracts of six letters to S.P.C.K., 14 May, 19 July, 19 and 27 Aug., 9 Sept., 28 Nov., ordering books.

Winchester, Hampshire Record Office; Parish Registers of Farringdon, Vols. 2M70/3, 2M70/4:
Entries and notes by Hales, *c.* 1723–41.

1724

London, S.P.C.K.; A.L.B. CR1/12, 7826:
Abstract of letter to S.P.C.K., 30 April, ordering books.

1725

London, S.P.C.K.; A.L.B. CR1/13, 8324, 8342, 8378:
Abstracts of three letters to S.P.C.K., 16 June, 5 and 6 July, ordering books.

1726

London, S.P.C.K.; A.L.B. CR1/13, 8841, 8910:
Abstracts of three letters to S.P.C.K., 13 June, 18 July, 1 Aug., ordering books.

1727

London, S.P.C.K.; A.L.B. CR1/14, 9287, 9294, 9351, 9531:
Abstracts of four letters to S.P.C.K., 15 and 19 June, 14 Aug., 30 Nov., ordering books.

London, Society for Propagation of the Gospel (S.P.G.); Letter Books (contemporary copies) A20/3, A20/10:
Two letters to S.P.G., 26 June, 5 Oct., concerning wife's legacy to the Society.

1728

London, British Museum; Sloane Mss 4049, ff. 79–80:
Letter to Sir Hans Sloane, 4 Jan. 1727/28, concerning solvent for urinary calculus.

London, British Museum; Add. Mss 19,783, ff. 61–3:
Letter to [unknown], 16 May, concerning putrefaction, tar water, distillation of gin.

London, Royal Society; Letter Book H. 3,133:
Fragment of a letter to Mr [Philip] Miller, 8 May, on cultivation of figs, reference to Dr Boerhaave's book of chymistry.

London, S.P.C.K.; A.L.B. CR1/14, 9617, 9649:
Abstracts of two letters to S.P.C.K., 27 Feb., 21 March 1727/28, ordering books and about distribution of books in Wales.

London, S.P.G.; Letter Book A21/3:
Letter to S.P.G., 8 April, on wife's legacy.

1729

Cambridge, Trinity College Library; R.4.42, ff. 25–30:
Three letters to John Mickleburgh, 21 June, 8 Oct., 8 Dec., on repeating experiments of the *Vegetable Staticks* and further experiments on calcareous incrustations.

London, S.P.C.K.; A.L.B. CR1/14, 10142, 10206; CR1/15, 10243, 10280, 10356, 10551:

Abstracts of five letters to S.P.C.K., 21 April, 23 June, 7 July, 1 Sept., 8 Dec., ordering books and about anon. donation for the Society.
Abstract of letter to Robert Hales, 28 July, praising Bishop of Man.

1730

London, S.P.C.K.; A.L.B. CR1/15, 10754, 10799, 10888:
Reference to letter to Luke Cotes, Dean of Middleham, *c.* May, on recent anonymous donation of books.
Abstract of two letters to S.P.C.K., 1 May, 10 Aug., ordering books.

1731

Cambridge, Trinity College Library; R.4.42, ff. 25–30:
Letter to John Mickleburgh, 18 Nov., on incrustations from water.

London, S.P.C.K.; A.L.B. CR1/16, 11204:
Abstract of letter to S.P.C.K., 26 April on the *Companion to the Altar.*

London, S.P.G.; Bray Associates, unbound Mss:
Letter from Daniel Waterland, Magdalene College, Cambridge, 5 Jan. 1730/31, response to Hales's query of 15 Dec. 1730 on presentation of books from Bray's Associates.

Oxford, Keble College; Thomas Wilson's Diary:
Record of letter from Hales, received 7 Dec., on donations to Diocese of Man.

1732

London, British Museum; Sloane Mss 4052, Vol. 17, ff. 147–8:
Letter to Sir Hans Sloane, 15 July, on a Mr Hodges and on corrections of haemastatical papers.

London, S.P.C.K.; A.L.B. CR1/16, 11543, 11876, 11937, 11993:
Abstract of four letters to S.P.C.K., 14 Feb. 1731/32, 21 Sept., 14 Nov., 21 Dec., on S.P.C.K. matters.

London, S.P.C.K.; A.L.B. CR1/16, 15200:
Abstract of letter to Hales from S.P.C.K., 18 Dec., on S.P.C.K. matters.

Oxford, Keble College; Thomas Wilson's Diary:
Record of Letters from Hales, 27 Feb. 1731/32, 21 Aug., 14 Sept., 4 Oct., on Manx donations, Georgia and Salzburgers.
Record of letter sent to Hales, 2 Aug., *via* Mr D. Hume.
Record of letters sent to Hales, 13 Jan., 28 Feb. 1731/32, 16 Sept., 4 Oct.,

appeal to Corporation of Sons of Clergy; personal, thanks for donations, reference to Hales's 'many worthy designs'.

1733

Cambridge, Trinity College Library; R.4.42, ff. 25–30:
Letter to John Mickleburgh, 17 May, sending copies of *Haemastaticks*, declaring intention to cease large series of experiments, hydrostatical ones on animals unsuited to 'our profession'.

London, S.P.C.K.; A.L.B. CR1/16, 12014, 12133, 12186, 12203, 12262, 15232; CR1/17, 15370, 15474, 15502; 'Soc. Letters', Vol. 27, pp. 2, 6, 46:
Abstracts of five letters to S.P.C.K., 4 Jan. 1732/33, 11 April, 22 and 31 May, 6 Aug., on S.P.C.K. matters.
Abstracts of four letters to Hales, 9 Jan. 1732/33, 29 May, 31 July, 16 Aug., on S.P.C.K. matters.
Abstracts of three letters to Hales, 29 May, 1 June, 2 Aug., recorded in 'Society Letters'.

Oxford, Keble College; Thomas Wilson's Diary:
Record of letters received from Hales, 16 Jan. 1732/33, 11 Dec., about preferment for Wilson.
Record of letter sent to Hales, 8 Dec., about preferment for Wilson.

1734

London, British Museum; Sloane Mss 4053, Vol. 18, ff. 123–4:
Letter to Sir Hans Sloane, 3 Jan. 1733/34, transmitting experiments of Mr Browne-Langrish; he would like to be a fellow of Royal Society.

London, S.P.C.K.; A.L.B. CR1/18, 12842, 12875, 12970:
Abstract of three letters to S.P.C.K., 26 Sept., 19 Oct., 24 Dec., on S.P.C.K. matters and ordering books.

London, S.P.G.; Letter Book A25/219:
Letter from Hales, 23 April, about anon. donation.

Oxford, Keble College; Thomas Wilson's Diary:
Record of letter received from Hales, 3 Aug., further Manx donation, servants turning Muggletonian.

1735

London, Royal College of Surgeons; Hunter-Baillie Collection:
Letter to Dr Robert Nesbitt, 11 Sept., experiments on medicinal waters (printed in *Postgraduate Medical Journal* 22 (1946), p. 121).

London, Royal Society; Letter Book H 3,134:
Letter to Dr Cromwell Mortimer, 17 May, declining to succeed Dr Dereham in abstracting meteorological diaries for Society. (Extract of letter to Mortimer, c. 18–19 May, printed in *Phil. Trans.* 44 [Appendix, 1746–47], pp. 693–5, referring to Mortimer's work on thermometers and Hales's proposal of a lead-wire pyrometer. May be part of letter cited above?)

London, S.P.C.K.; A.L.B. CR1/18, 12975, 12986, 13000, 13006, 13583;

Newman Private Letters, CN4/6, pp. 42–3; Society Letters, Vol. 31, p. 50:
Abstracts of five letters to S.P.C.K., 3, 11, 20, 27 Jan. 1734/35, 15 April, on S.P.C.K. matters and ordering books.
Drafts of letters to Hales from Henry Newman, 6, 13 Nov., on financial affairs of Robert Hales, ref. to Mr Oglethorpe waiting at Cowes for a wind.
Abstract of letter to Hales from S.P.C.K., 28 Jan. 1734/35, on S.P.C.K. matters.

1736

Cambridge, University Library; Corpus Christi College Mss 567:
Letter to Dr Nesbitt, 27 March, on experiments with cork.

London, S.P.C.K.; A.L.B. CR1/19, 13760, 13776, 13834, 13846:
Abstracts of four letters to S.P.C.K., 9 and 16 Sept., 5 and 10 Nov., on S.P.C.K. matters and ordering books.

Oxford, Keble College; Thomas Wilson's Diary:
Record of letters received from Hales, 23 Jan. 1735/36, 21 Sept., personal, reference to brandy shops.
Record of letter sent to Hales, 1 Nov., on poor health, canvassing for Gin Bill.

1737

Boston, Mass., Boston University; Newhall Collection:
Letter to Dr Nesbitt, Aug., on scientific matters including water analysis.

Cambridge, University Library; Corpus Christi College Mss 567:
Letter to Dr Nesbitt, 6 April, on experiments with mineral waters.

London, British Museum; Sloane Mss 4055, f. 37:
Letter to Sir Hans Sloane, 10 Jan. 1736/37, supporting Dr Battie's candidacy for position at Christ's Hospital.

London, S.P.C.K.; A.L.B. CR1/19, 14235:
Abstract of letter to S.P.C.K., 7 Sept., on William Curtis and his work.

1738

London, S.P.C.K.; A.L.B. CR1/19, 14514, 14672, 15245:
Abstracts of three letters to S.P.C.K., 21 April, 17 July, 21 Dec., on S.P.C.K. matters and ordering books.

1739

London, British Museum; Sloane Mss 4056, Vol. XXI, ff. 20, 46:
Letters to Sir Hans Sloane, 2 Jan., 5 Feb. 1738/39, on sea-water, putrefaction, paper on steel water.

London, Royal Society; Misc. Mss 58:
'Philosophical Experiments', 1739, printed as a book at the expense of the Royal Society.

1740

London, S.P.C.K.; A.L.B. CR1/20, 15703:
Abstract of letter to S.P.C.K., 9 Dec., recommending Dr Hartley as a subscribing member.

1741

London, British Museum; Add. Mss, 38,330 (Liverpool Papers, Vol. cxli), ff. 244–51:
'Collections of Some Observations on Bills of Mortality and Parish Registers', Derham's observations extended by Hales.

London, S.P.C.K.; A.L.B. CR1/21, 15755, 15806, 15815, 16002, 16053:
Abstracts of six letters to S.P.C.K., 24 Jan., — March, 17 March 1740/41, 6 April, 13 July, 10 Aug. 1741, on S.P.C.K. matters and ordering books.

1742

Cleveland, Ohio, U.S.A., Cleveland Medical Library Association; Hales Mss:

Letter to Dr William Lee, 26 Oct., on respirator for going into ships' holds. ventilators.

London, Royal Society; Letters and Papers, Decade I, 38:
Letter to Cromwell Mortimer, 23 Jan. 1741/42, 'On Ventilating the Holds of Ships'.

London, S.P.C.K., A.L.B. CR1/21, 16307:
Abstract of letter to S.P.C.K., 1 Feb. 1741/42, on S.P.C.K. matters and ordering books.

1743

London, S.P.C.K.; A.L.B. CR1/22, 321, 16783, 16930, 17041, 17139:
Abstract of letter to Hales, 5 July, on S.P.C.K. matters.
Abstracts of four letters to S.P.C.K., 3 Jan. 1742/43, 11 April, 25 July, 13
Nov., on S.P.C.K. matters and ordering books.

New York, Kew Gardens, Emil Offenbacher Bookseller; Catalogue 24, No.
80, Spring 1972:
Letter to Henri Louis Duhamel du Monceau, 18 July, on physiology of
bones, ventilators.

1744

London, Royal College of Physicians:
Letters to Thomas Yeoman, 21 Jan. 1743/44, 10 April, 21 Dec., on ventilators, other machinery (contemporary Ms copies).

London, Royal Society; Letters and Papers, Decade I, 260:
'On injecting a Liquor during Tapping', read 2 Feb. 1743/44 (published
Phil. Trans. 43 (1744–45), pp. 20–1).

London, S.P.C.K.; A.L.B. CR1/22, 347:
Abstract of letter from S.P.C.K., 22 Dec., on S.P.C.K. matters.

1745

London, Royal College of Physicians:
Letters to Thomas Yeoman, 4 and 22 Jan. 1744/45, 11 April, 4 and 18
July, 12 Aug., on ventilators, mills and other machinery (contemporary
Ms copies).
Letter to Edward Cave, 23 Sept., ventilators, tar-water (contemporary Ms
copy).

London, Royal College of Surgeons; Hunter-Baillie Collection:
Letter to [Mr Thomas Woodfall], 21 Jan. 1744–45, on his and Hartley's
treatise on Mrs Stephens's remedy.

London, Royal Society; Letters and Papers, Decade I, 351, 417, 419:
Fragment of letter to Martin Folkes, read 31 Jan. 1744/45, 'Of a monstrous
Calf', etc.
'A Proposal to bring small Stones out of the Bladder', read 31 Oct., with
revised copy (published *Phil. Trans.* 43 (1744–45), pp. 502–5).

London, S.P.C.K.; A.L.B. CR1/22, 17929, 365:
Abstract of letter to S.P.C.K., 1 March 1744/45, on books for Lady Blount.

Abstract of letter from S.P.C.K., 14 March 1744/45, on books for Lady Blount.

1746

London, Royal College of Physicians:
Letters to Thomas Yeoman, 11 March 1745/46, 21 June, on ventilators, mills and other machinery (contemporary Ms copies).

1747

London, S.P.C.K.; A.L.B. CR1/23, 18507, 18758:
Abstract of two letters to S.P.C.K., 13 July, received 15 Dec., ordering books.

1748

London, S.P.C.K.; A.L.B. CR1/23, 18909:
Abstract of letter to S.P.C.K., received 19 April, ordering books.

London, Sotheby's Auction; 14 Dec. 1964, Lot 184:
'Proposal for Checking in some Degree, the Progress of Fires', *c.* 1748, addressed to the Royal Society (published in *Phil. Trans.* 45 (1748), pp. 277–80).

1749

London, S.P.C.K.; A.L.B. CR1/23, 19324:
Abstract of letter to S.P.C.K., 30 Jan. 1748/49, ordering books.

London, S.P.G.; Bray Associates unbound Mss, Bray 9:
Letter to Herman Verelst, 21 June, on work of Georgia Trustees.

1750

London, Royal Society; Letters and Papers, Decade II, 77, 137:
'Some Considerations as to the cause of Earthquakes', read 5 April (published *Phil. Trans.* 46 (Appendix to 1750), pp. 669–83).
'Of the Residues from Purging Waters, also a letter by Swithin Adee on Jessop's Well', read 24 May (part published *Phil. Trans.* 46 (1750), pp. 446–51).

London, S.P.C.K.; A.L.B. CR1/23, 19905:
Abstract of two letters to S.P.C.K., received 12 April, 1 May, ordering books and on S.P.C.K. matters.

Oxford, Keble College; Thomas Wilson's Diary:
Record of letter sent to Hales, 3 Sept.

London, S.P.C.K.; A.L.B. CR1/23, 20592:
Abstract of letter to S.P.C.K., received 10 Sept., ordering books.

London, Wellcome Institute of the History of Medicine; Ms 5 1975:
Letter to Mr Woodward, 17 Aug., on Dr Hartley's publication of ways of giving Mrs Stephens's medicine.

1752

Boston, Mass., Boston University Library; Newhall Collection:
Letter to Mr Joynes, 21 Jan., on payment of account.

London, British Museum, Birch Mss 4309, ff. 23–9, 32–6, 30–1:
Letters to Thomas Birch, 6 Jan., 23 March, 11 and 18 April, 29 May, 3 June, 3 and 11 July, 30 Aug., 18 Dec., on Birch's life of Archbishop Wake, life of Archbishop Tillotson, Royal Society business and especially election of Mazeas as F.R.S., ventilators, electricity and lightning.
Letters to Hales from Thomas Birch, 24 April, 1 June, Royal Society business, especially election of Mazeas.

London, Linnean Society; Linnean Correspondence xvii:
Letters to John Ellis, 27 Jan., 3 Feb., 2 March, 15 Aug., 16 Sept., on seamoss, moss pictures, ventilators, Mr Pullein (all published in James Edward Smith, ed. *Linnean Correspondence*, Vol. II, pp. 25–9).

London, S.P.C.K.; A.L.B. CR1/23, 21038:
Abstract of letter to S.P.C.K., 5 Aug., on books for Maryland.

1753

Boston, Mass., Boston University Library; Newhall Collection:
Letter to [unknown, address obscured], on payment for North aisle of Teddington Church; see letter to Joynes, cited for 1752.

Edinburgh, University Library; Alston Papers LaIII 375/37–38:
Letters to Charles Alston, 26 March, 30 April, on lime water, Dr Whytt, ventilators, the stone.

London, British Museum; Middleton Papers, Vol. xli, Add. Mss 41, 843, ff. 119, 121, 122:
Letters to Mr William Wynne, Serjeant-at-Law, 18, c. 19, and 21 April, 12 and 17 May, fee farm rents, enquiries respecting estate of Charles Longueville.

Manchester, John Rylands Library; English Mss 19, iv, 301:

Reference to two letters to William Shipley, in letter from Shipley to Henry Baker, 12 Aug., on formation of Society for encouragement of Arts, Manufactures and Commerce.

1754

Edinburgh, University Library; Alston Papers LaIII 375/39–40:
Letters to Charles Alston, 26 Feb., 14 Nov., on preserving fresh water and fish, Dr Whytt, ventilators, ref. Alston's *Tirocinium Botanicum*.

London, Linnean Society; Linnean Correspondence, xvii:
Letters to John Ellis, 7 Jan., 20 May, 19 June, on Capt. Ellis, Hales suffering 'gravelly disorder', corallines, salubrity of air, ref. Pullein.

London, Royal Society; Letters and Papers, Decade II, 545:
'Use of Lime-Water to keep Water, Fish, etc. fresh', read 19 Dec. (published *Phil. Trans.* 48 (1754), pp. 826–31).

1755

Cleveland, Ohio, U.S.A., Cleveland Medical Library Association; Hales Mss:
Letter to Sir William Lee, 29 May, Leland benefactions, curing ill-tasting milk, distilling sea-water.

Edinburgh, University Library; Alston Papers LaIII 375/36:
Extract of letter to William Brownrigg, 28 May, transcribed in letter of Brownrigg to Charles Alston, 15 June, on efficiency of distillation.

London, Linnean Society; Linnean Correspondence xvii:
Letters to John Ellis, 22 and 29 Aug., 22 Oct., on Pullein and silk worms, adulteration of sugar, making of potash, ill-tasting milk (all published in J. E. Smith, ed., *Linnean Correspondence*, Vol. II, pp. 31–7).

London, Royal Society of Arts; Guard Book I, 16:
Letter to Society of Arts, 5 April, 'proposal for publishing a Book by Mr. Pullein on Silk-Worms'.

Reading, Berkshire County Record Office; Hartley Papers D/E, Hy F.79:
Letters to David Hartley, 13 July, 28 Aug., 9 Dec., on distilling sea-water, ventilators, foreign correspondence, ill-tasting milk, adulteration of sugar, sale of book on remedy for stone.

1756

Edinburgh, University Library; Alston Papers LaIII 375/36–41:

Letter to Charles Alston, 4 May, reference to Black's *Essay*, the stone, distillation, ventilators, Whytt's gift of *Physiological Essays*.

London, British Museum, Birch Papers, Add. Mss 4309, f. 41:
Letter to Thomas Birch, 20 Aug., on treatise on distillation of sea water.

London, Royal Society; Letters and Papers, Decade III, 106:
'Proposals to retard putrefaction of animals in hot climates' (reported in inventory of Royal Society papers, where it is said to have been read 17 Feb. 1756, and published *Phil. Trans.* 49 [1755–56], p. 544. But February 1756 meetings of the Royal Society were held on the 12 and the 19, and the *Phil. Trans.* reference is to an extract of a letter from Lady Belcher to Hales).

London, Royal Society of Arts; Guard Book I, Nos. 107, 114, 121, 127; III, No. 51:
Letters: to Dr D. W. Linden, 25 Feb., on cobalt; Society of Arts, 16 June, on premium for preserving casks; from Revd Wm. Henry, 13 June, on work of Dublin Society; (copy) from Alex. Macpherson, 3 Aug., on ventilator in Admiral Boscawen's flagship; to Lord Folkestone, Pres. Soc. of Arts, 2 March, on method of checking fires.

London, S.P.C.K.; A.L.B. CR1/24, 22664:
Abstract of letter to S.P.C.K., received 4 May, on S.P.C.K. matters.

Reading, Berkshire County Record Office; Hartley Papers D/E, Hy F79:
Letters to David Hartley, 24 Feb., 13 July, on tar-water, education of negro slaves.

1757

Cambridge, Trinity College Library; R.4.42, ff.25–30:
Letter to Edward Godfrey, 6 July, on preservation of food, reference to Brownrigg.

London, British Museum; Birch Papers, Add. Mss 4309, ff. 42, 44:
Letters to Thomas Birch, 26 March, 28 June, on Mrs Belcher's letter, correspondence with Duhamel du Monceau, Royal Society business, ventilators and paper on distillation.

London, Linnean Society; Linnean Correspondence xvii:
Letters to John Ellis, n.d. (1757?), 25 June, on plant 'Halesia', Pullein's book, preservation of clover, softening water, Mazeas and Duhamel du Monceau.

London, Royal Society of Arts; Guard Book III, No. 39:

Copy of letter to Dr James Stonhouse, *c.* Nov., on improving diet of the poor.

Reading, Berkshire County Record Office; Hartley Papers D/E, Hy F79:
Letters to David Hartley, 18 April, 28 September, on Hartley's 'calculus complaint', article on melon frames; visit from Hartley's son, ventilators for fleet, hatred of drams.

London, Sotheby (July 1973 catalogue):
Letter to Duhamel [de Nemours?], 16 Aug., 'Being 50 miles from London', on ventilators.

1758

London, British Museum; Add. Mss 19,683, f. 61:
Letter to Bishop Hildesley, 16 May, on evils of dram drinking, tar-water (published *Gentleman's Magazine* LXIV (1794), pp. 689–91).

London, British Museum; Birch Papers, Add. Mss 4309, f. 45:
Letter to Thomas Birch, 18 Dec., on Mr Marsham's ideas of the growth and planting of timber trees.

London, Linnean Society; Linnean Correspondence xvii:
Letters to John Ellis, 25 Feb., 21 Nov., on copies of *Treatise* on ventilators, preserving food, dram-drinking, cooling of houses (published in J. E. Smith, ed., *Linnean Correspondence*, Vol. II, pp. 40–2).

London, Linnean Society; Ellis's Notebook I, 11. 21 ver.–22 rect.:
Draft letter to Hales, 20 Nov., on Gov. Ellis, cooling of houses.

1759

Cleveland, Ohio, U.S.A., Cleveland Medical Library Association, Hales Mss:
Letter to Sir William Lee, 4 June, measurements of distance at sea, of longitude; ventilators, fresh water.

London, British Museum; Birch Papers, Add. Mss 4309, ff. 47, 48, 49:
Letters to Thomas Birch, 16 and 23 June, 13 July, on Marsham's communications respecting timber trees.

London, Linnean Society; Linnean Correspondence xvii:
Letter to John Ellis, 4 Jan., on Hales's illness, Ellis's scheme to cool houses, circulation of air in relation to life, Marsham's observations on trees, ref. to Dr Henry of Dublin.

London, S.P.C.K.; A.L.B. CR1/24, 23873:
Abstract of letter to S.P.C.K., 24 April, on S.P.C.K. matters.

London, Somerset House (transferred to Public Record Office, 1970):
Will of Stephen Hales, 30 Oct.

Oxford, Bodleian Library; Mss Eng. Misc. C113, f. 227:
Letter to William Stukeley, 23 Dec., on ventilators, Mr Yeoman, philanthropy (quoted by Clark-Kennedy, p. 239).

1760

London, Linnean Society; Peter Collinson Commonplace Book:
Letter to Peter Collinson, 8 Dec., on forwarding a letter written to Mr Elliot, ref. dram-drinking, copper spring, ventilators, sea-water and rheumatism.

London, Royal Society; Letters and Papers, Decade IV, 20:
'A Proposal to prevent noxious Effects of Exposures to Dews at Night in hot Countries', read 19 June.

London, Royal Society of Arts; Guard Book I, No. 1; II, 28; IV, 108, 111, 118:
Copy of letter to William Lewis, 16 Feb., on marking of sheep.
Letters to Society of Arts, 20 Feb., 15 Feb., on ventilator for Society's Great Room; reply to request of opinion of method of marking sheep.
Letters to Society of Arts, addressed to Lord Folkestone, 19 and 26 Feb., on Dr Lewis's method of marking sheep.

London, S.P.C.K.; A.L.B. CR1/24, 24419, 24441:
Abstract of two letters to S.P.C.K., 14 and 28 Oct., ordering books.

London, Wellcome Institute of the History of Medicine; Ms 56474:
Letter to Lord Barrington, 10 Jan., recommending the use of ventilators for the preservation of horses going to Germany.

Oxford, Bodleian Library [Ms Bradley 45], 16451, f. 56:
Letter to Richard Bradley, 25 Nov., on a subject similar to perpetual motion, ventilators (cited by Clark-Kennedy, p. 244).

APPENDIX TWO

Published writings of
Stephen Hales

(Items marked with * used in this work)

1727

Vegetable Staticks: or An Account of some Statical Experiments on the Sap in Vegetables: being an Essay towards a Natural History of Vegetation. Also, a Specimen of an Attempt to Analyse the Air by a great Variety of Chymio-Statical Experiments (London, W. and J. Innys and T. Woodward, 1727).
*— reprinted by photo-offset, with foreword by Michael Hoskin (London, Oldbourne Press, 1961), subsequent editions published by Macdonald & Co., London and American Elsevier Inc., New York.

1728

*'An Account of a Machine for Measuring any depth in the Sea, with great expedition and certainty, shewn to the Royal Society, by J. T. Desaguliers . . . and contriv'd by the Rev. Mr. Stephen Hales . . . and Himself', *Phil. Trans.* 35 (1727–28), pp. 559–62.

1731

Vegetable Staticks (London, 1731), 2nd ed.

1733

Statical Essays: Containing Haemastaticks; or An Account of some Hydraulick and Hydrostatical Experiments made on the Blood and Blood Vessels of Animals . . ., Vol. 2 (London, W. Innys and R. Manby, and T. Woodward, 1733).
*— reprinted by photo-offset, with foreword by André Cournand (New York, Hafner Publishing Company, New York Academy of Medicine, History of Medicine Series 22, 1964).

1734

A Sermon preached before the Trustees for establishing the colony of Georgia in America; and before the associates of the late Rev. Dr. Thomas Bray, for converting the negroes in the British plantation, and for other good purposes . . . (London, T. Woodward, 1734).

*A Friendly Admonition to the Drinkers of Brandy, and other Distilled Spirituous Liquors (London, Joseph Downing, 1734)
*— 2nd ed. (London, Joseph Downing, 1734).

1735

A Friendly Admonition to the Drinkers of Brandy . . . 3rd ed. (London, M. Downing, 1735).
La Statique des végétaux, et l'analyse de l'air, translated by Buffon (Paris, 1735).

1738

Statical Essays: Containing Vegetable Staticks . . ., 3rd ed. (London, 1738).

1739

*Philosophical Experiments: containing useful, and necessary instructions for such as undertake long voyages at Sea. Showing how sea water may be made fresh and wholesome; and how fresh-water may be preserv'd sweet. How biscuit, corn, etc. may be secured from weevel, maggots, and other insects. And flesh preserv'd in hot climates, by salting animals whole. To which is added, an account of several experiments and observations on chalybeate or steel-waters . . . (London, W. Innys and R. Manby, 1739)

1740

*An Account of some experiments and Observations on Mrs. Stephens's medicines for dissolving the Stone (London, 1740).
Statical Essays: Containing Haemastaticks . . ., 2nd ed. (London, 1740).

1743

*A Description of Ventilators: whereby Great Quantities of Fresh Air May with Ease be conveyed into Mines, Gaols, Hospitals, Work-Houses and Ships, In Exchange for their Noxious Air. An Account also of their Great Usefulness in many other Respects: As in Preserving all Sorts of Grain Dry, Sweet, and free from being Destroyed by Weevels, both in Grainaries and Ships: And in Preserving many other sorts of Goods . . . (London, W. Innys, R. Manby, T. Woodward, 1743).
*'Some Observations of the very Ingenious Dr. Hales, in his Treatise of Ventilators', Gentleman's Magazine XIII (1743), pp. 432–33.

1744

*'A Method of conveying Liquors into the Abdomen during the Operation of Tapping', Phil. Trans. 43 (1744–45), pp. 20–1.

Description of Ventilators, French translation by P. Demours (Paris, 1744), noted in *Gentleman's Magazine* XIV (1744), registry of books.

Haemastatique, ou la Statique des Animaux (Geneva, Philibert, 1744), translated by de Sauvages.

1745

*An Account of some Experiments and Observations on Tar Water; wherein is shown the quantity of tar that is therein. And also a method proposed, both to abate that quantity . . . and to ascertain the strength of the tar-water (London, 1745).

*'A Proposal to bring small passable Stones soon and with Ease out of the Bladder', *Phil. Trans.* 43 (1745), pp. 502–5.

*'A Description of a Back-Heaver, which will winnow and clean corn, both much sooner and better, than by the common methods of doing it', *Gentleman's Magazine* XV (1745), pp. 353–4.

*'Preserving of quantities of corn, etc. in granaries', *Gentleman's Magazine* XV (1745), p. 640.

1746

*'An Account of several methods to preserve Corn well by Ventilation', *Gentleman's Magazine* XVI (1746), pp. 315–18.

*Notice: Tuesday 30 Aug. 1746. Reference to success of ventilators in Newgate, also ventilator in frigate *Success*, transporting recruits for Georgia, *Gentleman's Magazine* XVI (1746), p. 494.

*'Some Remarks on the boasted Liquid Shell', *Gentleman's Magazine* XVI (1746), p. 520.

1747

An Account of some Experiments and Observations on Tar Water . . ., 2nd ed. (London, 1747).

*Note: Dr Hales doubts that electricity promoted vegetation, *Gentleman's Magazine* XVII (1747), pp. 270–1.

*Notice of Middlesex County Hospital for Small Pox, Stephen Hales one of four Vice-Presidents, *Gentleman's Magazine* XVII (1747), pp. 270–1.

*'A Description of a very great Improvement which is made to the Back Heaver . . .', *Gentleman's Magazine* XVII (1747), pp. 310–12.

1748

Statick d. Gewächse oder angestellte Versuche mit d. Saft in Pflantzen . . . (Halle, Renger, 1748), translated by Christian Wolff.

*'A Proposal for checking in some Degree the Progress of Fires', *Phil. Trans.* 45 (1748), pp. 277–80.

*Extract of a letter . . . concerning some Electrical Experiments, *Phil. Trans.* 45 (1748), pp. 409–11.

1749

*'Method proposed . . . for checking fires', abstracted from *Phil. Trans.*, *Gentleman's Magazine* XIX (1749), p. 554.
*Notice: 29 Oct. 1749. Ventilators to be installed in Savoy Prison. Also into each of transports carrying Germans to British Plantations. *Gentleman's Magazine* XIX (1749), p. 282.

1750

Some Considerations on the Causes of Earthquakes (London, R. Manby and H. S. Cox, 1750).
**Some Considerations on the Causes of Earthquakes*, 2nd ed. (London, 1750).
Expériences Physiques (Paris, 1750), French translation of *Philosophical Experiments* of 1739.
*'An Examination of the Strength of several of the principal purging Waters, especially that of Jessop's Well . . .', *Phil. Trans.* 46 (1749–50), pp. 446–51.
*'Some Considerations on the Causes of Earthquakes', *Phil. Trans.* 46 (Appendix to 1750), pp. 669–83 (text reprinted separately, see above).
*'A Letter from the Rev. Stephen Hales . . . serving to inclose a Letter . . . from Walter Bowman . . . concerning an Earthquake . . .', *Phil. Trans.* 46 (Appendix to 1750), pp. 684–7.
*'Account of a Pamphlet, intitled, Some Considerations on the Causes of Earthquakes', *Gentleman's Magazine* XX (1750), pp. 169–71.
*Notice, of 29 Aug. 1750. Ventilators installed in *Sheerness*, 20–gun ship at Deptford. Worked by a windmill, intended to preserve timbers, *Gentleman's Magazine* XX (1750), p. 379.

1751

Considérations sur la cause physique des tremblements de terre . . . (Paris, 1751), translated G. Mazeas.
* *The Wisdom and Goodness of God in the Formation of Man, Being an anniversary sermon preached before the Royal College of Physicians* . . . according to the Institution of Dr Croun (London, 1751).
*'An Account of the bucket Sea-gage to find the different Degrees of coolness and saltness of the Sea', *Phil. Trans.* 47 (1750–51), pp. 214–16.

1752

'Reflexions physiques sur les causes des tremblements de terre', in *Histoire des tremblements de terre arriv's a Lima . . . et autres lieux* (Le Haye, 1752).

*'A Description of the Ventilators which are fixed in Newgate; where being worked by a Windmill they draw the foul air out of the several Wards . . .', *Gentleman's Magazine* XXII (1752), pp. 179–82.

*'A Description of the Windmill, which is fixed on Newgate to work the Ventilators . . .', *Gentleman's Magazine* XXII (1752), p. 182.

1753

*'An Account of the good Effect of Ventilators, in Newgate and the Savoy Prison', *Gentleman's Magazine* XXIII (1753), pp. 70–1.

*(Pringle, John), 'An Account of several Persons seized with the Jail Fever, by working in Newgate, and of the manner by which the Infection was communicated to one entire Family', *Gentleman's Magazine* XXIII (1753), pp. 71–4, introduced by a letter, dated 12 Feb. 1753, by Stephen Hales.

*'Some Considerations about Means to draw the foul Air out of the sick Rooms of occasional Army-Hospitals, in private Houses in Towns', *Gentleman's Magazine* XXIII (1753), p. 173. Extracted from Pringle's *Observations on the Diseases in the Army*, with Hales's recommendation noted on use of small exterior ventilator.

1754

A Friendly Admonition to the Drinkers of Brandy . . ., 5th ed. with additions (London, 1754).

*'An Account of some Trials to keep Water and Fish sweet, with Lime-Water', *Phil. Trans.* 48 (1754), pp. 826–31.

*'A further Account of the Success of Ventilators, etc.', *Gentleman's Magazine* XXIV (1754), pp. 115–16.

*'A Description of a Sea Gage', *Gentleman's Magazine* XXIV (1754), pp. 215–19.

*'A Proposal for the more speedily and effectually curing Men, Ships, and Goods, of Pestilential Infection', *Gentleman's Magazine* XXIV (1754), pp. 543–4.

1755

*'An Account of the great Benefit of blowing showers of fresh Air up through distilling Liquors', *Phil. Trans.* 49 (1755–56), pp. 312–32.

*'An Account of the great Benefit of Ventilators in many Instances, in preserving the Health and Lives of People, in Slave and other Transport Ships', *Phil. Trans.* 49 (1755–56), pp. 332–9.

*'An Account of some Trials to cure the ill Taste of Milk, which is occasioned by the Food of Cows, either from Turnips, Cabbages or Autumnal Leaves, etc. Also to sweeten stinking Water, etc.', *Phil. Trans.* 49 (1755–56), pp. 339–47.

*'Extract of some Tryals made . . . to keep Water and Fish sweet with Lime-water, etc.', *Gentleman's Magazine* XXV (1755), pp. 310–12.

1756

An Account of a useful Discovery to distill double the usual Quantity of Sea-water, by blowing Showers of Air up through the distilling Liquor; and an Account of the great Benefit of Ventilators in many Instances, in preserving the Health and Lives of People, in Slave and other Transport Ships . . . Also an Account of the good Effect of blowing Showers of Air up through Milk thereby to cure the ill Taste which is occasioned by some kinds of Foods of Cows (London, R. Manby, 1756). Separate reprint of three Royal Society Papers.

An Account of a useful Discovery, etc., 2nd ed. (London, 1756).

*J. Wall, 'An Essay on the Waters of the Holy Well at Malvern, Worcestershire', *Phil. Trans.* 49 (1755–56), pp. 459–68. Includes extract of a letter from Hales to Mr Clare, dated 25 Oct. 1750.

*'Method of obtaining Plenty of fresh Sea water', *Gentleman's Magazine* XXVI (1756), pp. 78–9.

*'An Account of some Tryals to cure ill tasting milk and Stinking Water by Ventilators of blowing up Showers of Air though them', *Gentleman's Magazine* XXVI (1756), pp. 130–1.

1757

*'Rational and easy Methods to purify the Air and regulate its Heat in Melon-Frames and hot Green-houses', *Gentleman's Magazine* XXVII (1757), pp. 165–6.

*'Farther Improvements in the methods of distilling Sea-Water', *Gentleman's Magazine* XXVII (1757), pp. 503–4.

*'An Account of rational and easy Methods to purify the Air, and regulate its Heat, in melon Frames and hot Greenhouses', *General Magazine of Arts and Sciences* 6 (1757), p. 524.

1758

A Treatise on Ventilators. Wherein an Account is given of the happy Effects of the several Trials which have been made of them . . . As also of what farther Hints and Improvements . . . have occurred since the Publication of the former Treatise. Part Second (London, R. Manby, 1758).

1762

A New-Year's Gift to Dram-Drinkers, being an earnest address to them: from the late S.H. . . . . reprinted out of his second Volume on Ventilators. To which is prefixed an Epistle to them by W. Henry (Dublin, 1762).

1769

Statical Essays: containing I. Vegetable Staticks . . . II. Haemastaticks . . ., 4th ed. of I and 3rd ed. of II (London, 1769).

1776

Statica de' Vegetabili ed analisi dell'aria (Napoli, Gaetano Castellano, 1776), transl. with commentary by Signora D. M. A. Ardinghelli.

1779–80

La Statique des Végétaux, et celle des Animaux (Paris, 1779–80), 2nd ed. of Buffon transl. of *Vegetable Staticks*, revised by Sigaud de la Fond; 2nd ed. of Sauvages' translation of *Haemastaticks*.

1800

A Friendly Admonition to the Drinkers of Brandy (London, Society for Promoting Christian Knowledge, Religious Tracts, Vol. II, 1800), 'another' edition.

1807

A Friendly Admonition to the Drinkers of Brandy (London, F. & C. Rivington, for the Society for Promoting Christian Knowledge, Religious Tracts, Vol. II, 1807), 'sixth' ed. with additions.

Portraits and monuments
of and to Stephen Hales

Cambridge: Corpus Christi College:

c. 1720: A portrait described as S. H. by Knapton, sold by Captain Eric C. Palmer, Christie's, 24 May 1957. The National Portrait Gallery note that it is of about 1720 on costume and is near the style of Richard van Bleek, and that by comparison with the Hudson portrait, it seems unlikely to represent S.H.

London: National Portrait Gallery:

1759: Portrait in oil on canvas, studio of Thomas Hudson.

1759: Mezzotint of Hudson's portrait by James McArdell.

1799: Rough etched portrait for *G.M.* (Jan. 1799, p. 9).

1810: Engraving of Hudson's portrait by James Hopwood for one of Robert John Thornton's *Elementary Botanical Plates*, where the original painting is wrongly attributed to Francis Cotes.

London: R.S.A.:

1778: Portrait of S. H. after Hudson included in painting of the Distribution of Premiums in The Society of Arts, No. 5 in series 'The progress of Human Knowledge' by James Barry.

London: Westminster Abbey:

1762: Monument by Joseph Wilton in South Transept with portrait medallion of S. H. mourned by figures of Religion and Botany.

Teddington: Middlesex, St Mary's Church:

1761: Tomb beneath floor of Church Tower with inscription above.

1911: Inscription on tablet affixed to North wall of Tower.

1960: East window by A. E. Buss showing S. H. and Thomas Traherne as votary figures.

Winterthur, Wilmington, Delaware: Henry Francis Du Pont Winterthur Museum:

1734: Portrait of S. H. included in the 'Trustees of the Colony of Georgia receiving the Indians' by Harman Verelst.

Family trees

DESCENDANTS OF SIR JOHN HALES,
BARON OF THE EXCHEQUER TEMP. HENRY VIII

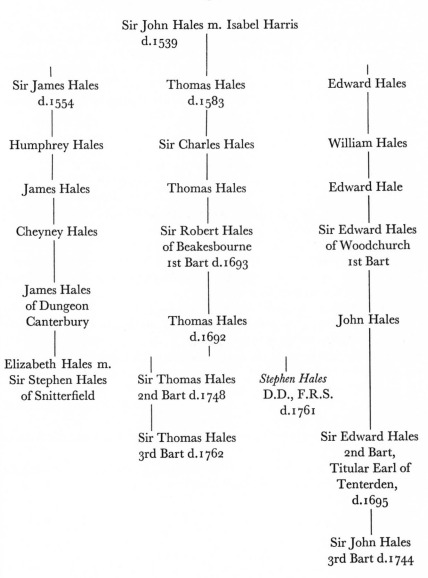

Sir John Hales m. Isabel Harris
d.1539

Sir James Hales
d.1554

Thomas Hales
d.1583

Edward Hales

Humphrey Hales

Sir Charles Hales

William Hales

James Hales

Thomas Hales

Edward Hale

Cheyney Hales

Sir Robert Hales
of Beakesbourne
1st Bart d.1693

Sir Edward Hales
of Woodchurch
1st Bart

James Hales
of Dungeon
Canterbury

Thomas Hales
d.1692

John Hales

Elizabeth Hales m.
Sir Stephen Hales
of Snitterfield

Sir Thomas Hales
2nd Bart d.1748

Stephen Hales
D.D., F.R.S.
d.1761

Sir Thomas Hales
3rd Bart d.1762

Sir Edward Hales
2nd Bart,
Titular Earl of
Tenterden,
d.1695

Sir John Hales
3rd Bart d.1744

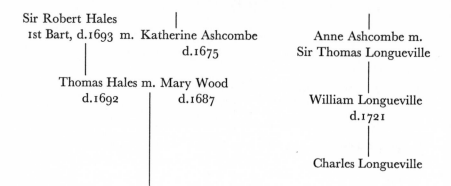

Sir Robert Hales
1st Bart, d.1693 m. Katherine Ashcombe
d.1675

Thomas Hales m. Mary Wood
d.1692   d.1687

Anne Ashcombe m.
Sir Thomas Longueville

William Longueville
d.1721

Charles Longueville

CHILDREN OF THOMAS AND MARY HALES

1. Robert b.1664 d.1671
2. Sir Thomas b.1665 d.1748 m. Mary Pym 7s. 5 dau.
3. Charles b.1667 d.1747
4. Mary b.1668 d.1732 m. The Hon. Robert Booth D.D.
5. Catherine b.1670
6. Ann b.1671 m. Samuel Mills, Steward of Archiepiscopal Temporal Court
7. Margaret b. and d. 1673
8. Robert b.1674 d.1735 m. Sarah Andrews 2 dau.
9. William b.1675 d.1729 m. Mary Gillow 2s. 7 dau.
10. *Stephen* b.1677 d.1761 m. Mary Newce
11. Elizabeth b.1679 d.1749 m. Rev. John Metcalfe 1 dau.
12. James b. and d. 1683

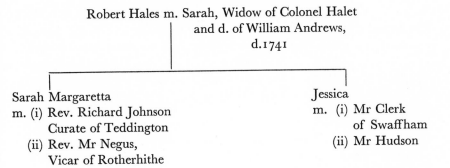

Robert Hales m. Sarah, Widow of Colonel Halet
and d. of William Andrews,
d.1741

Sarah Margaretta
m. (i) Rev. Richard Johnson
    Curate of Teddington
  (ii) Rev. Mr Negus,
    Vicar of Rotherhithe

Jessica
m. (i) Mr Clerk
    of Swaffham
  (ii) Mr Hudson

THE HALES/MARSHAM AND THE MARSHAM/BOUVERIE CONNECTIONS

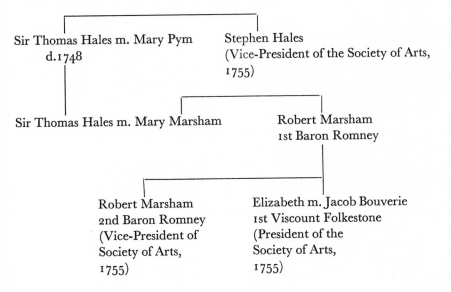

Sir Thomas Hales m. Mary Pym
d.1748

Stephen Hales
(Vice-President of the Society of Arts,
1755)

Sir Thomas Hales m. Mary Marsham

Robert Marsham
1st Baron Romney

Robert Marsham
2nd Baron Romney
(Vice-President of
Society of Arts,
1755)

Elizabeth m. Jacob Bouverie
1st Viscount Folkestone
(President of the
Society of Arts,
1755)

201

General bibliography

Manuscript Collections

Boston, Massachusetts, U.S.A., Boston University: Newhall Collection.
Cambridge, Corpus Christi College: Mss 567, Nesbett Letters.
    Trinity College Library: R. 4.42.
    University Library: Ms Dd 12.53(A).
Cleveland, Ohio, U.S.A., Cleveland Medical Library Association.
Edinburgh, University Library: Alston Papers.
London, Borough of Richmond, York House, Twickenham: Teddington
    Vestry Minutes.
Middlesex, Teddington, St Albans Church: Parish Registers.
    British Museum: Add. Mss 6271, f. 3.
    Birch Mss, 4222, ff. 167–8.
    Liverpool Papers (Add. Mss 38,330), xcli, ff. 244–51.
    Middleton Papers (Add. Mss 41, 843).
    Portland Mss 29191, ff. 196–7.
    Sloane Mss 4042, f. 94; 4078, f. 164, 280.
    Goldsmiths' Company Records.
    Kensington and Chelsea Library (Local History Department): Parish
        Poor Rate Book, 1683–1728.
    Cuttings File.
    Linnean Society: Linnean Correspondence.
    Collinson, Mss.
    Middlesex County Record Office: Teddington Manor Court Book, 1764–71.
    Public Record Office: State Papers Domestic, S.P. 361229.
    Royal College of Physicians: Yeoman Papers (copies).
    Royal College of Surgeons: Hunter-Baillie Collection
    Royal Society: Journal Book, 1714–20.
    Letter Book, H. 3, 133, 134.
    Letters and Papers, Decade I, II, III, IV.
    Misc. Mss 58.
    Royal Society of Arts: Guard Books I, II, III, IV.
    Loose Archives, E 1/23, Minutes of Committees.
    Minutes and Transactions, 'Dr. Templeman's Transactions'.
    Subscription Book.

Society for Promoting Christian Knowledge (S.P.C.K.):
Abstract Letter Books CR1/11, CR1/12, CR1/13, CR1/14, CR1/15, CR1/20, CR1/21.
Henry Newman Correspondence, CN 2.9.
Minute Book, Vol. X.
Pocket Book, FT 8/1.
Society for Propagation of the Gospel in Foreign Parts (S.P.G.):
Bray Associates' Papers – American Papers.
Minutes, Vols. I, II.
Journal of Minutes, 1731, 1733, 1734, 1736, 1737, 1740, 1746/47, Vol. 15.
Will of Revd Dr Thomas Bray.
Somerset House: Will of Sir Robert Hales, 1693.
Will of Mary Hales, 20 Sept. 1720.
Will of Stephen Hales, 1759.
(All transferred to Public Record Office, 1970.)
Victoria and Albert Museum: Forster Collection, Baker-Arderon Correspondence, III.
Wellcome Institute of the History of Medicine: Ms 5 1975; Ms 56474.
Manchester, John Rylands Library: English Mss 19, IV, 339; V, 30103.
Reading, Berkshire County Record Office: Hartley Papers, S/E, Hy f. 79.
Winchester, Hampshire Record Office: Farringdon Parish Registers.
Windsor, Windsor Castle: Royal Archives, Establishment Books, 21–7.

Theses

Bligh, K. V., 'A descriptive list of part of the Bouverie collection: documents relating to the estates of the families of Pym, Hales and Bouverie in Kent and Somerset', unpublished thesis Diploma in Archive Administration, London University, 1966.
Brown, Theodore M., 'The Mechanical Philosophy and the "Animal Œconomy" – A Study in the Development of English Physiology in the Seventeenth and Early Eighteenth Century', unpublished Ph.D. dissertation, Princeton University, Princeton, New Jersey, 1968.
Gilbert, Nona, 'The Work of Stephen Hales (1677–1761) and its Influence on his Contemporaries and Successors', unpublished M.Sc. Thesis, University College, London, 1957.

Books and Articles

(in addition to the D.A.B., D.N.B. and O.E.D.)
Abbey, Charles, J. and Overton, John H., *The English Church in the Eighteenth Century* (London, 1887).
Accum, Frederick, *A Practical Treatise on Gas-Light* (London, 1815).

A[llan], D. G. C., 'Dr. Hales and the Society, 1753–61: (i) Before the Foundation', Studies in the Society's Archives XXVI, *Journal of the Royal Society of Arts* 110 (1962), pp. 855—9.

A[llan], D. G. C., 'Dr. Hales and the Society, 1753–61: (ii) After the Foundation', Studies in the Society's Archives XXVII, *Journal of the Royal Society of Arts* 111 (1963), pp. 53–7.

Allan, D. G. C., 'Dr. Hales of Teddington and the Society of Arts, 1753–1761', *Middlesex Local History Council Bulletin* 14 (1962), p. 17.

Allan, David G. C., *William Shipley: Founder of the Royal Society of Arts* (London, 1968, 1980).

Allan, David G. C., *The Houses of the Royal Society of Arts*, 2nd ed. (London, 1974).

Allen, William O. B. and McClure, Edmund, *Two Hundred Years: The History of the Society for Promoting Christian Knowledge, 1698–1898* (London, 1898).

Archaeologia Cantiana 53 (1941), p. 94, 'Description of Herne Church'.

Austen, Jane, *The Novels of Jane Austen*, ed. R. W. Chapman, 3rd ed. (Oxford 1933).

Bailey, William, *The Advancement of Arts, Manufactures, and Commerce; Or, Description of the Useful Models and Machines Contained in the Repository of the Society for the Encouragement of Arts, Manufactures and Commerce . . .* (London, 1772).

Baker, John, *Abraham Trembley of Geneva, Scientist and Philosopher 1710–1784* (London, 1952).

[Baker, John], *The Diary of John Baker, Barrister of the Middle Temple, Solicitor-General of the Leeward Islands*, ed. P. C. Yorke (London, 1931).

Bale, F., *Church of St. Mary Teddington* (Teddington, n.d.).

Ball, W. W. Rouse, *Cambridge Papers* (London, 1918).

Barbaste, Mathieu, *Etude Biographique, Philosphique, Médicale et Botanique sur François Boissier de Sauvages* (Montpellier, 1851).

Barry, James, *An Account of a Series of Pictures in the Great Room of the Society of Arts* (London, 1783).

[Bath, Marquis of], *Calendar of the Manuscripts of the Marquis of Bath preserved at Longleat, Wiltshire* (London, 1904).

Bentley, Richard, *Eight Sermons Preach'd at the Honourable Robert Boyle's Lecture*, 5th ed. (Cambridge, 1724).

[Bentley, Richard], *The Works of Richard Bentley*, ed. A. Dyce, Vol. III (London, 1838).

Berkeley, Edmund and Berkeley, Dorothy S., *Dr. Alexander Garden of Charles Town* (Chapel Hill, N.C. 1969).

[Berkeley, George], *The Works of George Berkeley, Bishop of Cloyne*, ed. A. A. Luce and T. E. Jessup, Vols. 5 and 8 (London, 1953, 1956).

Berry, Henry F., *A History of the Royal Dublin Society* (London, 1915).

Betham, William, *The Baronetage of England*, Vol. II (London, 1802).
Holy Bible, annotated, Adam Clarke (London, 1825).
Black, Joseph, *Lectures on the Elements of Chemistry*, ed. John Robison (Edinburgh, 1803).
Blomfield, Joseph, *St. George's, 1733–1933* (London, 1933).
Boerhaave, Hermann, *A New Method of Chemistry*, transl. Peter Shaw and Ephraim Chambers (London, 1727).
Bonnet, Charles, 'An Abstract of some new Observations upon Insects', *Phil. Trans.* 42 (1743), pp. 458–87.
[Bonnet, Charles], *Memoires Autobiographique de Charles Bonnet de Genève*, ed. Raymond Savioz (Paris, 1948).
The Book of Common Prayer (London, 1753).
Boss, J. M. N., 'A collection of some observations on bills of mortality and parish registers: an unpublished manuscript by Stephen Hales, F.R.S. (1677–1761)', *Notes and Records of the Royal Society of London*, Vol. 32, No. 2 (March 1978), pp. 131–47.
Boswell, James, *Boswell's Life of Johnson*, ed. George Birkbeck Hill, revised L. F. Powell, Vol. V (Oxford, 1950).
Bourde, André J., *The Influence of England on the French Agronomes, 1750–1789* (Cambridge, 1953).
Bradley, Richard, 'Observations and Experiments relating to the motion of the Sap in Vegetables', *Phil. Trans.* 29 (1716), pp. 486–90.
Brande, William, 'A Letter on the Differences in the Structure of Calculi, which arise from their being formed in different Parts of the Urinary Passages; and on the Effects that are produced on them, by the internal Use of solvent Medicines', *Phil. Trans.* 98 (1808), pp. 223–43.
Brewer, James N., *London and Middlesex*, Vol. IV (London, 1816).
Brooks, Chandler McC. and Cranefield, Paul F., eds., *Historical Development of Physiological Thought* (New York, 1959).
Buess, Heinrich, 'William Harvey and the Foundation of Modern Haemodynamics by Albrecht von Haller', *Medical History* 14 (1970), pp. 175–82.
[Buffon, Georges Louis Leclerc, Comte de], *Des Manuscrits de Buffon*, ed. P. Flourens (Paris, 1860).
Buffon, Georges Louis Leclerc, Comte de, 'Preface du Traducteur', in Stephen Hales's, *La Statique des Végétaux et celle des Animaux* (Paris, 1779).
Bultmann, W. A., 'A Layman proposes Protestant Union: Robert Hales and the Helvetic Churches, 1700–1705'. *Church History* 27 (1958), pp. 32–45.
Burchell, Howard B., 'Editorial: Stephen Hales, September 17, 1677–January 4, 1761', *Circulation, An Official Journal of the American Heart Association* 23 (1961), pp. 1–6.
Burget, G. E., 'Stephen Hales', *Annals of Medical History* 7 (1925), pp. 109–16.
Burgh, James, *Crito, or Essays on Various Subjects* (London, 1766).

[Bute, Earl of], *A Prime Minister and his son from the correspondence of the 3rd Earl of Bute and Lt. General the Hon. Sir Charles Stuart, K.B.*, ed. Mrs E. S. Wortley (London, 1925).

Butler, Weeden, *Memoirs of Mark Hildesley, D.D., Lord Bishop of Sodor and Man* (London, 1799).

[Campbell, Archibald], *The Sale of Authors, A Dialogue, In Imitation of Lucian's Sale of Philosophers* (London, 1767).

Candler, Allen D., *The Colonial Records of the State of Georgia*, Vols. I–III (Atlanta, Georgia, 1904).

[Cavendish, Henry], *The Scientific Papers of the Honourable Henry Cavendish*, ed. Sir Edward Thorpe, Vol. 2 (Cambridge, 1921).

Central Council for the Care of Churches, *The Parochial Libraries of the Church of England* (London, 1959).

Chaplin, Arnold, 'The History of Medical Education in the Universities of Oxford and Cambridge, 1500–1850', *Proceedings of the Royal Society of Medicine* 13 (1920), History Section, pp. 83–107.

Chew, V. K., *Physics for Princes* (London, 1968).

Church, Leslie F., *Oglethorpe, a Study of Philanthropy in England and Georgia* (London, 1932).

Clarke, W. K. Lowther, *Eighteenth Century Piety* (London, 1944).

Clarke, W. K. Lowther, *A History of the S.P.C.K.* (London, 1959).

Clark-Kennedy, Archibald E., *Stephen Hales, D.D., F.R.S.; an Eighteenth Century Biography* (Cambridge, 1929).

Blay, John W., ed., *The Registers of St. Paul's Cathedral* (London, 1899).

Clegg, Samuel, Jr, *A Practical Treatise on the Manufacture of Coal-Gas* (London, 1841).

Clement, Mary, ed., *Correspondence and Minutes of the S.P.C.K. Relating to Wales, 1699–1740* (Cardiff, 1952).

Cohen, I. Bernard, *Franklin and Newton* (Philadelphia, 1956).

Cockayne, George E., ed., *Complete Baronetage* (London, 1903).

[Colden, Cadwallader], *Letters and Papers of Cadwallader Colden*, New York Historical Society Collections, Vol. V (New York, 1919).

Coleby, L. J. M., 'John Francis Vigani, first professor of chemistry in the University of Cambridge', *Annals of Science* 8 (1952), pp. 42–60.

Collinson, Peter, Memoir of Stephen Hales, *Gentleman's Magazine* XXXIV (1764), pp. 273–8; also published in *Annual Register* 7 (1764), 'Characters', pp. 42–9.

A Companion to the Altar; showing the nature and necessity of a Sacramental preparation . . . according to what the Church of England requires from her communicants, 11th ed. (London, 1729).

[Condorcet, M. J. A. N. de Caritat, Marquis de], *Correspondance Inédité de Condorcet et de Turgot, 1770–1779*, ed. Charles Henry (Paris, [1961]).

Cooper, Thomas, *Some Information concerning Gas Lights* (Philadelphia, 1816).

[Coram, Thomas], 'Letters', *Massachusetts Historical Society Proceedings* 56 (3 ser. 1922–23), pp. 19–56.

Cotes, Roger, *Hydrostatical and Pneumatical Lectures*, ed. Robert Smith (London, 1738).

Cowie, Leonard W., *Henry Newman, An American in London 1708–43* (London, 1956).

Crane, V. W., 'Dr Thomas Bray and the Charitable Colony Project, 1730', *William and Mary Quarterly* 19 (3rd Series, 1962), p. 53.

Crane, V. W., 'The Philanthropists and the Genesis of Georgia', *American Historical Review* 27 (1922), p. 64.

Dade, Harry C. T., *Parish Church of St. Alban the Martyr, Teddington, and the old Parish Church of St. Mary, Teddington* (Teddington, 1957).

Darwin, Erasmus, *Phytologia* (London, 1800).

Davies, Richard, *The General State of Education in the Universities: With a particular View to the Philosophical and Medical Education: set forth in An Epistle Inscribed to the Reverend Doctor Hales* (Bath, 1759).

Davy, Sir Humphry, *Elements of Agricultural Chemistry* (London, 1813).

Dawson, Percy M., 'Stephen Hales, the Physiologist', *Bulletin of the Johns Hopkins Hospital* 15 (1904), pp. 232–237.

Debrett, John, ed., *The Baronetage of England*, Vol. I, (London, 1808).

Desaguliers, Jean T., 'An Account of an Instrument for changing the Air of the Room of Sick People', *Phil. Trans.* 39 (1735–36), pp. 41–3.

Desaguliers, Jean T., Review of the Vegetable Staticks, *Phil. Trans.* 34 (1726–7), pp. 264–91; 35 (1727–28), pp. 323–31.

[Dodington, George Bubb], *The Political Journal of George Bubb Dodington*, ed., J. Carswell and L. A. Dralle (Oxford, 1965).

DuFay, Charles, 'Cinquième Memoir sur L'Electricité', *Memoires de l'Academie Royale des Sciences* (1734, Amsterdam ed.), pp. 490–91.

Duhamel du Monceau, Henri Louis, 'Concerning the Method of making slips and Layers take Effect', *Gentleman's Magazine* XIX (1749), pp. 155–57.

Duhamel du Monceau, Henri Louis, *The Elements of Agriculture*, trans. and revised, Philip Miller (London, 1764).

Duhamel du Monceau, Henri Louis, 'Of raising without Earth', *Gentleman's Magazine* XIX (1749), pp. 259–66.

Edwards, Averyl, *Frederick Louis, Prince of Wales 1707–1751* (London, 1957).

Edwards, David L., *A History of the King's School, Canterbury* (London, 1957).

[Egmont, John Perceval, Earl of], *The Journal of the Earl of Egmont; abstract of the Trustees Proceedings for Establishing the Colony of Georgia, 1732–1738*, ed. E. G. McPherson (Athens, Georgia, 1962).

[Egmont, John Perceval, Earl of], Manuscripts of the Earl of Egmont;

Diary of the First Earl of Egmont, Viscount Perceval, 3 Vols. (London, Historical Manuscripts Commission, 1920–23).

Ellis, John, *An Essay towards a Natural History of the Corallines and other Marine Productions of the like kind, Commonly found on the Coast of Great Britain and Ireland* (London, 1755).

European Magazine 21 (1791), p. 429, 'Memoir of Rev. Mr. Richard Johnson'.

Evans, Joan, *A History of the Society of Antiquaries* (London, 1956).

Everitt, Alan M., *The Community of Kent and the Great Rebellion, 1640–60* (Leicester, 1966).

Fant, H. B., 'The Prohibition Policy of the Trustees for Establishing the Colony of Georgia in America', *Georgia Historical Quarterly* 17 (1933), pp. 286–92.

Filby, Frederick A., *A History of Food Adulteration and Analysis* (London, 1934).

Fines, John, 'The Last Years of Stephen Hales', *Letter of the Corpus Association* (Corpus Christi College, Cambridge), No. 47 (Michaelmas, 1968), pp. 27–32.

Franklin, Kenneth J., *A Short History of Physiology* (London, 1949).

Freind, John, *Emmenologia*, transl. Thomas Dales (London, 1729).

Freind, John, *Chymical Lectures: In which almost all the Operations of Chymistry are reduced to their True Principles and Laws of Nature* (London, 1712).

Fussell, George E., *More Old English Farming Books, from Tull to the Board of Agriculture, 1731–1798* (London, 1950).

Fussell, George E., 'Stephen Hales, 1677–1761: A Kentish founder of modern science', *Fertilizer and Feeding Stuffs and Farm Supplies Journal* 39 (No. 6, March 18, 1955), pp. 217–19.

Gentleman's Magazine XVII (1747), pp. 270–71, 'Notice of the Middlesex County Hospital'.

Gentleman's Magazine XXXII (1762), p. 444, 'Notice of Westminster Abbey Memorial to Hales, 2 September 1762'.

Gentleman's Magazine LV (1785), p. 323, 'Note of death of Dr. Husband Messiter'.

Geoffroy, Etienne François, *Tractatus de Materia Medica* (Paris, 1741), Vol. I, 'De Fossilibus'.

[George III, King], *Letters from George III to Lord Bute*, ed. R. Sedgwick, (London, 1939).

Gibbs, F. W., 'George Wilson (1631–1711)', *Endeavour* 12 (1953), pp. 182–85.

Gibbs, F. W., 'Peter Shaw and the Revival of Chemistry', *Annals of Science* 7 (1951), pp. 211–37.

Gibbs, F. W., 'William Lewis, M.D., F.R.S., 1708–1781', *Annals of Science* 8 (1952), pp. 122–48.

Goodfield, G. June, *The Growth of Scientific Physiology* (London, 1960).

Gourli, Norah, *Prince of Botanists, Carl Linnaeus* (London, 1953).

Grew, Nehemiah, *Anatomy of Plants*, ed. with introduction, Conway Zirkle (New York, 1965).

Greene, Thomas, *The Sacrament of the Lord's Supper Explained to the Meanest Capacities* . . . (London, 1710).

Guerlac, Henry, 'The Continental Reputation of Stephen Hales', *Archives Internationales d'Histoires des Sciences* 30 (1951), pp. 392–404.

Guerlac, Henry, 'Joseph Black and Fixed Air . . .', *Isis* 48 (1957), pp. 124–51, 433–56.

Guerlac, Henry, 'Lavoisier and His Biographers', *Isis* 45 (1954), pp. 51–62.

Guerlac, Henry, *Lavoisier – The Crucial Year* (Ithaca, N.Y., 1961).

Haley (Hayley), W., 'Extract from the Ode to John Howard . . .', *Annual Register* 23 (1780), pp. 206–7; reprinted in William Hayley, *Poems and Plays*, Vol. 1 (London, 1785), pp. 123–37.

Hall, A. Rupert, *The Abbey Scientists* (London, 1966).

Hall, Thomas S., *Ideas of Life and Matter, Studies in the History of General Physiology, 600 B.C.—1900 A.D.* (Chicago, 1969).

Haller, Albrecht von, *First Lines of Physiology*, transl. and annot. William Cullen, with intro. Lester S. King (New York, 1966).

Hanks, Lesley, *Buffon avant l'Histoire Naturelle* (Paris, 1966).

Harris, D. Fraser, 'Stephen Hales, the Pioneer in the Hygiene of Ventilation', *The Scientific Monthly* 3 (1931), pp. 440–54.

Hasted, Edward, *History of Kent* (London, 1782).

[Hauksbee, Francis and Whiston, William], *A Course of Mechanical, Optical, Hydrostatical and Pneumatical Experiments. To be performed by Francis Hauksbee; and the Explanatory Lectures read by William Whiston, M.A.* (London [1714]).

Henry, William, *A New Year's Gift to Dram-Drinkers, being an earnest Address to them: from the late S. H.* (Dublin, 1762).

[Hildesley, Bishop Mark], Letter of Bishop Hildesley to Dr. Tothwell, *c.* 1761, *Gentleman's Magazine* LXXI, Part ii (1801), p. 713.

Hoadly, Benjamin, *Three Lectures on the Organs of Respiration* (London, 1740).

Home, Everard, 'Some Observations on Mr. Brande's Paper on Calculi', *Phil. Trans.* 98 (1808), pp. 244–48.

Hoskin, Michael A., ' "Mining All Within": Clarke's Notes to Rohault's *Traite de Physique, The Thomist* 24 (1961), pp. 353–63.

Hoskins, S. Elliott, 'Researches on the Decomposition and Disintegration of Phosphatic Vesical Calculi, and on the introduction of chemical decomponents into the living bladder', *Phil. Trans.* 133 (1843), pp. 7–16.

Hudson, Derek and Luckhurst, Kenneth W., *The Royal Society of Arts, 1754–1954* (London, 1954).

Huxham, John, 'A Letter . . . concerning Polypi taken out of the Hearts, of several Sailors . . .' *Phil. Trans.* 42 (1742–43), pp. 123–26.

Huxley, George, 'Roger Cotes and Natural Philosophy', *Scripta Mathematica* 26 (1961), pp. 231–38.

Jernegan, M. W., 'Slavery and Conversion in the Colonies', *American Historical Review* 21 (1916), pp. 504–27.

Johnson, Richard, *Grammatical Commentaries: being an Apparatus to a New National Grammar: by way of Animadversion upon the Falsities, Obscurities, Redundancies and Defects of Lilly's System now in Use* . . . (London, 1706).

Jones, Griffith, *Welch Piety, or a farther account of the Circulating Welch Charity Schools* (London, 1755).

Jones, Henry Bence, *Gravel, Calculus and Gout: the Application of Liebig's Physiology to these Diseases* (London, 1872).

Jones, Henry Bence, 'On the Dissolution of Urinary Calculi in dilute Saline Fluids . . . by the aid of Electricity', *Phil. Trans.* 143 (1853), pp. 201–16.

Jones, Mary G., *The Charity School Movement; a Study of Eighteenth Century Puritanism in Action* (Cambridge, 1938).

Jurin, James, 'An Account of some Experiments relating to the Specific Gravity of Human Blood', *Phil. Trans.* 30 (1717–19), pp. 1000–1014.

Keill, James, *Anatomy of the Humane Body Abridged: or a short and full view of all parts of the body. Together with their several uses drawn from their compositions and structure* (London, 1759), 12th ed.

Keill, James, *Essays on Several Parts of the Animal Oeconomy* (London, 1738), 4th ed.

Keill, John, *An Introduction to Natural Philosophy: or Philosophical Lectures read in the University of Oxford Anno. Dom. 1700* (London, 1720).

Keill, John, 'In qua Leges Attractionis aliaque Physices Principia traduntur', *Phil. Trans.* 26 (1708–09), pp. 97–110; transl. as: 'On the laws of Attraction and other Physical Properties' in *Phil. Trans. Abridged*, ed. Charles Hutton, George Shaw and Richard Pearson, Vol. 5 (London, 1809), pp. 407–24.

Kemp, Eric W., *Counsel and Consent* (London, 1961).

L.L., 'Dr. Stephen Hales', *Notes and Queries* 4 (2nd Series, 1851), p. 343.

Lecky, William E. H., *History of England in the Eighteenth Century*, Vol. I (New York, 1878).

LeFanu, W. R., 'Preserving Mineral Water. A letter of 1735 from Stephen Hales, F.R.S.', *Post-Graduate Medical Journal* 22 (1946), pp. 121–22.

Leslie, John, *Elements of Natural Philosophy* (Edinburgh, 1829).

Lewis, William, *Commercium Philosophico-Technicum* (London, 1763).

Libby, Margaret Sherwood, *The Attitude of Voltaire to Magic and the Sciences* (New York, 1935).

Lindeboom, Gerrit A., *Hermann Boerhaave, the Man and his Work* (London, 1968).

Lillywhite, Bryant, *London Coffee Houses* (London, 1963).

Logan, James, '. . . concerning the crooked and angular Appearance of the Streaks, or Darts of Lightning . . .' *Phil. Trans.* 39 (1735-36), p. 240.

Lydekker, John W., *Thomas Bray 1658–1730; founder of Missionary Enterprise* (Philadelphia, 1943).

Lysons, Daniel, *Environs of London*, Vol. III, (London, 1792–96).

McCain, James R., *Georgia as a Proprietary Province; The Execution of a Trust* (Boston, Mass., 1917).

Macalister, Alexander, *The History of the Study of Anatomy in Cambridge* (Cambridge, 1891).

McCloy, Shelby T., *French Inventions of the Eighteenth Century* (Louisville, Kentucky, 1952).

McClure, Edmund, ed., *A Chapter in English Church History . . . S.P.C.K. Minutes and Correspondence 1698–1704* (London, 1888).

McCormmach, Russell, 'Henry Cavendish: A Study of Rational Empiricism in Eighteenth-Century Natural Philosophy', *Isis* 60 (1969), pp. 293–306.

McKendrick, John G., 'Abstract of Lectures on Physiological Discovery. Lecture I. The Circulation of the Blood, A Problem in Hydrodynamics', *British Medical Journal* 1 (1883), pp. 654–55.

Marcet, Alexander, *An Essay on the Chemical History and Medical Treatment of Calculus Disorders* (London, 1819).

Marshall, Dorothy, *Eighteenth Century England* (New York, 1962).

Masters, Robert, *The History of Corpus Christi College, Cambridge. Part II. Of its Principal Members* (Cambridge, 1755).

Miller, Perry, 'Bentley and Newton', in I. B. Cohen, ed., *Isaac Newton's Papers and Letters on Natural Philosophy* (Cambridge, Mass., 1958), pp. 271–78.

Miller, Philip, *The Gardener's Dictionary* (London, 1752), 6th ed.

Mortimer, Thomas, *A concise Account of the Rise, Progress, and Present State of the Society for the Encouragement of Arts, Manufactures and Commerce, Instituted at London, Anno MDCCLIV, Compiled from the Original Papers of the first Promoters of the Plan; and from other Authentic Records* (London, 1763).

[Newman, Henry], *Henry Newman's Salzburger Letterbooks*, ed. George F. Jones (Athens, Ga., 1966).

Newton, Sir Isaac, *The Mathematical Principles of Natural Philosophy* [Principia], transl. Andrew Motte (London, 1729).

[Newton, Isaac], *Isaac Newton's Papers and Letters on Natural Philosophy and Related Documents*, ed. I. B. Cohen (Cambridge, Mass., 1958).

Nichols, John, *Illustrations of the Literary History of the Eighteenth Century* (London, 1817).

Nicolson, Marjorie and Rousseau, George S., *'This Long Disease, My Life', Alexander Pope and the Sciences* (Princeton, 1968).

Oliver, Francis W., ed., *Makers of British Botany* (Cambridge, 1913).

Page, William, ed., *Victoria History of Hampshire*, Vol. III (London, 1908).

Page, William, ed., *Victoria History of the County of Middlesex*, Vol. I (London, 1906).

Page, William, ed., *Victoria History of Nottingham*, Vol. II (London, 1910).

Partington, James R., *A History of Chemistry*, Vol. III (London, 1962).

Peachey, George C., *A Memoir of William and John Hunter* (Plymouth, 1924).

Pearson, George, 'Experiments and Observations tending to show the Composition of Urinary Concretions', *Phil. Trans.* 88 (1798), pp. 15–46.

Pennington, E. L., 'Thomas Bray's Associates and their Work among Negroes', *Proceedings of the American Antiquarian Society* (1938), p. 31.

Philosophical Transactions . . . Abridged, eds. Charles Hutton, George Shaw and Richard Pearson, Vols. 7, 30 (London, 1809).

Pitcairne, Archibald, *The Philosophical and Mathematical Elements of Physick. In Two Books. The First containing the Theory: The Second the Practice. Compos'd for the Use of all who study the Art of Medicine*, transl. by John Quincy, 2nd ed. (London, 1745).

Pope, Alexander, *Of the Characters of Women* (London, 1734/5).

Price, F. G. Hilton, *A Handbook of London Bankers* (London, 1890).

Pullein, Samuel, *The Culture of Silk: or an Essay on its rational Practice and improvement . . . for the use of the American Colonies* (London, 1758).

[Pyle, Edmund], *Memoirs of a Royal Chaplain, 1729–1763. Correspondence of Edmund Pyle, D.D., with Samuel Kerrich, D.D.*, ed. Albert Hartshorne (London, 1905).

Radnor, William Pleydell-Bouverie, Earl of, 'The First President—the inaugural address of the 200th session', *Journal of the Royal Society of Arts* 102 (1953), pp. 9–13.

Rappaport, Rhoda, 'G.-F. Rouelle: an Eighteenth-Century Chemist and Teacher', *Chymia* 6 (1960), pp. 68–101.

Rappaport, Rhoda, 'Rouelle and Stahl—The Phlogistic Revolution in France', *Chymia* 7 (1961), pp. 73–102.

Raven, Charles E., *John Ray, Naturalist, his Life and Works* (Cambridge, 1950).

Reed, Howard S., 'Jan Ingenhousz, Plant Physiologist, with a History of the Discovery of Photosynthesis', *Chronica Botanica* 11 (1949), pp. 285–396.

Rees, Abraham, ed., *The Cyclopaedia; or Universal Dictionary of Arts, Sciences, and Literature* (London, 1819).

Reese, Trevor R., *Colonial Georgia, A Study in British Imperial Policy in the Eighteenth Century* (Atlanta, Ga., 1963).

Renbourn, E. T., 'The Natural History of Insensible Perspiration; a forgotten Doctrine of Health and Disease', *Medical History* 4 (1960), pp. 135–52.

Reynolds, Susan, ed., *Victoria History of the County of Middlesex*, Vol. III (London, 1962).

Richmann, Georg W., 'On the force of water in freezing', *Novi-Commentarii Academiae Scientiarum Imperialis Petropolitanae* 1 (1747), p. 276

R[obins,] B [enjamin], *New Principles of Gunnery, containing the Determination of the Force of Gunpowder* (London, 1742).

Robinson, Eric, 'The Profession of Civil Engineer in the Eighteenth Century: A Portrait of Thomas Yeoman, F.R.S., 1704?–1781', *Annals of Science* 18 (1962, publ. 1964), pp. 195–215.

[Rohault, Jacques], *Rohault's System of Natural Philosophy*, ed. with notes, by Samuel Clarke, transl. John Clarke (London, 1723).

Royal Society, *The Record of the Royal Society for the Promotion of Natural Knowledge* (London, 1940), 4th ed.

Russell, Kenneth, *British Anatomy 1525–1800. A Bibliography* (Parksville, Victoria, Australia, 1963).

Russell-Wood, J., 'A Biographical Note on William Brownrigg, M.D., F.R.S. (1711–1800)', *Annals of Science* 6 (1950), pp. 186–96.

Russell-Wood, J., 'The Scientific Work of William Brownrigg, M.D., F.R.S. (1711–1800)', *Annals of Science* 6 (1950), pp. 436–47; 7 (1951), pp. 77–94, 199–206.

Rutt, John Towill, *Life and Correspondence of Joseph Priestley*, Vol. I (London 1831–32).

Sachs, Julius von, *History of Botany (1530–1860)*, transl. Henry E. F. Garnsey (Oxford, 1890).

Sachs, Julius von, *Lectures on the Physiology of Plants*, transl. H. Marshall Ward (Oxford, 1887).

Sachs, Julius von, *Text-Book of Botany, Morphological and Physiological*, transl. and annot. Alfred W. Bennett and W. T. Thiselton Dyer (Oxford, 1875).

Sauvage, François Boissier de, 'Avertissement du traducteur', in Etienne Hales, *Haemastatique, Ou La Statique des Animaux* (Geneva, 1744).

Saye, Albert B., *Georgia's Charter of 1732* (Athens, Ga., 1942).

Schofield, Robert E., *Mechanism and Materialism: British Natural Philosophy in an Age of Reason* (Princeton, N.J., 1970).

Secker, Thomas, *Sermon before the London Infirmary* . . . (London, 1754).

Sevin, Nathan, 'William Lewis (1708–1781) as a chemist', *Chymia* 8 (1962), pp. 63–88.

Shugg, W., 'Humanitarian Attitudes in the early Animal Experiments of the Royal Society', *Annals of Science* 24 (1968), pp. 227–38.

Sinclair, Hugh M. and Robb-Smith, A. H. T., *Short History of Anatomy Teaching in Oxford* (Oxford, 1950).

Singer, Dorthea Waley, 'Sir John Pringle and his Circle—Part II. Public Health', *Annals of Science* 6 (1950), pp. 229–61.

Smith, James Edward, ed., *A Selection of the Correspondence of Linnaeus, and other Naturalists*, (London, 1821).

Society of Arts, *To the Publick* [printed 'Premium List'] (London, 1755).

Solly, Edward, 'Dr. Stephen Hales, not Hale', *Notes and Queries* 7 (6th Series, 1883), pp. 352–3.

[Spence, Joseph], *Joseph Spence: Observations, Anecdotes and Characters of Books and Men*, ed. J. M. Osborn, Vol. I. (Oxford, 1966).

Stokes, Henry P., *Corpus Christi* (London, 1898).

Stonhouse, James, 'Expedients for alleviating the Distress occasioned by the present dearness of Corn', *Gentleman's Magazine* XXVIII (1758), pp. 17–20.

[Stukeley, William], *The Family Memoirs of The Rev. William Stukeley, M.D. and the Antiquarian and other Correspondence of William Stukeley, Roger and Samuel Gale, etc.*, ed. W. C. Lukis (Durham, 1882–3).

[Suffolk, Henrietta, Countess of], *Letters to and from Henrietta, Countess of Suffolk, and second husband, the Hon. George Berkeley, from 1712 to 1767*, ed. J. W. Croker (London, 1824).

Sutton, Samuel, *An Historical Account of a New Method for Extracting the Foul Air out of Ships* (London, 1858, reprint of 1759 ed.).

Sykes, Norman, *Edmund Gibson, Bishop of London, 1669–1748: a Study in Politics and Religion in the Eighteenth Century* (London, 1926).

Sykes, Norman, *Church and State in England in the XVIIIth Century* (Cambridge, 1934).

Tanner, Joseph R., *The Historical Register of the University of Cambridge to the Year 1910* (Cambridge, 1917).

Thompson, Henry P., *Thomas Bray* (London, 1954).

Thoms, William J., *The Book of the Court* (London, 1838).

Thorpe, Jocelyn, 'Stephen Hales, D.D., F.R.S., 1677–1761', *Notes and Records of the Royal Society* 3 (1940–41), pp. 53–63.

Tull, Jethro, *Horse-Hoeing Husbandry* (London, 1762), 4th ed.

[Twining, Thomas], *Recreations and Studies of a Country Gentleman of the Eighteenth Century: being Selections from the Correspondence of the Reverend Thomas Twining, M.A.*, ed. R. Twining (London, 1888).

Venn, John and Venn, John A., *Alumni Cantabrigienses: A Biographical List of all the known Students, Graduates and Holders of Office at the University of Cambridge, from the Earliest Times to 1900* (Cambridge, 1922).

Viseltear, Arthur J., 'Joanna Stephens and the Eighteenth Century Lithontriptics; a Misplaced Chapter in the History of Therapeutics', *Bulletin of the History of Medicine* 42 (1968), pp. 199–220.

[Voltaire], *Oeuvres Complètes de Voltaire*, ed. Louis Moland (Paris, 1879), Vol. 22, 'Conseils à un Journaliste . . . Sur La Philosophie', pp. 241–43.

Walker, John, 'Experiments on the Motion of Sap in Trees', *Transactions of the Royal Society of Edinburgh* 1 (1788), Part II, pp. 3–40.

Wall, J., 'An Essay on the Waters of the Holy Well at Malvern, Worcestershire', *Phil. Trans.* 49 (1756), pp. 459–68.

[Walpole, Horace], *The Yale Edition of Walpole's Correspondence*, ed. W. S. Lewis, Vol. 20. (London, 1960)

Warren, Christopher, 'A Letter . . . containing further Accounts of injecting medicated Liquors into the Abdomen . . .', *Phil. Trans.* 43 (1744–45), pp. 47–8. (By the same person whose later paper signed Warrick, is cited in this bibliography.)

Warrick, Christopher, 'A Further Account of the Success of some Experiments of injecting Claret, &c. into the abdomen, after Tapping', *Phil. Trans.* 49 (1755–56), pp. 485–89. (See also Warren and Warwick.)

[Wesley, Charles], *The Journal of the Rev. Charles Wesley, M.A.*, ed. Thomas Jackson (London, 1849).

[Wesley, John], *The Journal of the Rev. John Wesley, A.M.*, ed. Nehemiah Curnock, Vol. I (London, 1909–13).

Whiston, William, *Memoirs of the Life of Mr. William Whiston* (London, 1749).

White, Gilbert, 'Letters to Robert Marsham', ed. J. E. Harting, *Transactions of the Norfolk and Norwich Naturalists Society* 2 (1875), pp. 152–54.

Wilkie, Christopher H., *The Parish Register of St. Peter's – Beakesbourne* (Canterbury, 1896).

[Wilson, Thomas], *The Diaries of Thomas Wilson, D.D., 1731–37 and 1750. Son of Bishop Wilson of Sodor & Man*, ed. C. L. S. Linnell (London, 1964).

[Wilson, Thomas], *Distilled Spirituous Liquors the Bane of the Nation* (London, 1736), 2nd ed.

Winstanley, D. A., *Unreformed Cambridge. A Study of Certain Aspects of the University in the Eighteenth Century* (Cambridge, 1935).

[Woodforde, James], *The Diary of a Country Parson, the Reverend James Woodforde 1758–81*, ed. J. Beresford (Oxford, 1926).

Wordsworth, Christopher, *Scholae Academicae: Some Account of the Studies at English Universities in the Eighteenth Century* (Cambridge, 1877).

Select index

217

218